Nuffield Maths 3
Teachers' handbook

# Nuffield Maths 3

a revised and extended version of
the Nuffield Mathematics Teaching Project

# Nuffield Maths 5-11
# Teachers' Handbook

Published for the Nuffield Foundation by Longman Group Ltd

General editor:

Eric A. Albany, *Senior lecturer in mathematics education, The Polytechnic, Wolverhampton*

Authors of this volume:

Paul Latham, *Inspector of Schools, Metropolitan Borough of Wirral*

Percy Truelove, *Former Deputy Head, Oak Meadow Primary School, Wolverhampton*

Contributing authors:

Eric Albany

Raymond Bull, *Senior lecturer in mathematics education, The Polytechnic, Wolverhampton*

Illustrator:

Chris Williamson

We are grateful to:

Mrs Jean Parrack and the children of Stewart Fleming School, Anerley, London SE20 for the cover photograph.


LONGMAN GROUP LIMITED
*Longman House,*
*Burnt Mill, Harlow, Essex CM20 2JE, England*
*and Associated Companies throughout the World.*

First published 1980
Fifth impression 1985
ISBN 0 582 19177 7

Photoset in Monophoto Plantin 110 and 194

Produced by Longman Group (FE) Ltd
Printed in Hong Kong

**Note**
In the 'revised money version', the halfpenny has been taken out, the 20p coin inserted, and the £1 coin included where relevant. All other chapters in this book remain unchanged.

# Contents

# Foreword

As organizer of 'Nuffield Mark I', I am delighted to have the opportunity of welcoming the present publication, which in effect is Nuffield Mark II. The original project started in 1964 with the aim of 'producing a contemporary course', an urgent need at the time when the 11-plus examination in arithmetic was on its way out and there was a realization that neither its contents nor the methods of teaching for it were producing happy or numerate children (the overwhelming majority of people in that era grew up to hate and fear the subject).

The decision was taken at that time to produce only guidance for the teachers of primary children and not materials for the children themselves. Arguments will continue to rage as to whether this was a wise decision. I can defend it vigorously on many counts *at that time*, but I am also glad to be on record as saying that about ten years later there would be the acceptance and the need for the production of pupils' materials as well.

And so, of course, it has turned out. Very many teachers have asked for more guidance and more materials to be put into the hands of their pupils, and this is just what Mark II has set out to achieve. It is very fortunate that this enterprise has been directed by Eric Albany. He is a staunch Nuffield man who contributed a lot to Mark I. His ability, shrewdness and sense of both humour and proportion have ensured that Mark II should complete the task of 'producing a contemporary course' which children can enjoy. Of equal importance, they will be helped to think for themselves and to acquire relevant skills to the very best of their ability. Eric Albany and his team have produced materials which will set a standard of excellence for many years to come.

Among the many institutions and people to whom the Foundation owes thanks for their help, I must especially acknowledge the part played by the Polytechnic, Wolverhampton in allowing the full-time secondment of Eric Albany to the project and also the assistance given by Wolverhampton and Walsall Education Committees in providing accommodation and facilities for the project staff. We are extremely grateful to all those teachers and schools who have taken part in the trials of the new materials. I would also like to express our thanks to William Anderson, Publications Manager of the project and his colleagues, to the project secretary, Kathleen Norton, and to our publishers, Longman Group Ltd, who have devoted so much effort and such skill to the editing, design and production of the materials.

Geoffrey Matthews

*Chairman of the Nuffield Foundation*
*Primary Mathematics Consultative Committee*
*Professor Emeritus, Chelsea College,*
*University of London*

# Introduction

*Nuffield Maths 5–11* is based on the original *Nuffield Mathematics Teaching Project* but is revised in the light of experience, and extended to include the full range of pupils' materials.

*Nuffield Maths 3 Pupils' Book* is a *non-expendable* text intended for children approximately 7 to 8 years old. As many children of this age will be making the transition from using expendable materials such as the worksheets for *Nuffield Maths 1 and 2*, a good deal of space in *Nuffield Maths 3 Pupils' Book* is devoted to examples showing how to set out computations.

In order to allow children to concentrate on accurate copying of printed information and orderly presentation of written work, much of *Nuffield Maths 3* revises and reinforces topics which may have been covered already. This will also enable children who have not used *Nuffield Maths 1 and 2* to 'slot' into the scheme.

For the sake of convenience, the teacher is referred to as 'she' and the pupil as 'he' in this book.

## Aims and objectives

The general aim of the *Nuffield Maths 5–11* Project is to promote understanding of the concepts and proficiency in the basic skills of mathematics in children of the 5–11 age range.

The objectives of the Teachers' Handbooks are:
a) To give teachers clear guidance on the content, method and timing appropriate at each stage of the course;
b) To give practical, 'down to earth' suggestions for teaching Number, Measurement and Shape, using activities suitable for children with a wide range of abilities and backgrounds;
c) To give guidance in the use of both homemade and commercially available apparatus;
d) To encourage the development of a healthy, inquisitive attitude towards mathematical patterns and structures;
e) To suggest ways of dealing with children's difficulties.

## Using the Materials

The materials of the *Nuffield Maths 5–11* Project can be used in a variety of classroom organisations including individual work, group or class teaching. This should prove particularly useful to the teacher who tends to vary the type of organisation to suit particular topics. Whichever system is used, it is important for teachers to remember the following points:
a) Children learn at different rates and so will not reach the same stage simultaneously;

b) Young children learn by doing and by discussion;
c) As well as finding out and 'discovering' things about mathematics, children need to be *told* things about mathematics, particularly if new vocabulary is involved.

The obvious line of development for a primary child learning mathematics would seem to be:

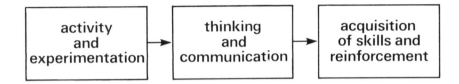

*Activity and experimentation* may vary from a child 'finding out by fiddling' to a structured or teacher-led activity.

*Thinking and communication* involves discussion, sometimes between children, sometimes between teacher and children. Discussion leads to recording in various forms:
a) copying and completing statements – in this case, □ is intended to be replaced by a numeral so that □ + 6 = 15, for example, would be copied and completed as 9 + 6 = 15;
b) drawing or completing shapes or diagrams;
c) recording estimates and measurements;
d) using tabulations such as addition squares or investigating patterns on 100 squares.

Often children spend more time ruling up a table or chart than actually performing the calculations needed to complete it. To overcome this, *Nuffield Maths 3 Spiritmasters* are available from which copies can be run off ready for children's use.

*Acquisition of skills and reinforcement*   Apart from the obvious benefits of having certain useful skills and facts at one's fingertips, there is the question of building up confidence and enjoyment – 'I can do these, Miss. Can I have some more?'

The important thing is that these three elements form a *sequence*. The exercises in the Pupils' Book are seen as part of the last element of the sequence. Additional exercises, to be used as extra practice or for assessment, are available as part of the *Nuffield Maths 3 Spiritmasters* pack.

## Chapter format

Each of the 24 chapters in the Teachers' Handbook is set out as follows:

### 1 For the teacher:
A brief outline of what is being attempted in the chapter, where it is leading, and what may need to be revised before starting.

### 2 Summary of the stages:
Setting out the stages contained within a chapter.

### 3 Vocabulary

A list of the words and phrases which the children will need to be able to use and understand if they are to appreciate and explore the ideas in each chapter. The teacher may wish to include some of these words and phrases in work on language.

### 4 Equipment and apparatus

The sort of materials such as boxes, containers, pots, sticks, pictures, sorting toys, buttons, counters, cubes, beads, string, sand, plasticine, etc. which the teacher may need to collect in advance.

### 5 Working with the children

Suggestions for introducing and developing each stage through discussion, teacher-led activities, games, etc.; hints for making number lines, charts, models, displays and simple apparatus; how to check-up, where necessary, that a child understands a particular stage.

### 6 Pages from the Pupils' Book and Spiritmasters

These provide an invaluable link between teaching notes and pupils' material. *Answers* to specific and computational questions in the Pupils' Book are given on pages 151 to 158.

A number of useful grids are available in Spiritmaster form. As well as these, there is practice material for each of the chapters in the **Pupils' Book**. These practice sheets are reproduced for the teacher's reference.

### 7 References and resources

A list of books and commercially produced materials which are appropriate for the chapter. No commercially produced equipment is deemed essential but is suggested as a possible alternative to homemade or environmental materials. Occasionally the Teachers' Guides published by the original *Nuffield Foundation Mathematics Teaching Project* may be listed in this section. These guides are now out of print but may be found in libraries and schools and they still make a valuable contribution to mathematics education.

# Chapter 1

# Addition 1

## For the teacher

This chapter concentrates on the addition of numbers giving totals up to 20. For many children this will be a reinforcement of work done previously but the importance of a thorough knowledge of basic addition facts cannot be over-stressed. The previous experience of many children may have been limited to the use of expendable materials such as the worksheets produced by this Project. When starting to use non-expendable books, children will need to be given time to acquire the necessary skills of copying accurately from the printed page and setting down their computations in a neat and orderly way.

The transition from:

### 'Write the answer in the frame.'

$$5 + 7 \quad = \boxed{12}$$

to: 'Copy into your book and complete.'

$$5 + 7 = \boxed{\phantom{12}}$$

$$5 + 7 \quad = 12$$

will take some children longer than others.

The establishment of reasonable standards of presentation cannot begin too early. Learning good habits, such as the careful placing of figures, will pay dividends and reduce frustration and inaccuracy later – particularly when dealing with numerals containing two or more digits.

For example:

$$\begin{array}{r} 13 \\ +4 \\ \hline 57 \end{array} \quad \text{instead of} \quad \begin{array}{r} 13 \\ +\ 4 \\ \hline 17 \end{array} \qquad \begin{array}{r} 62 \\ +\ 34 \\ \hline 654 \end{array} \quad \text{instead of} \quad \begin{array}{r} 62 \\ +34 \\ \hline 96 \end{array} \ \text{etc.}$$

## Summary of the stages

1  Pairs that make 10

2  Making an addition square

3  A useful discovery (the commutative property)

# Vocabulary

Pairs, column, row, addition square, total, zero, double, sloping, order, count on, diagonal.

# Equipment and apparatus

Squared paper, rods or interlocking cubes, strips of squared paper for number lines.

# Working with the children

## 1   Adding – pairs which make 10

Of all number pairs, those which add together to make ten are probably the most important. Sound experience in using these number pairs will assist in subsequent work in addition and subtraction.

The children should be given a $10 \times 10$ square. On this they can see the 'step' pattern which can be made by colouring in the respective number pairs. See page 6 for diagram as in *Pupils Book*.

This 'step' pattern can also be made by using structural apparatus such as Stern rods, Cuisenaire rods, or interlocking cubes (Unifix, Multilink, Metriblocs, etc.). Having gained initial experience children should be given frequent opportunities to practise using and to memorise the number pairs making 10.

*The tens race*

The aim of this game is to encourage quick responses. In Race 1, when the child sees '7' he should respond as quickly as possible with the answer '3'.

Some teachers may wish the children to use scrap paper for recording the number pairs, for example, $7 + 3$, $2 + 8$, etc. Children may compete with each other or individually against the clock.

*Adding zero*

Adding zero frequently presents problems. Children may become confused because when we add to something we usually make it bigger, whereas adding zero leaves the original number as in $7 + 0 = 7$. Such confusion is often due to lack of understanding of the meaning of 'zero'. Its use as a space filler when considering place value is dealt with elsewhere. For the time being, discussion can be limited to the 'nothingness' of zero. The teacher may ask how many pencils there are in an empty jar, or how many cakes there are on an empty plate – and relate the children's responses to the symbol '0'.

## 2   Making an addition square

(*Nuffield Maths 3 Spiritmasters*, Grid 1)

Each child will need a piece of squared paper 12 squares long and 12 squares wide. Thick lines are drawn to separate the left-hand column and the bottom row from the 'body' of the square. It is a good idea to use a colour for the numerals in the left-hand column and bottom row and for the + sign in the bottom left-hand corner. It is important to make sure that the children are familiar with the words 'column' (up and down like

Nelson's Column) and 'row' (across as in church or in assembly).

The 'inverted L' shaped piece of card or paper is suggested for those children whose fingers may wander from the correct column or row.

Once the addition square has been completed and checked, finding and discussing number patterns in the square should be encouraged.

The activity on 'doubles' leads to finding and shading these numbers on the square. The word *diagonal* (the line across the square from corner to corner) may be introduced. The 'doubles' lie on the diagonal joining bottom left and top right corners.

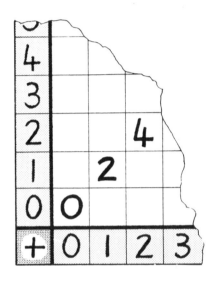

| + | 0 | 1 | 2 | 3 | 4 | 5 | 6 | 7 | 8 | 9 | 10 |
|---|---|---|---|---|---|---|---|---|---|---|----|
| 10 | 10 | | | | | | | | | | 20 |
| 9 | | 10 | | | | | | | | 18 | |
| 8 | | | 10 | | | | | | 16 | | |
| 7 | | | | 10 | | | | 14 | | | |
| 6 | | | | | 10 | 12 | | | | | |
| 5 | | | | | 10 | | | | | | |
| 4 | | | | 8 | 10 | | | | | | |
| 3 | | | 6 | | | 10 | | | | | |
| 2 | | 4 | | | | | 10 | | | | |
| 1 | 2 | | | | | | | 10 | | | |
| 0 | 0 | | | | | | | | | | 10 |

The other diagonal (top left to bottom right) is formed by a line of 10's. The practice questions given in Blocks A to I have answers greater than 10. These are found in the part of the square which is above and to the right of the 'tens' diagonal'.

Further practice can be given by using the 'Moving Targets' mentioned in *Nuffield Maths 2 Teachers' Handbook*.

Two circles are cut from stiff card, one with 5 cm diameter, the other 8 cm. The circles are divided into eight sectors or 'slices' and fixed together with a brass paper fastener. Numerals are written in the spaces so that when the 'spokes' are lined up, eight addition problems are given:

$10 + 5 = 15$
$5 + 6 = 11$
$4 + 7 = 11$
$9 + 8 = 17$, etc.

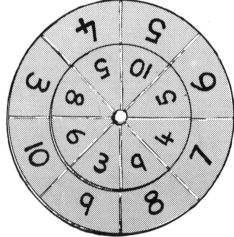

When the inner circle is moved round, another eight addition problems appear, and so on.

### 3   A useful discovery (the commutative property)

The addition square not only helps to establish number bonds but also demonstrates that addition is *commutative* – or, to use language which is probably more suitable for children at this level: 'The order in which we add two numbers does not alter the total.'

For example:   $3 + 5 = 8$
and              $5 + 3 = 8$

By using colours to ring, frame or shade numbers in pairs on the addition square, some children may appreciate the commutative property of addition by seeing that, for example, the 11 obtained from $2 + 9$ has a 'twin' $(9 + 2 = 11)$ on the other side of the 'doubles diagonal'.

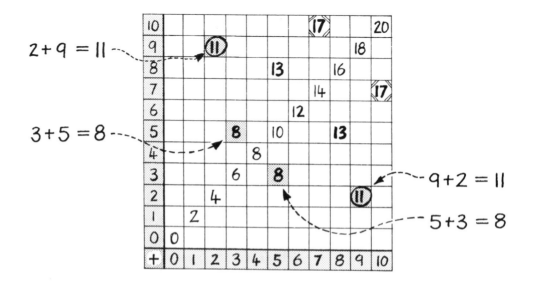

By carefully folding the square along the 'doubles diagonal', each answer drops on to its 'twin'.

Rods or interlocking cubes and the number line are also used to demonstrate the commutative property of addition. Apart from a large number line displayed in the classroom, it is a great help if each child has an individual number line – preferably a strip of 2 cm squared paper on which the vertical *lines* are marked from 0 to 20. (*Nuffield Maths 3 Spiritmasters*, Grid 5.)

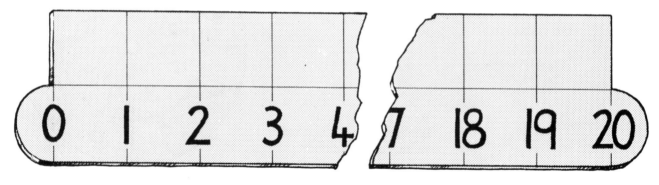

Many children are aware of the commutative property and will appear quite slick at completing such examples as:

$$\square + 6 = 15 = 6 + \square \quad \text{or} \quad 8 + \square = 12$$
$$\square + 4 = 12$$

The problem is one of *recognition* of situations where the commutativity of addition can be utilized.

Examples of two types of situation where the commutative property can be used are provided:

1 If $12 + 9 = 21$ is known, then $9 + 12 = \square$ does not require any further work.

2 When adding by counting on, it is easier to start at 16 and count on 3, for example, than to start at 3 and count on 16.

Although exercises are provided, there is no substitute for constant reinforcement by the teacher as situations arise when the commutative property can be of assistance to the child.

To quote from *Nuffield Maths 2 Teachers' Handbook*:

> 'The prospect of trying to get children to remember all the possible combinations of numbers which give totals up to twenty may seem daunting. However, if we approach the task systematically, using practical aids, building on what is known and gradually extending the experience and knowledge of the children, they will increase their facility with numbers. It must be remembered that this new knowledge and facility will only be retained if opportunities are given for practice and reinforcement – preferably in short, regular "doses". (Those odd five-minute sessions, for example).'

The full appreciation of the commutative property of addition and the recognition of its value in halving the number of facts to be known, is seen as one of the ways in which we can use a systematic approach to the all-important acquisition of number bonds.

*Nuffield Maths 3 Spiritmasters Practice 1* (see page 7)
This provides practice for adding pairs of numbers with totals up to 20, using both a horizontal and vertical layout. It is suggested that these can be set as required, or a child can attempt to beat his own previous record of the number answered correctly in a set time.

# Pages from the Pupils' Book and Spiritmasters

## Chapter 1: Addition 1

### Adding – pairs that make 10

To remind you of the pairs of numbers that make 10,
either use rods or cut out a piece of squared paper
10 squares by 10 squares and colour it like this:

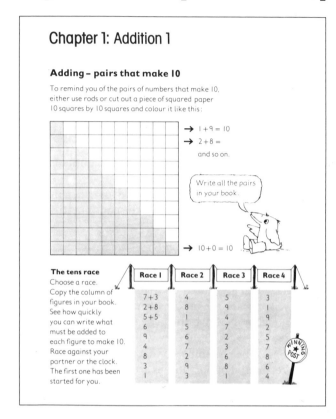

→ 1 + 9 = 10

→ 2 + 8 =

and so on.

Write all the pairs in your book.

→ 10 + 0 = 10

### The tens race

Choose a race.
Copy the column of
figures in your book.
See how quickly
you can write what
must be added to
each figure to make 10.
Race against your
partner or the clock.
The first one has been
started for you.

| Race 1 | Race 2 | Race 3 | Race 4 |
|--------|--------|--------|--------|
| 7+3 | 4 | 5 | 3 |
| 2+8 | 8 | 9 | 1 |
| 5+5 | 1 | 4 | 9 |
| 6 | 5 | 9 | 2 |
| 9 | 6 | 7 | 5 |
| 4 | 7 | 3 | 7 |
| 8 | 2 | 6 | 8 |
| 3 | 8 | 8 | 6 |
| 1 | 3 | 1 | 4 |

WINNING POST

---

### Making an addition square

Take a piece of squared paper, 12 squares by 12 squares,
and make an addition square like this:

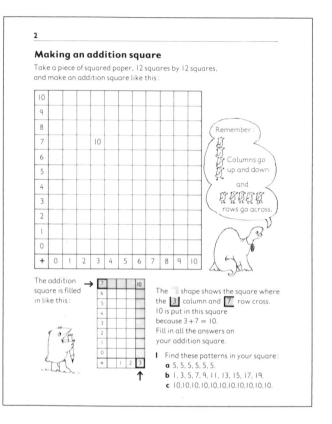

| + | 0 | 1 | 2 | 3 | 4 | 5 | 6 | 7 | 8 | 9 | 10 |

Remember:

Columns go up and down

and

rows go across.

The addition
square is filled
in like this:

The ⌐ shape shows the square where
the 3 column and 7 row cross.
10 is put in this square
because 3 + 7 = 10.
Fill in all the answers on
your addition square.

1 Find these patterns in your square:
a 5, 5, 5, 5, 5, 5.
b 1, 3, 5, 7, 9, 11, 13, 15, 17, 19.
c 10, 10, 10, 10, 10, 10, 10, 10, 10, 10.

---

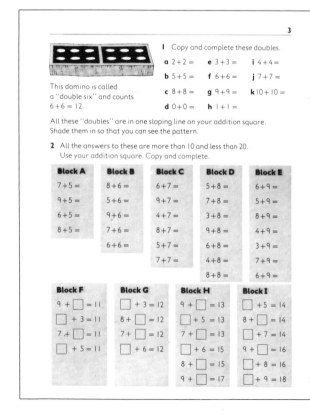

This domino is called
a "double six" and counts
6 + 6 = 12.

1 Copy and complete these doubles.

a 2+2 =    e 3+3 =    i 4+4 =
b 5+5 =    f 6+6 =    j 7+7 =
c 8+8 =    g 9+9 =    k 10+10 =
d 0+0 =    h 1+1 =

All these "doubles" are in one sloping line on your addition square.
Shade them in so that you can see the pattern.

2 All the answers to these are more than 10 and less than 20.
Use your addition square. Copy and complete.

| Block A | Block B | Block C | Block D | Block E |
|---------|---------|---------|---------|---------|
| 7+5 = | 8+6 = | 6+7 = | 5+8 = | 6+9 = |
| 9+5 = | 5+6 = | 9+7 = | 7+8 = | 5+9 = |
| 6+5 = | 9+6 = | 4+7 = | 3+8 = | 8+9 = |
| 8+5 = | 7+6 = | 8+7 = | 9+8 = | 4+9 = |
|  | 6+6 = | 5+7 = | 6+8 = | 3+9 = |
|  |  | 7+7 = | 4+8 = | 7+9 = |
|  |  |  | 8+8 = | 6+9 = |

| Block F | Block G | Block H | Block I |
|---------|---------|---------|---------|
| 9 + ☐ = 11 | ☐ + 3 = 12 | 9 + ☐ = 13 | ☐ + 5 = 14 |
| ☐ + 3 = 11 | 8 + ☐ = 12 | ☐ + 5 = 13 | 8 + ☐ = 14 |
| 7 + ☐ = 11 | 7 + ☐ = 12 | 7 + ☐ = 13 | ☐ + 7 = 14 |
| ☐ + 5 = 11 | ☐ + 6 = 12 | ☐ + 6 = 15 | 9 + ☐ = 16 |
|  |  | 8 + ☐ = 15 | ☐ + 8 = 16 |
|  |  | 9 + ☐ = 17 | ☐ + 9 = 18 |

---

### A useful discovery

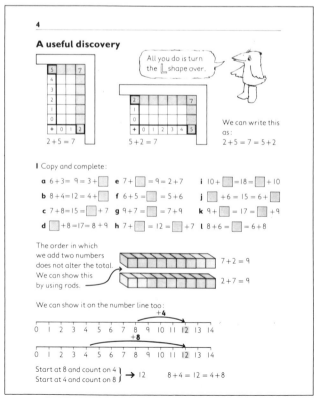

2 + 5 = 7

5 + 2 = 7

All you do is turn the L shape over.

We can write this as:

2 + 5 = 7 = 5 + 2

1 Copy and complete:

a 6+3 = 9 = 3+☐    e 7+☐ = 9 = 2+7    i 10+☐ = 18 = ☐+10
b 8+4 = 12 = 4+☐    f 6+5 = ☐ = 5+6    j ☐+6 = 15 = 6+☐
c 7+8 = 15 = ☐+7    g 9+7 = ☐ = 7+9    k 9+☐ = 17 = ☐+9
d ☐+8 = 17 = 8+☐    h 7+☐ = 12 = ☐+7    l 8+6 = ☐ = 6+8

The order in which
we add two numbers
does not alter the total.
We can show this
by using rods.

7 + 2 = 9

2 + 7 = 9

We can show it on the number line too:

+4

0 1 2 3 4 5 6 7 8 9 10 11 12 13 14

+8

0 1 2 3 4 5 6 7 8 9 10 11 12 13 14

Start at 8 and count on 4 ⎫ → 12
Start at 4 and count on 8 ⎭

8 + 4 = 12 = 4 + 8

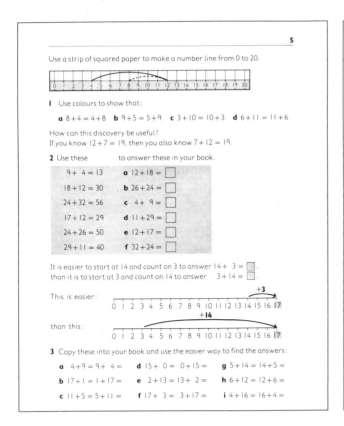

### 5

Use a strip of squared paper to make a number line from 0 to 20.

**I** Use colours to show that:

**a** 8+4 = 4+8   **b** 9+5 = 5+9   **c** 3+10 = 10+3   **d** 6+11 = 11+6

How can this discovery be useful?
If you know 12+7 = 19, then you also know 7+12 = 19.

**2** Use these        to answer these in your book.

| | |
|---|---|
| 9+ 4 = 13 | **a** 12+18 = ☐ |
| 18+12 = 30 | **b** 26+24 = ☐ |
| 24+32 = 56 | **c** 4+ 9 = ☐ |
| 17+12 = 29 | **d** 11+29 = ☐ |
| 24+26 = 50 | **e** 12+17 = ☐ |
| 29+11 = 40 | **f** 32+24 = ☐ |

It is easier to start at 14 and count on 3 to answer 14+ 3 = ☐,
than it is to start at 3 and count on 14 to answer 3+14 = ☐.

This is easier:

than this:

**3** Copy these into your book and use the easier way to find the answers:

**a** 4+9 = 9+ 4 =   **d** 15+ 0 = 0+15 =   **g** 5+14 = 14+5 =

**b** 17+1 = 1+17 =   **e** 2+13 = 13+ 2 =   **h** 6+12 = 12+6 =

**c** 11+5 = 5+11 =   **f** 17+ 3 = 3+17 =   **i** 4+16 = 16+4 =

---

**Practice material
for use with Nuffield Maths 3 Pupils' Book**

**Practice I**                                Name_____

Chapter I: Addition I

| A | B | C | D |
|---|---|---|---|
| 9+8 = 17 | 5+7 = 12 | 11+3 = 14 | 4+8 = 12 |
| 11+1 = 12 | 12+2 = 14 | 5+9 = 14 | 17+2 = 19 |
| 4+9 = 13 | 13+6 = 19 | 11+7 = 16 | 15+1 = 16 |
| 13+4 = 17 | 6+7 = 13 | 12+8 = 20 | 8+7 = 15 |
| 9+6 = 15 | 14+3 = 17 | 9+7 = 16 | 12+6 = 18 |
| 15+5 = 20 | 16+4 = 20 | 13+2 = 15 | 11+9 = 20 |
| 16+2 = 18 | 4+7 = 11 | 15+3 = 18 | 14+1 = 15 |
| 8+6 = 14 | 19+1 = 20 | 14+5 = 19 | 7+8 = 15 |
| 18+1 = 19 | 12+4 = 16 | 7+9 = 16 | 11+5 = 16 |
| 6+6 = 12 | 8+9 = 17 | 8+8 = 16 | 5+8 = 13 |

**E**

| 7 | 14 | 5 | 17 | 11 | 7 | 14 | 11 | 18 | 8 |
|---|---|---|---|---|---|---|---|---|---|
| +7 | +6 | +8 | +1 | +2 | +6 | +2 | +6 | +2 | +8 |
| 14 | 20 | 13 | 18 | 13 | 13 | 16 | 17 | 20 | 16 |

**F**

| 12 | 3 | 5 | 15 | 7 | 13 | 16 | 9 | 6 | 12 |
|---|---|---|---|---|---|---|---|---|---|
| +7 | +8 | +6 | +4 | +9 | +7 | +1 | +7 | +9 | +3 |
| 19 | 11 | 11 | 19 | 16 | 20 | 17 | 16 | 15 | 15 |

**G**

| 12 | 16 | 13 | 8 | 14 | 9 | 13 | 15 | 8 | 3 |
|---|---|---|---|---|---|---|---|---|---|
| +5 | +3 | +5 | +7 | +4 | +6 | +3 | +2 | +9 | +9 |
| 17 | 19 | 18 | 15 | 18 | 15 | 16 | 17 | 17 | 12 |

Nuffield Maths 3 Spiritmasters          Nuffield Maths 3 Pupils' Book          9

# References and resources

Shuard, H. and Williams, M., *Primary Mathematics Today* (chapter 9), Longman Group Ltd 1970

Pleuger, W. H., *A Guide to the use of Stern Apparatus*, E.S.A.

*Dial-a-sum*, Triman Classmate

# Chapter 2

# Shape 1

## For the teacher

This chapter revises and extends some of the basic principles covered in Chapter 8 (Shape 2) of the *Nuffield Maths 2 Teachers' Handbook*.

It cannot be stressed too strongly that no amount of formal exercise work can take the place of practical activities when dealing with shape. The child must have the opportunity to manipulate cut-out shapes, to move them around, to fit them together and to see them in all possible positions. Many children recognise shape A as a square but cannot say what shape B is because they have never manipulated a cut-out square.

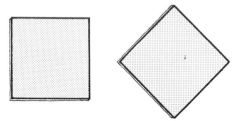

Throughout this work children should be encouraged to look for shapes in the environment and to collect pictures to be stuck in class books which can be made in the shape.

## Summary of the stages

1  Sorting and classifying – straight and curved lines

2  Plane shapes with 3 or more sides

3  Axes of symmetry

## Vocabulary

Straight, curved, triangle, square, rectangle, oblong, quadrilateral, pentagon, hexagon, octagon, symmetry, symmetrical, axis, axes, exactly.

## Equipment and apparatus

Card, squared or 'dot' paper, geoboards, elastic bands, string, mirrors (plastic), pegboard and pegs, carbon paper.

## Working with the children

### 1  Sorting and classifying – straight and curved lines

In everyday life we accept that the straight line is the shortest distance

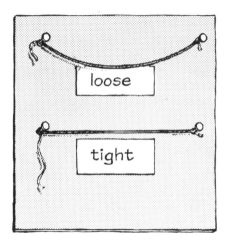

between two points and this may be demonstrated to children in a number of ways.

If we allow a piece of string to sag between two nails and then pull it until the string is tight and in a straight line we find we have used less string.

Two skittles placed some distance apart enable children to compare how many paces it takes to go from one to the other by different routes and to see that the straight line is the shortest distance.

The exercises in the Pupils' Book involve first sorting and then drawing shapes with straight sides, curved sides or both straight and curved sides.

## 2　Plane shapes with three or more sides

In these exercises no attempt is made to discover anything about the shapes but that they have a certain number of sides and the same number of corners. At a later stage the properties of shapes will be considered and the 'corners' will become angles.

A triangle is a shape with three sides and three corners.
A quadrilateral is a shape with four sides and four corners.
A pentagon is a shape with five sides and five corners.
A hexagon is a shape with six sides and six corners.
An octagon is a shape with eight sides and eight corners.

It is unfortunate that most commercially-produced sets of shapes are *regular*, that is, those with all sides and angles equal. For example, the pentagon is only produced as in Figure A, whereas Figures B, C and D are also pentagons. Figure A is the *regular* pentagon.

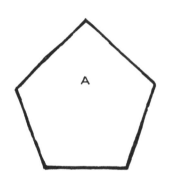
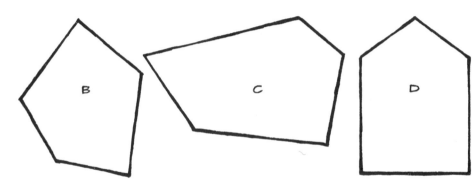

It is important that the child recognises each of these shapes as a pentagon. For this reason *no* emphasis has been laid at this stage on the regular shapes.

Using a nailboard or geoboard in the first instance allows children to make plane shapes quickly and easily. After some experience of this activity, the children can begin to record either on specially prepared 'dot sheets' or on squared paper.

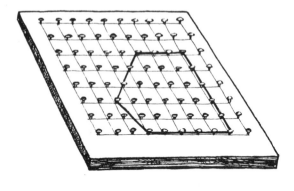 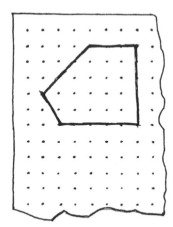 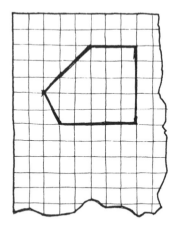

## 3   Axes of symmetry

First ideas of symmetry were introduced in *Nuffield Maths 2* where emphasis was placed on children's natural feeling for symmetry in their art and constructional play and examples of symmetry in the environment, particularly in nature.

The word *balance* was used to describe a shape or picture which is 'alike on both sides' of the line of balance or *axis of symmetry*.

The practical activities suggested in *Nuffield Maths 2 Teachers' Handbook* are repeated here to be used as reinforcement of first ideas on symmetry or as an introduction for those children who are meeting the topic for the first time.

## Activities

*Blot patterns*  Fold a piece of paper down the middle.
Open out and put a blob of paint on the fold.
Fold the paper again and carefully press down on the paper.
Open out and let paint dry. The picture will display a back to front pattern with the axis running along the fold of the paper.

*String patterns* Fold a piece of paper in half.

Cover a piece of string with paint.

Open paper and place string on one half, near the fold, leaving one end of the string over the edge of the paper.

Place one hand firmly on the folded paper and pull the string out by the loose end.

Open up and allow paint to dry. The picture again will display a back to front pattern with the *axis of symmetry* running down the fold.

*Paper folding and cutting* Fold a piece of paper in half.

Cut a shape out of the double thickness.

When opened out and mounted on a coloured sheet, a symmetrical shape shows through.

If the paper is folded three or four times before cutting, several axes of symmetry can be shown:

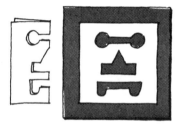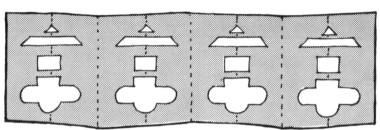

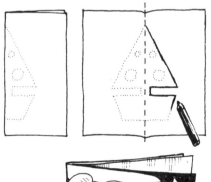

*Pin pricking and carbon patterns*
Fold a piece of paper in half.

Draw any shape on one side up to the fold.

Prick through the paper with a pin along the line of the drawn shape.

Open up the paper and draw over the pin holes.

Again, the *line of balance* or *axis of symmetry* is along the fold.

carbon side

A similar effect is obtained by folding a sheet of carbon paper with the carbon on the *outside*, placing it inside a paper 'cover' and drawing on the front of the 'cover'.

A symmetrical design will appear when the paper is opened out.

11

*Mirrors*, which can now be obtained in unbreakable plastic, are very useful for showing the symmetry of environmental shapes, geometrical shapes and letters.

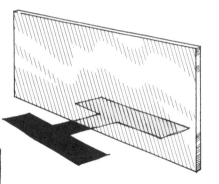
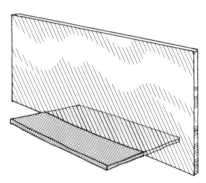

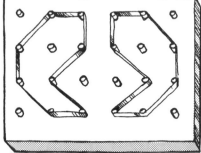

*Geoboards, pegboards etc.* A chalk line drawn on a geoboard is used as the axis of symmetry. Children use rubber bands to make symmetrical patterns or to make the 'other half' of a shape made by a partner.

Similar activities may be designed using: pegs and pegboard, beads threaded to make a symmetrical necklace, or centicubes on a baseboard. Here, colour as well as pattern must be considered to achieve complete balance.

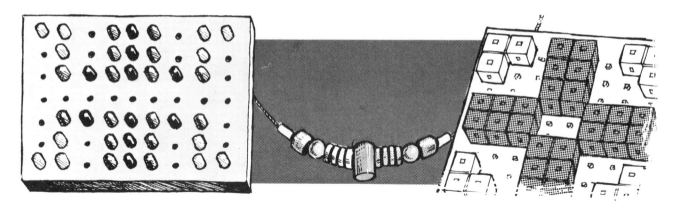

# Pages from the Pupils' Book and Spiritmasters

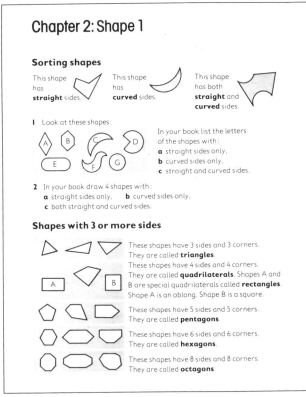

## Chapter 2: Shape 1

### Sorting shapes

This shape has **straight** sides.

This shape has **curved** sides.

This shape has both **straight** and **curved** sides.

**I** Look at these shapes.

In your book list the letters of the shapes with:
**a** straight sides only,
**b** curved sides only,
**c** straight and curved sides.

**2** In your book draw 4 shapes with:
**a** straight sides only,    **b** curved sides only,
**c** both straight and curved sides.

### Shapes with 3 or more sides

These shapes have 3 sides and 3 corners.
They are called **triangles**.

These shapes have 4 sides and 4 corners.
They are called **quadrilaterals**. Shapes A and B are special quadrilaterals called **rectangles**.
Shape A is an oblong. Shape B is a square.

These shapes have 5 sides and 5 corners.
They are called **pentagons**.

These shapes have 6 sides and 6 corners.
They are called **hexagons**.

These shapes have 8 sides and 8 corners.
They are called **octagons**.

---

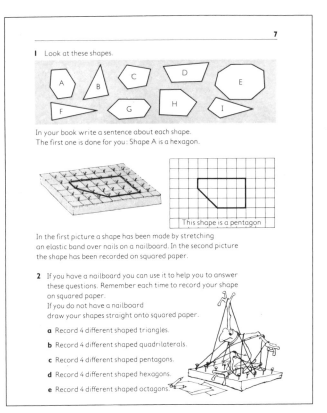

**I** Look at these shapes.

In your book write a sentence about each shape.
The first one is done for you: Shape A is a hexagon.

This shape is a pentagon

In the first picture a shape has been made by stretching an elastic band over nails on a nailboard. In the second picture the shape has been recorded on squared paper.

**2** If you have a nailboard you can use it to help you to answer these questions. Remember each time to record your shape on squared paper.
If you do not have a nailboard draw your shapes straight onto squared paper.

**a** Record 4 different shaped triangles.

**b** Record 4 different shaped quadrilaterals.

**c** Record 4 different shaped pentagons.

**d** Record 4 different shaped hexagons.

**e** Record 4 different shaped octagons.

---

### Axes of symmetry

Copy this quadrilateral onto squared paper and then cut it out.

The cut-out shape can be folded so that one part fits exactly onto the other.

If a shape can be folded like this so that one part fits exactly on the other, we say that it has an axis of symmetry.

axis of symmetry

Some shapes have more than one axis of symmetry.
A cut-out square can be folded in 4 different ways so that one part fits exactly on the other.

A square has 4 axes of symmetry.

**I** Copy these shapes onto squared paper, cut them out and fold them to discover how many axes of symmetry they have.
Record your results in your book.

---

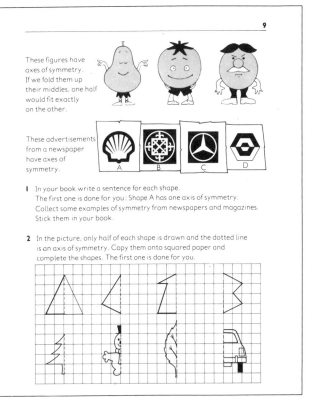

These figures have axes of symmetry.
If we fold them up their middles, one half would fit exactly on the other.

These advertisements from a newspaper have axes of symmetry.

**I** In your book write a sentence for each shape.
The first one is done for you: Shape A has one axis of symmetry.
Collect some examples of symmetry from newspapers and magazines.
Stick them in your book.

**2** In the picture, only half of each shape is drawn and the dotted line is an axis of symmetry. Copy them onto squared paper and complete the shapes. The first one is done for you.

---

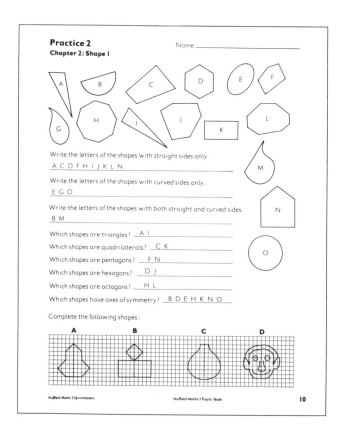

# References and resources

Ingleby, T. and Taylor, J., *Shapes series* (six books), Longman Group Ltd

Nuffield Mathematics Teaching Project, *Beginnings* ▽, *Shape and Size* ▽, *Environmental Geometry*, Nuffield Teachers' Guides, Chambers/Murray 1969 (See Introduction, page xii.)

Shuard, H. and Williams, E., *Primary Mathematics Today* (chapters 11 and 12), Longman Group Ltd 1970

Walter, Marion, *Mirror Books* (supplied with metal mirrors), Andre Deutsch

*Tracing Shapes*, E. J. Arnold

*Copyprint Grids*, Copyprint

*Basic Shapes Metrirule, Basic Shapes Set, Early Cognitive Experiences, Mosaic Shapes, Related Shapes, Shape Tracer and Recognition Kit*, Invicta Plastics

*Altair Design Pads 1*, Longman Group Ltd

*2 Centimetre Cubes, Geometry Models, Shapes Board Set, Shape Silhouettes*, Metric Aids

*Centicube Baseboard and Centicubes, Geoshape Stencils, Mirrors* (unbreakable plastic), Osmiroid

*3-D Geometry Rubber Stamps, Mammoth Table and Floor Tiles, Plane Geometry Rubber Stamps, Symmetry and Reversal Pairing Cards*, Philip & Tacey

*Multi-purpose Mosaic Shapes, Wooden Cones, Cylinders and Spheres*, Taskmaster

# Chapter 3

# Place value

## For the teacher

This chapter contains a little more reading than usual but it is hoped that the material it contains will be given a considerable amount of teacher direction and support. The aim is to stimulate interest in the recording of numbers and the advantages of place value in any recording system.

A full understanding of the concept of place value is acquired very gradually and experience of grouping and exchanging is much more likely to lead to this understanding than the mechanical chanting of such misleading phrases as 'put down three and carry one'.

Grouping in threes, fours, fives and sixes involves only very simple number bonds and enables children to use the all-important principle of exchange without being confused by larger amounts of material. This type of activity is not seen as an end in itself, but as a means to an end.

Alongside skill and facility in computation, it is important that children develop an appreciation of the economy of a number system based on place value.

Some teachers may develop the ideas in this chapter into a small topic, giving rise to discussion, written work, surveys, artwork and indeed the development of the children's own counting system.

## Summary of the stages

1  Tallying

2  Place value – practical examples

## Vocabulary

Tally, survey, record, position, represents, columns.

## Equipment and apparatus

Egg boxes and large beads, a calendar, interlocking cubes, squared paper for 'home-made' place value apparatus. For traffic survey – a board and clip with a duplicated sheet showing columns and headings suggested.

## Working with the children

### 1  Tallying

Early man used tallying to keep count of objects without using conventional numbers. Recording was achieved on a one-to-one basis, for example, one notch would be cut in a piece of wood, or one pebble placed in the soil, for each object counted. It is important for children to experience these ancient skills if they are to gain a true understanding of number.

One particular form of tallying involves the use of ̶1̶1̶1̶1̶ 11 (that is, one group of 5 and 2 units). Experience with this form of tallying helps to establish the concept of 'representation'. Although made up of single strokes, ̶1̶1̶1̶1̶ quite clearly *represents* 5, and can be recognised and counted as such. The *changed form* represents a new quantity – *sets of 5*. This is precisely the concept we are trying to establish when we teach 'tens and units'. The '1' in '15', for example, represents a set of ten units although in this instance it is the *position* and not the *appearance* of the symbol which has *changed*.

The first exercise provides experiences in translating a 'tally number' into a conventional number by finding the number contained in the sets of five and then adding on the units.

|||| |||| ||||   11
5,    10,    15, and 2 makes 17

This is taken a stage further by providing a '||||| column', thus

|||| ||||   111   becomes

| |||| | 1 |
|---|---|
| 2 | 3 |

It is important for the child to call this, '2 sets of five and 3 units' or to read the numerals figure by figure as 'two, three' and not as 'twenty-three' because 'twenty' is a special word for 'two sets of *ten*'.

*Word and traffic surveys*
This activity is aimed at providing a practical experience in using the tally-method for counting. It is important to convey to the children that keeping a tally is not something old-fashioned, but a very useful skill even today.

If the weather or other conditions make a traffic survey impracticable, a word survey is a good alternative. A page in a reading book is selected and tallying is used to count such things as:

How many times the word 'the' occurs on the page.
or    How many words with more than 5 letters there are.
or    The number of sentences with 2 words, how many with 3 words, 4 words, etc.

One could, perhaps, discuss with the children the possible advantages of keeping a tally compared to continuous counting.

## 2   Place value – practical examples

The first example provides experience in making groups of 5. Some children may need practical experience with re-grouping. 'Choc-bars' can be made from rectangular pieces of card and elastic bands, or envelopes can be provided to group five together to form a box.

The second example provides experience in making groups of 6 using egg boxes.

The third example is less practical although nevertheless realistic. By using weeks and days, experience is provided in making groups of 7. Activities involving a calendar are particularly useful here.

The main teaching point with all three exercises is to establish that it is possible to record a group of objects under a *new name* which represents a new value although the same digits are being used.

For example:

1 box    and    4 eggs

2 trays    and    2 cakes

A numeral may refer to different things depending upon its *position* – the numeral on the left giving the number of sets or groups; the numeral on the right giving the number of 'units' not put into full sets. Thus in the egg example, 1 box and 4 eggs, the 1 is worth more than the 4 because it means a full box. In the cake example, 2 trays and 2 cakes, the 2 on the left is worth more than the 2 on the right.

If children need additional practice, some of the re-grouping activities suggested in Chapter 2 of *Nuffield Maths 2 Teachers' Handbook* can be used. For example: Interlocking unit cubes such as Centicubes, Multilink, Metricubes or Unifix are matched to the coloured squares on a board. The cubes are then linked to make 'longs' according to the instructions on one of the separate cards.

| Match | longs | units |
|---|---|---|
|  |  |  |

When I match and group in 3's there are ☐ longs and ☐ units.

When I match and group in 4's there are ☐ longs and ☐ units.

The child carries out the matching and grouping, puts numeral cards in the frames on the board and copies the completed card into his book.

This activity may be extended to include a third column giving a further grouping of 'longs' into 'squares'.

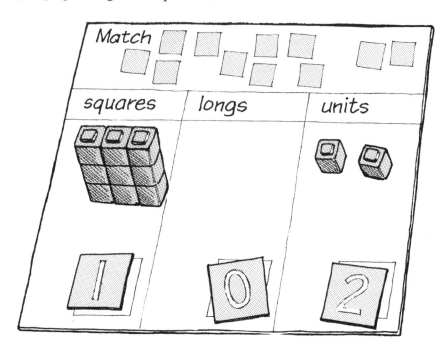

The advantage of this type of material is that the units are *actually fixed together* to make a group of 3, 4, 5, etc. in the form of a 'long' and, later, the 'longs' are joined to make 'squares'.

*Use of multi-base arithmetic blocks*
Many schools have multi-base apparatus, e.g. Dienes, Tillich Blocks or Multi-Base Blocks, but if this is not available the children can make simple apparatus from card marked in 1 cm squares.

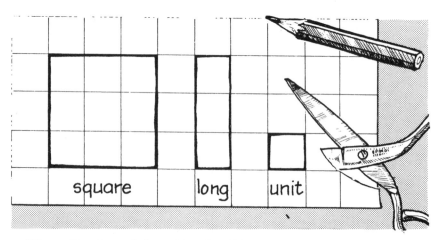

They will each need about 30 units, 10 longs and 4 squares, which should be cut from the card.

Although in multi-base apparatus these are three-dimensional, the flat card will serve as an adequate aid at this stage as we are only concerned with practice in regrouping.

The children should be given the opportunity to experiment with the apparatus before commencing the exercises. They may set out their pieces in sequential patterns, make pictures with them, etc.

To avoid confusion, the names units, longs and squares are given to the pieces as shown above.

The first part of each exercise establishes the relationship between units, longs and squares. This is followed by the *physical exchanging* of pieces which is fundamental to the regrouping process. It is important to establish the correct routine from the start:

1   Take the required number of units.
2   Exchange the units, a few at a time, for longs, and record in terms of longs and units.
3   Exchange the longs, a few at a time, for squares and record as squares, longs and units.

For example, grouping in 3's.

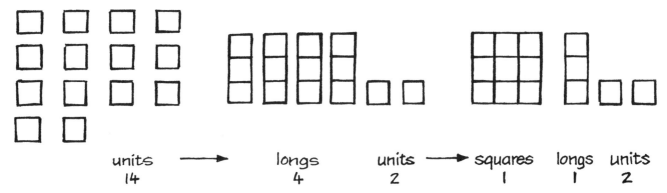

| units | | longs | units | | squares | longs | units |
|-------|--|-------|-------|--|---------|-------|-------|
| 14 | → | 4 | 2 | → | 1 | 1 | 2 |

One of the main advantages of using small bases such as 3 or 4 is that they provide experience of two exchange operations using a manageable number of units and very simple number bonds.

Some schools have multi-base apparatus but tend to use base 10 only. In order to experience 2 exchange operations (that is, the use of 3 columns) in base 10 at least a hundred units are needed – an unmanageable number compared with 9 units in base 3 or 16 units in base 4. Moreover, because our number system is based on 10, a particular set of units is represented in the same form when expressed in longs and units or tens and units.

For example:

| | Longs | Units |
|---|-------|-------|
| 28 units | 2 | 8 |

In other words, because of the child's familiarity with base 10, it becomes more difficult to assess if he has gained understanding from the experience of exchange or is merely giving a mechanical response. A child may be able to state that 28 units is made up of 2 tens and 8 units but does he really understand the significance of the value of the 2 tens? Using bases other than 10 provides a check on this.

Although the diagram for grouping in tens shows a square representing 100, the exercises only deal with 2-digit numbers. The children should 'set out' the correct number of 'longs' to represent tens and unit pieces to represent 'ones' or units before completing each line in the table.

For example,
the child sets out

and then records:

| 1 ten and 2 units | 10+2 | 12 | twelve |

This gives a physical representation of the number, followed by a description in words of the pieces. Then the numerical values of the pieces are listed separately in so-called 'extended notation' (10 + 2). The numeral is then written in figures and finally in word form.

# Pages from the Pupils' Book and Spiritmasters

## Chapter 3: Place value

### Tallying

Many years ago, when people lived in caves and simple huts, they knew nothing about the numbers we use today.
How do you think this man was able to tell his friend on the other side of the river how many weapons he had?

Who had more weapons?

Sometimes they made knots along a piece of string, or made patterns with stones or shells. We say that they made a tally.

Early merchants used a different way of tallying to help them count their goods.

| | represents | |
|---|---|---|
| II | → | 2 barrels |
| ₩ | → | 5 barrels |
| ₩ ₩ III | → | 13 barrels |
| ₩ I | → | 6 barrels |

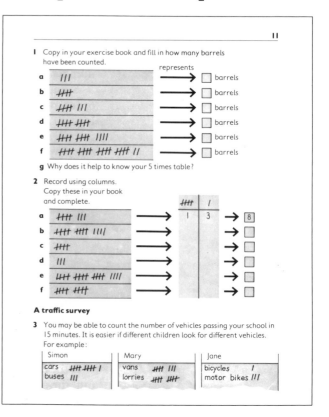

1  Copy in your exercise book and fill in how many barrels have been counted.

represents

a  III → ☐ barrels
b  ₩ → ☐ barrels
c  ₩ III → ☐ barrels
d  ₩ ₩ → ☐ barrels
e  ₩ ₩ IIII → ☐ barrels
f  ₩ ₩ ₩ ₩ II → ☐ barrels

g  Why does it help to know your 5 times table?

2  Record using columns.
Copy these in your book and complete.

| | | | | ₩ | I | |
|---|---|---|---|---|---|---|
| a | ₩ III | → | | 1 | 3 | → 8 |
| b | ₩ ₩ IIII | → | | | | → ☐ |
| c | ₩ | → | | | | → ☐ |
| d | III | → | | | | → ☐ |
| e | ₩ ₩ ₩ IIII | → | | | | → ☐ |
| f | ₩ ₩ | → | | | | → ☐ |

### A traffic survey

3  You may be able to count the number of vehicles passing your school in 15 minutes. It is easier if different children look for different vehicles.
For example:

| Simon | | Mary | | Jane | |
|---|---|---|---|---|---|
| cars | ₩ ₩ I | vans | ₩ III | bicycles | I |
| buses | III | lorries | ₩ ₩ | motor bikes | III |

## Panel 12

**Understanding place value**

At Mr Sweet's factory, 5 choc-bars are packed into a box. If he had 8 bars he would say, "I have one full box and three bars," and he would record:

| boxes | units |
|---|---|
| 1 | 3 |

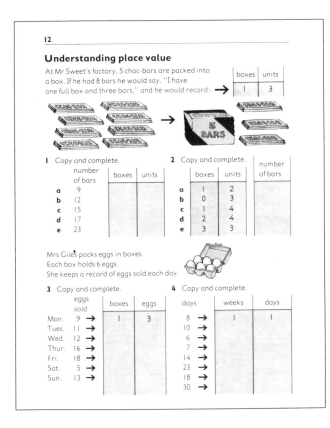

**1** Copy and complete.

| | number of bars | boxes | units |
|---|---|---|---|
| a | 9 | | |
| b | 12 | | |
| c | 15 | | |
| d | 17 | | |
| e | 23 | | |

**2** Copy and complete.

| | boxes | units | number of bars |
|---|---|---|---|
| a | 1 | 2 | |
| b | 0 | 3 | |
| c | 1 | 4 | |
| d | 2 | 4 | |
| e | 3 | 3 | |

Mrs Giles packs eggs in boxes.
Each box holds 6 eggs.
She keeps a record of eggs sold each day.

**3** Copy and complete.

| | eggs sold | | boxes | eggs |
|---|---|---|---|---|
| Mon. | 9 | → | 1 | 3 |
| Tues. | 11 | → | | |
| Wed. | 12 | → | | |
| Thur. | 16 | → | | |
| Fri. | 18 | → | | |
| Sat. | 5 | → | | |
| Sun. | 13 | → | | |

**4** Copy and complete.

| days | | weeks | days |
|---|---|---|---|
| 8 | → | 1 | 1 |
| 10 | → | | |
| 6 | → | | |
| 7 | → | | |
| 14 | → | | |
| 23 | → | | |
| 18 | → | | |
| 30 | → | | |

## Panel 13

**Grouping in threes**

3 units make a long.
3 longs make a square.

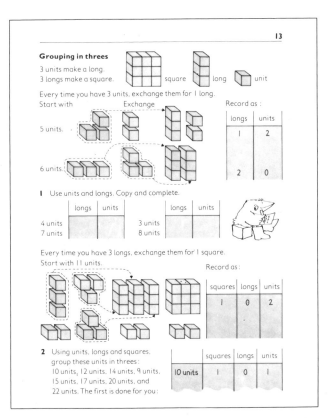

square    long    unit

Every time you have 3 units, exchange them for 1 long.

Start with    Exchange    Record as :

| | longs | units |
|---|---|---|
| 5 units. | 1 | 2 |
| 6 units. | 2 | 0 |

**1** Use units and longs. Copy and complete.

| | longs | units | | longs | units |
|---|---|---|---|---|---|
| 4 units | | | 3 units | | |
| 7 units | | | 8 units | | |

Every time you have 3 longs, exchange them for 1 square.
Start with 11 units.

Record as :

| squares | longs | units |
|---|---|---|
| 1 | 0 | 2 |

**2** Using units, longs and squares, group these units in threes:
10 units, 12 units, 14 units, 9 units, 15 units, 17 units, 20 units, and 22 units. The first is done for you :

| | squares | longs | units |
|---|---|---|---|
| 10 units | 1 | 0 | 1 |

## Panel 14

**Grouping in fours**

4 units make a long.
4 longs make a square.

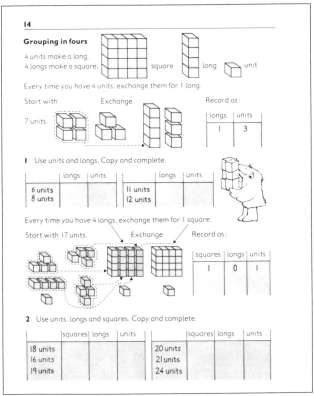

square    long    unit

Every time you have 4 units, exchange them for 1 long.

Start with    Exchange    Record as :

| | longs | units |
|---|---|---|
| 7 units. | 1 | 3 |

**1** Use units and longs. Copy and complete.

| | longs | units | | longs | units |
|---|---|---|---|---|---|
| 6 units | | | 11 units | | |
| 8 units | | | 12 units | | |

Every time you have 4 longs, exchange them for 1 square.
Start with 17 units.

Exchange    Record as :

| squares | longs | units |
|---|---|---|
| 1 | 0 | 1 |

**2** Use units, longs and squares. Copy and complete.

| | squares | longs | units | | squares | longs | units |
|---|---|---|---|---|---|---|---|
| 18 units | | | | 20 units | | | |
| 16 units | | | | 21 units | | | |
| 19 units | | | | 24 units | | | |

## Panel 15

**Grouping in tens**

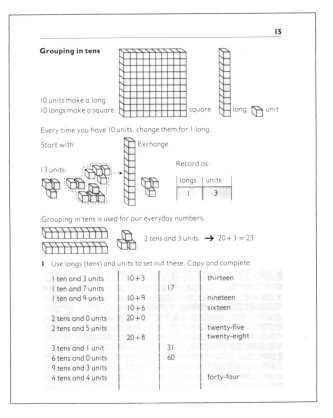

10 units make a long.
10 longs make a square.

square    long    unit

Every time you have 10 units, change them for 1 long.

Start with    Exchange    Record as :

| | longs | units |
|---|---|---|
| 13 units. | 1 | 3 |

Grouping in tens is used for our everyday numbers.

2 tens and 3 units  →  20 + 3 = 23

**1** Use longs (tens) and units to set out these. Copy and complete.

| | | | |
|---|---|---|---|
| 1 ten and 3 units | 10 + 3 | | thirteen |
| 1 ten and 7 units | | 17 | |
| 1 ten and 9 units | 10 + 9 | | nineteen |
| | 10 + 6 | | sixteen |
| 2 tens and 0 units | 20 + 0 | | |
| 2 tens and 5 units | | | twenty-five |
| | 20 + 8 | | twenty-eight |
| 3 tens and 1 unit | | 31 | |
| 6 tens and 0 units | | 60 | |
| 9 tens and 3 units | | | |
| 4 tens and 4 units | | | forty-four |

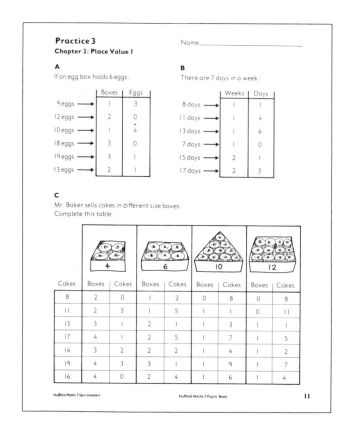

**Practice 3**
**Chapter 3: Place Value I**

Name_____

**A**

If an egg box holds 6 eggs:

| | Boxes | Eggs |
|---|---|---|
| 9 eggs → | 1 | 3 |
| 12 eggs → | 2 | 0 |
| 10 eggs → | 1 | 4 |
| 18 eggs → | 3 | 0 |
| 19 eggs → | 3 | 1 |
| 13 eggs → | 2 | 1 |

**B**

There are 7 days in a week:

| | Weeks | Days |
|---|---|---|
| 8 days → | 1 | 1 |
| 11 days → | 1 | 4 |
| 13 days → | 1 | 6 |
| 7 days → | 1 | 0 |
| 15 days → | 2 | 1 |
| 17 days → | 2 | 3 |

**C**

Mr. Baker sells cakes in different size boxes.
Complete this table.

| Cakes | Boxes (4) | Cakes (4) | Boxes (6) | Cakes (6) | Boxes (10) | Cakes (10) | Boxes (12) | Cakes (12) |
|---|---|---|---|---|---|---|---|---|
| 8 | 2 | 0 | 1 | 2 | 0 | 8 | 0 | 8 |
| 11 | 2 | 3 | 1 | 5 | 1 | 1 | 0 | 11 |
| 13 | 3 | 1 | 2 | 1 | 1 | 3 | 1 | 1 |
| 17 | 4 | 1 | 2 | 5 | 1 | 7 | 1 | 5 |
| 14 | 3 | 2 | 2 | 2 | 1 | 4 | 1 | 2 |
| 19 | 4 | 3 | 3 | 1 | 1 | 9 | 1 | 7 |
| 16 | 4 | 0 | 2 | 4 | 1 | 6 | 1 | 4 |

Nuffield Maths 3 Spiritmasters · Nuffield Maths 3 Pupils' Book · 11

# References and resources

Nuffield Mathematics Teaching Project, Computation and Structure ②
Nuffield Teachers' Guides, Chambers/Murray 1969 (See Introduction page xii.)

McIntosh, A. *How basic are bases?* Article in *Junior Education*, July 1978

Shuard, H. and Williams, M., *Primary Mathematics Today* (chapter 13), Longman Group Ltd 1970

*Centicubes*, Osmiroid

*Dienes M.A.B., Multilink*, E.S.A.

*Multibase Blocks*, Metric Aids

*Tillich Blocks*, E. J. Arnold

*Unifix Cubes, Unifix Retaining Frames*, Philip & Tacey

# Length 1

## For the teacher

This chapter revises and reinforces some of the basic work covered in Chapter 7 (Length 2) of *Nuffield Maths 2 Teachers' Handbook*. Some children will have been introduced to these ideas already but will benefit from the revision. For others this chapter will be a valuable introduction to measurement of length.

The order of the work is both logical and important. The children begin by using parts of their bodies for measuring. They are shown that the choice of unit is governed by the length to be measured: that is, they will use smaller units such as digits for the shorter measurements. The children are given experience of estimating and comparing the estimates with the measurements taken. They are also introduced to the problem of 'the bit left over' and the need to use two units for more accurate measurement.

Before the children use standard measures, it is important that they appreciate the need for them. This is realised through discussion of the weaknesses of arbitrary measures. When set the same task different children will come to different conclusions using arbitrary measures. Once the need for standard measures is realised the children work with first the metre and then the 10-centimetre (decimetre) rod.

## Summary of the stages

1   Measuring with parts of the body. (Estimating before measuring.)

2   Measuring with more than one unit

3   Towards a standard measure

4   The metre

5   The 10-centimetre (decimetre) rod

## Vocabulary

Shorter, longer, shortest, longest, order of length, handspan, palm, digit, cubit, length, width, height, distance, estimate, stride, footprint, metre, pace, standard unit, 10-centimetre or decimetre, column.

## Equipment and apparatus

Most things to be measured will be in the average classroom. Other things required are: coloured sticky paper, metre rods, 10-centimetre rods (orange rod from Cuisenaire or Colour Factor or any base 10 long from multibase materials which use a 1 cm unit).

## Working with the children

### 1   Measuring with parts of the body

Man used parts of the body as arbitrary measures before the introduction of standard measures. The children should use these arbitrary measures

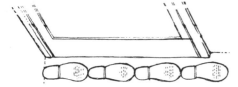

first so that through discussion of the problems that arise and the inadequacies of such measures, they realise the need for the standard measures we use today.

At this stage accuracy is not as important as the need for the correct technique when measuring. The children should work within a controlled situation from the start. Whichever part of the body is used, the children should be shown how to place the 'units' close together starting at the very edge of the object to be measured.

*Estimating before measuring*

It is very important that children develop some skill in estimating. All too often children take a wild guess when asked to estimate a measurement, rather than think carefully and make a reasonable judgement. Preliminary activities should include oral work when the child is asked to 'imagine', for example, how many handspans will measure the length of a table. Skill at estimating is more likely to develop if children are encouraged to go through three steps:

1  Estimate by 'imagining' the units along the length.

Estimate:
7 handspans

Measure:
6 handspans

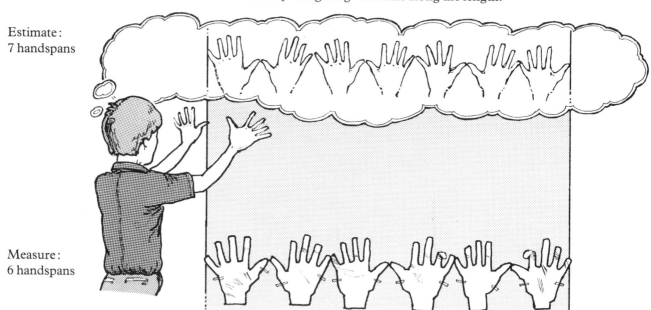

2  Measure the length in the chosen units.

3  Compare the estimate with measurement to see 'How close I was'. 'The measurement is 1 handspan less than my estimate.'
   (*Nuffield Maths 3 Spiritmasters*, Grids 6 and 7.)

This sequence should be followed with the same unit over a range of measurements. For example, using handspans as the unit, steps 1, 2 and 3 are taken for the length of a table, then the width of a window and so on. In this way the experience gained in making the first estimate is carried over to the next.

The skills of estimating and measuring are extended to use other limb measurements over longer distances. At this stage the children need not take account of any 'bits left over' but may use such phrases as 'just over 5 paces' or 'nearly 6 full spans'.

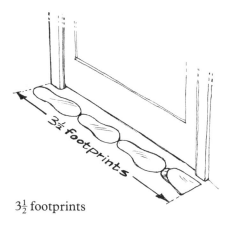

$3\frac{1}{2}$ footprints

When measuring in full spans the children need to work in pairs. One child marks the spot before the partner repositions himself for the next full span measurement.

Some children tend to 'lose count' when using handspans, footprints, etc. To help overcome this problem paper cut-outs, made by using limbs as templates, can be placed end to end first and then counted. Lengths of string or strips of paper may be cut to the size of the child's cubit, pace or full-span. Cut-outs also have another advantage – they can be folded in half or in quarters for the 'bit left over' to give a more accurate measurement.

Discussion about the results of these measuring activities should be steered to bring out the fact that the parts of the body vary in length from one individual to another. This is important in the build-up to the introduction of standard units.

## 2 Measuring with more than one unit

This section helps to establish two important aspects of measurement:
1 The use of smaller units to measure the 'bits left over'.
2 Possible relationships between the units used.
Later on the child will be introduced to recording measurement in terms of one unit, for example, 3.241 metres. Although this measure is conveniently expressed in terms of one unit (metres) it represents several units (metres, decimetres, centimetres, and millimetres). The Metric System's use of base 10 makes the need less obvious, but it is still essential that children recognise the need for and have experience of working with more than one unit of measure.

It may be necessary to give guidance on the selection of appropriate units. Obviously the second unit will be smaller than the first and some children may discover approximate relationships between units for themselves, for example, '2 handspans make a cubit' or '12 digits make a handspan.'

## 3 Towards a standard measure

By cutting strips of paper to represent the lengths of several children's handspans and comparing them on a bar-chart, the point made earlier about arbitrary units is emphasised. If a group of children each mark off the length of *six* handspans, the difference will be made even more obvious.

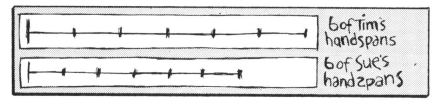

Discussion about these differences should lead the children to appreciate that a measure is needed that is the same for everyone – that is, a *standard* measure.

## 4 The metre

Having discussed the disadvantages of arbitrary units such as handspans, cubits, etc. in the previous stage, the children should be allowed to check that all metre sticks are the same length and, unlike limb measures, do not vary from person to person. A metre is always the same length whether it is used by a giant or a dwarf!

To help children to become familiar with the metre, it is used as a standard of comparison when making lists of objects or distances which are shorter than, about, and longer than a metre. Activities similar to those for limb measures, involving first estimation and the measurement are repeated but this time the units are metres. The symbol m can be introduced as standing for metre or metres so that 5 m, for example, means five metres. No full stop is required after the m unless it comes at the end of a sentence.

Children's ability to deal with 'the bit left over' will vary. Some may give results such as, 'Just over 5 metres' or 'Nearly 4 metres'; others may be able to use approximate fractions of a metre. This approach can be encouraged by providing a piece of string or strip of paper cut to a metre length which can be folded.

$2\frac{1}{2}$ metres

This may be a good moment to remind children that, unlike counting, no measurement can be absolutely exact.

The Pupils' book does not contain suggestions for use of the trundle or click wheel as not all schools have them and it is not easy to produce a 'home-made' version. Most children enjoy using the trundle wheel but its use needs to be carefully introduced and supervised by the teacher, or the child may regard it as a plaything rather than a measuring instrument. The child should be helped to understand the working of a trundle wheel by such questions as 'Why does it click?', 'What do you have to do to make it click?', 'How far does it travel between two clicks?'

A useful introductory activity is to run the trundle wheel along a metre stick first making sure that the wheel is in the 'click' position when put at the start of the metre stick. Alternatively a metre length of string can be put round the circumference of the wheel.

### 5 The 10-centimetre (decimetre) rod

After sufficient practice and experience of measuring with the metre stick, the decimetre or 10-centimetre rod may be introduced so that parts of a metre can be measured. The relationship between the 10 cm rod and the metre stick is covered in the first question.

An orange Cuisenaire/Colour Factor rod or a base 10 'long' from multibase apparatus (check that it is 10 cm long) can be used. Its handy size enables children to gain further experience of a repeated standard unit but it is not intended that it should become a commonly used measure. While the child is still mastering the physical skills of measuring, using the decimetre rod is a valuable interim stage before dealing with large numbers of centimetres.

As very few objects to be found in the classroom measure an exact number of metres, the child will find the 10-centimetre a useful second unit.

The metre stick and decimetre rods are used to measure objects in the same way as two body measures were used previously. See *Nuffield Maths 3 Spiritmasters*, Grid 8.

# Pages from the Pupils' Book and Spiritmasters

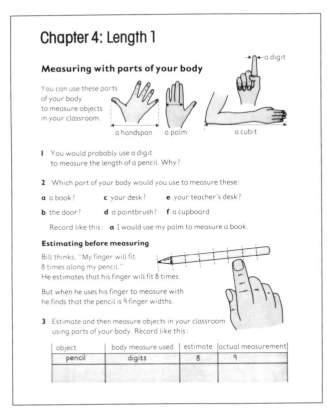

## Chapter 4: Length 1

### Measuring with parts of your body

You can use these parts of your body to measure objects in your classroom.

a handspan    a palm    a cubit    a digit

1   You would probably use a digit to measure the length of a pencil. Why?

2   Which part of your body would you use to measure these:

**a** a book?    **c** your desk?    **e** your teacher's desk?

**b** the door?    **d** a paintbrush?    **f** a cupboard

Record like this: **a** I would use my palm to measure a book.

### Estimating before measuring

Bill thinks, "My finger will fit 8 times along my pencil." He estimates that his finger will fit 8 times.

But when he uses his finger to measure with he finds that the pencil is 9 finger widths.

3   Estimate and then measure objects in your classroom using parts of your body. Record like this:

| object | body measure used | estimate | actual measurement |
|--------|-------------------|----------|--------------------|
| pencil | digits | 8 | 9 |
|  |  |  |  |

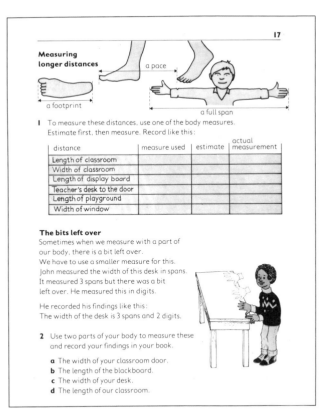

17

### Measuring longer distances

a footprint    a pace    a full span

1   To measure these distances, use one of the body measures. Estimate first, then measure. Record like this:

| distance | measure used | estimate | actual measurement |
|----------|-------------|----------|--------------------|
| Length of classroom |  |  |  |
| Width of classroom |  |  |  |
| Length of display board |  |  |  |
| Teacher's desk to the door |  |  |  |
| Length of playground |  |  |  |
| Width of window |  |  |  |

### The bits left over

Sometimes when we measure with a part of our body, there is a bit left over. We have to use a smaller measure for this. John measured the width of this desk in spans. It measured 3 spans but there was a bit left over. He measured this in digits.

He recorded his findings like this: The width of the desk is 3 spans and 2 digits.

2   Use two parts of your body to measure these and record your findings in your book.

   **a** The width of your classroom door.
   **b** The length of the blackboard.
   **c** The width of your desk.
   **d** The length of our classroom.

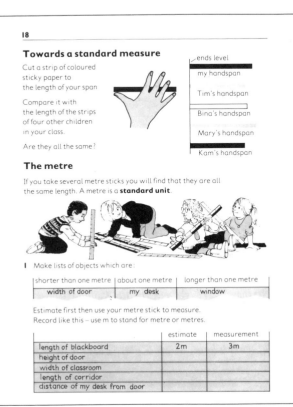

18

### Towards a standard measure

Cut a strip of coloured sticky paper to the length of your span

Compare it with the length of the strips of four other children in your class.

Are they all the same?

ends level
my handspan
Tim's handspan
Bina's handspan
Mary's handspan
Kam's handspan

### The metre

If you take several metre sticks you will find that they are all the same length. A metre is a **standard unit**.

1   Make lists of objects which are:

| shorter than one metre | about one metre | longer than one metre |
|------------------------|-----------------|----------------------|
| width of door | my desk | window |

Estimate first then use your metre stick to measure. Record like this – use m to stand for metre or metres.

|  | estimate | measurement |
|--|----------|-------------|
| length of blackboard | 2m | 3m |
| height of door |  |  |
| width of classroom |  |  |
| length of corridor |  |  |
| distance of my desk from door |  |  |

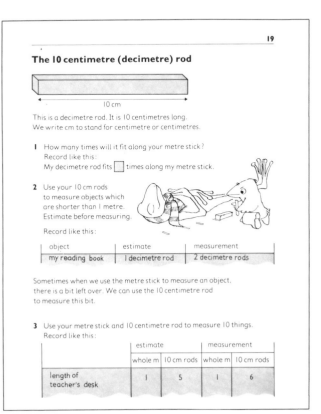

19

### The 10 centimetre (decimetre) rod

10 cm

This is a decimetre rod. It is 10 centimetres long. We write cm to stand for centimetre or centimetres.

1   How many times will it fit along your metre stick? Record like this:
   My decimetre rod fits [ ] times along my metre stick.

2   Use your 10 cm rods to measure objects which are shorter than 1 metre. Estimate before measuring.

Record like this:

| object | estimate | measurement |
|--------|----------|-------------|
| my reading book | I decimetre rod | 2 decimetre rods |

Sometimes when we use the metre stick to measure an object, there is a bit left over. We can use the 10 centimetre rod to measure this bit.

3   Use your metre stick and 10 centimetre rod to measure 10 things. Record like this:

|  | estimate | | measurement | |
|--|----------|--|-------------|--|
|  | whole m | 10 cm rods | whole m | 10 cm rods |
| length of teacher's desk | 1 | 5 | 1 | 6 |

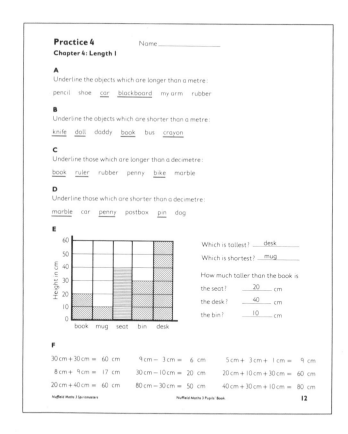

**Practice 4**                     Name_____

Chapter 4: Length I

**A**

Underline the objects which are longer than a metre:

pencil   shoe   <u>car</u>   <u>blackboard</u>   my arm   rubber

**B**

Underline the objects which are shorter than a metre:

<u>knife</u>   <u>doll</u>   daddy   <u>book</u>   bus   <u>crayon</u>

**C**

Underline those which are longer than a decimetre:

<u>book</u>   <u>ruler</u>   rubber   penny   <u>bike</u>   marble

**D**

Underline those which are shorter than a decimetre:

<u>marble</u>   car   <u>penny</u>   postbox   <u>pin</u>   dog

**E**

Which is tallest? ___desk___

Which is shortest? ___mug___

How much taller than the book is

the seat? ___20___ cm

the desk? ___40___ cm

the bin? ___10___ cm

**F**

30 cm + 30 cm = 60 cm       9 cm − 3 cm = 6 cm        5 cm + 3 cm + 1 cm = 9 cm

8 cm + 9 cm = 17 cm         30 cm − 10 cm = 20 cm      20 cm + 10 cm + 30 cm = 60 cm

20 cm + 40 cm = 60 cm       80 cm − 30 cm = 50 cm      40 cm + 30 cm + 10 cm = 80 cm

Nuffield Maths 3 Spiritmasters          Nuffield Maths 3 Pupils' Book          12

# References and resources

Nuffield Mathematics Teaching Project, *Checking up 2*, *Computation and Structure* ②, Nuffield Teaching Guides, Chambers/Murray 1967 (See Introduction page xii.)

Shuard, H. and Williams, E., *Primary Mathematics Today* (Chapter 5), Longman Group Ltd 1970

*The Giant Colour Book of Maths*, Hamlyn

*100 cm rule, Roll-up Height Measure, Set of Metre Sticks*, E. J. Arnold

*First Metre Rod*, E.S.A.

*Metristick, Trundle Wheel*, Invicta Plastics

*10 m Wall Measure, Calliper, Flexible Height Measure, Height Measure and Floor Stand, Measuring Tapes, Set of Metre Sticks*, Nicolas Burdett

*10 m Tape Measure, Depth Gauge, Graduated Callipers*, Osmiroid

*1 Metre Graduated Paper Strips, Metre Measuring and Comparison Rods Set, Metre Measuring Tapes, Metric-Aid Metre Tape, Metric Measuring Scale*, Philip & Tacey

*Flexible 1 m Measures, Measuring Tapes, Metre Rules*, Taskmaster.

# Chapter 5

# Addition 2

## For the teacher

This chapter provides further experience in 'counting on', with emphasis on patterns and relationships rather than knowledge of number bonds. The child cannot be expected to know every addition bond but should be able to recognise patterns and relationships that exist in our number system.

To help the child it is essential that a form of number track is available. This could be:

a) a number line going round the room,

b) a number ladder going up the wall,

c) children's own number lines – preferably strips cut from large pieces of squared paper,

d) a commercially made number track such as Multilink, Stern, Centicube or metre rule.

In *Nuffield Maths 1 Teachers' Handbook* and *Nuffield Maths 2 Teachers' Handbook* reference was made to two sorts of number track:

### The Number *Line*

0  1  2  3  4  5

Numerals label equally – spaced *points*.

The number line is less confusing if *lengths* are used to represent numbers:

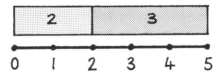

0  1  2  3  4  5

This has an obvious link with measuring activities since zero, the starting point, is clearly marked.

Using the number line as a physical model of abstract number has certain advantages later on – particularly when representing fractions or negative numbers.

$-1$    $0$   $+\frac{1}{2}$   $+1$

### The Number *Strip*

| 1 | 2 | 3 | 4 | 5 |

Equal segments labelled by numerals in the *spaces*.

The number strip may be familiar to children through games such as 'Snakes and Ladders' or 'Hopscotch'. Notice that these games usually have a 'start' space rather than a 'zero'.

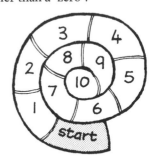

The number strip leads naturally to the 100 square, a 'conveniently packed' number strip which occupies less space and is very versatile when illustrating number patterns.

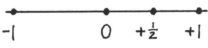

## Summary of the stages

1　Counting on from 10, 20, 30 . . .

2　The associative property of addition

3　Patterns in addition

4　Inequalities

5　Practice activities: (a) magic squares, (b) the 'computer'

## Vocabulary

Equal to, greater than, less than, equaliser, record, row, column, diagonal, total, computer, input, output.

## Equipment and apparatus

Strips of squared paper for number lines, teacher's demonstration number line or ladder, number track, 100 squares, equaliser(s).

## Working with the children

### 1　Counting on from 10, 20, 30 . . .

This is an obvious but very necessary stage in the child's number development. Although the section is called 'counting on' it is hoped that these exercises will serve as a link with the concept of place value which was introduced in Chapter 2 of *Nuffield Maths 2 Teachers' Handbook* and developed in Chapter 3 of this book.

On the completion of these exercises the child should realise that if 6 is added to 10, 20, 30 the answer will be 16, 26, 36 respectively. A practical demonstration of this can be given on the number line which should be displayed in the classroom.

It is very useful if each child makes his own number line using a strip of squared paper. This could be glued and folded in such a way that it forms a 'pull out feature' in the child's mathematics book. *Nuffield Maths 3 Spiritmasters*, Grid 5.

### 2　The associative property of addition

Another important aspect of addition is the 'associative property', i.e. when adding 3 or more numbers it does not matter in which *order* the operations are carried out. For example:

$$(4+3)+2 = 7+2 = 9$$
$$4+(3+2) = 4+5 = 9$$
$$(4+2)+3 = 6+3 = 9$$

It is important that children are given ample opportunities to see that the order in which three or more numbers are added does not alter the total.

The associative property is now extended and combined with the child's knowledge of addition pairs making 10.

In the first exercise children should be encouraged to set out their work as shown in the Pupils' book, drawing lines to show addition pairs making 10. For example:

$$3 + 6 + 7 + 4 + 2$$
$$10 + 10 + 2 = 22$$

### 3 Patterns in addition

Number ladders or number lines are an invaluable aid for showing patterns and relationships associated with addition. For example:

If $\quad 4 + 5 = \phantom{0}9$
then $\quad 14 + 5 = 19$
and $\quad 24 + 5 = 29$, and so on.

If a '5 piece' is used against a number line or ladder this can be demonstrated quite simply.

'5 piece'

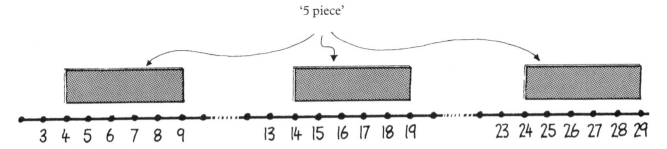

It is often difficult to display a number line or strip extending much beyond twenty because of the space it occupies. The 100-square, a 'conveniently packed' number strip, overcomes this difficulty and has the added advantage of emphasising the *pattern* of numbers up to a hundred. (Remember, we are using the word 'strip' when the numerals are written in the *spaces*). In making the transition from a number strip to the 100 square, some children may need to be shown how to move from the end of one line to the start of the next when counting on from 8 to 13, for example.

| 1 | 2 | 3 | 4 | 5 | 6 | 7 | 8 | 9 | 10 |
|---|---|---|---|---|---|---|---|---|---|
| 11 | 12 | 13 | 14 | 15 | 16 | 17 | 18 | 19 | 20 |
| 21 | 22 | 23 | 24 | 25 | 26 | 27 | 28 | 29 | 30 |
| 31 | 32 | 33 | 34 | 35 | 36 | 37 | 38 | 39 | 40 |
| 41 | 42 | 43 | 44 | 45 | 46 | 47 | 48 | 49 | 50 |
| 51 | 52 | 53 | 54 | 55 | 56 | 57 | 58 | 59 | 60 |
| 61 | 62 | 63 | 64 | 65 | 66 | 67 | 68 | 69 | 70 |
| 71 | 72 | 73 | 74 | 75 | 76 | 77 | 78 | 79 | 80 |
| 81 | 82 | 83 | 84 | 85 | 86 | 87 | 88 | 89 | 90 |
| 91 | 92 | 93 | 94 | 95 | 96 | 97 | 98 | 99 | 100 |

The 100-square is a rich source of activities for reincforcing and extending children's number knowledge. Here are some examples:

Use a 'stepped cover' to show
26 is 2 rows of 10 and 6
$26 = 10 + 10 + 6$
$26 = 20 + 6$, etc.

| 1 | 2 | 3 | 4 | 5 | 6 | 7 | 8 | 9 | 10 |
|---|---|---|---|---|---|---|---|---|----|
| 11 | 12 | 13 | 14 | 15 | 16 | 17 | 18 | 19 | 20 |
| 21 | 22 | 23 | 24 | 25 | 26 | | | | |

Counting on.
'Start at two and count on in threes'.
This can be done orally or by the
child either colouring or 'framing'
the squares.

| 1 | 2 | 3 | 4 | 5 | 6 | 7 | 8 | 9 | 10 |
|---|---|---|---|---|---|---|---|---|----|
| 11 | 12 | 13 | 14 | 15 | 16 | 17 | 18 | 19 | 20 |
| 21 | 22 | 23 | 24 | 25 | 26 | 27 | 28 | 29 | 30 |
| 31 | 32 | 33 | 34 | 35 | 36 | 37 | 38 | 39 | 40 |

Counting on
in tens,
starting at ten.

Counting on
in tens from
any number.

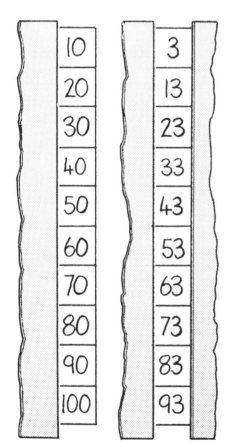

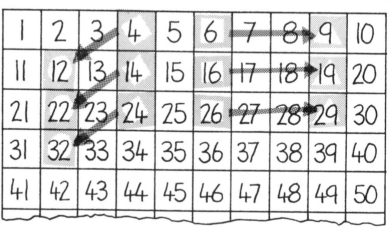

| 1 | 2 | 3 | 4 | 5 | 6 | 7 | 8 | 9 | 10 |
|---|---|---|---|---|---|---|---|---|----|
| 11 | 12 | 13 | 14 | 15 | 16 | 17 | 18 | 19 | 20 |
| 21 | 22 | 23 | 24 | 25 | 26 | 27 | 28 | 29 | 30 |
| 31 | 32 | 33 | 34 | 35 | 36 | 37 | 38 | 39 | 40 |
| 41 | 42 | 43 | 44 | 45 | 46 | 47 | 48 | 49 | 50 |

$4 + 8 = 12$          $6 + 3 = 9$
$14 + 8 = 22$         $16 + 3 = 19$
$24 + 8 = 32$         $26 + 3 = 29$

A large 100-square displayed in the classroom will provide many
opportunities for talking about numbers, especially during those odd 'five-
minute sessions'. Smaller, expendable copies of the 100-square enable
children to find patterns and relationships for themselves. *Nuffield Maths 3
Spiritmasters*, Grid 3.

It is important to remember that children need lots of time to become
familiar with the appearance, sound, composition and 'system' of numbers
up to 100 before being pushed too far into computing with them.

### 4 Inequalities

It is important at this stage not to become too pre-occupied with equalities. It is just as valid in some circumstances for the child to be able to recognise inequalities. Experience, therefore, should be provided to allow the child to discover and record number combinations which are *not* equal.

Inequalities can be demonstrated very effectively by using an equaliser. If the equaliser fails to balance inequality exists.

If there is an inequality, one number must be 'greater than' or 'less than' another number. The signs $>$ and $<$ can be used as 'shorthand' but if children find difficulty in remembering which way round the signs go, it is worth remembering, 'The wider end is the larger.' For example:

$8 > 2$
8 'is greater than' 2
$3 < 7$
3 'is less than' 7

In *Nuffield Maths 1 Teachers' Handbook* towers of cubes were used to introduce $>$ and $<$:

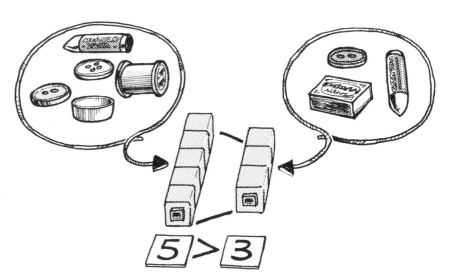

The pupils' exercise practises using the correct symbol ($=$, $>$ or $<$).

### 5 Practice activities

a) *Magic squares*
Before starting Magic Squares it is advisable to remind the children of the words:

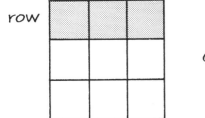

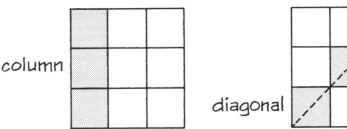

and to introduce the word *cell* as the name for one of the small squares.

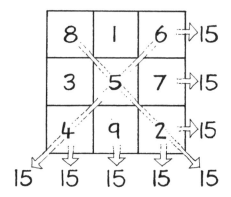

This is an example of a 3 × 3 Magic Square. The total for each row, each column and each diagonal is the same. The example is a 'normal' magic square because it makes use of consecutive whole numbers starting from 1, that is it uses the numbers 1 to 9 in the 9 'cells'.

When children are given a Magic Square containing some empty cells, one line (a row, a column or a diagonal) must be complete. This will enable the children to find the 'line total' for the square – in this example 15. He will then need to solve 'missing number' problems in order to complete the square, for example:

$$8 + 2 + \square = 15$$

To make additional examples for children to complete, the first Magic Square may be rotated or reflected and different cells left blank:

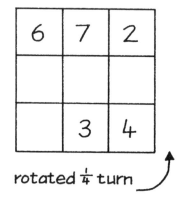

rotated ¼ turn

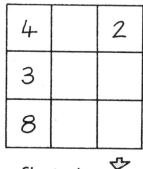

reflected

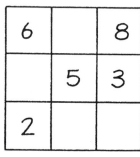

reflected

Once a normal Magic Square is made others can be produced by adding the same number to each cell. For example, adding 2 to each cell:

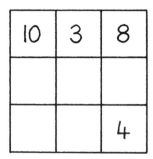

Magic Squares give lots of practice in simple addition and subtraction. Later on they will be used to give practice with larger numbers.

b) *The 'computer'*

These days children hear a lot about computers and this activity, using a 'home-made computer', provides motivation and extra practice. The teacher may use it to promote 'speed addition' by emphasising that computers are normally very *fast* and provide *accurate* answers.

There may be an opportunity for the class to make a computer in craft lessons, using cardboard boxes. If large enough, children could take it in turns to sit inside with a pack of answer cards. As one child places a number in the 'input' slot, the 'computer child' passes the correct answer through the 'output' slot. If the 'computer' is switched to 'add 3' for example, inputs and outputs may be recorded on a 'print out' tape:

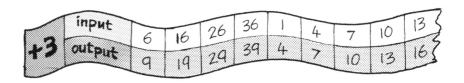

See *Nuffield Maths 3 Spiritmasters*, Grid 2.
This style of recording can also provide opportunities for investigating number patterns and relationships.

# Pages from the Pupils' Book and Spiritmasters

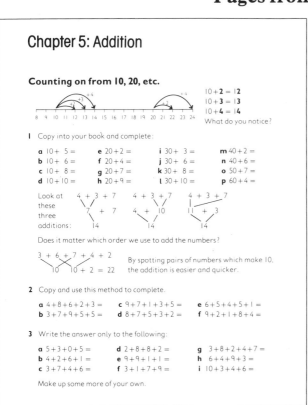

## Chapter 5: Addition

### Counting on from 10, 20, etc.

$10+2 = 12$
$10+3 = 13$
$10+4 = 14$
What do you notice?

1  Copy into your book and complete:

a 10+ 5 =        e 20+2 =        i 30+ 3 =        m 40+2 =
b 10+ 6 =        f 20+4 =        j 30+ 6 =        n 40+6 =
c 10+ 8 =        g 20+7 =        k 30+ 8 =        o 50+7 =
d 10+10 =        h 20+9 =        l 30+10 =        p 60+4 =

Look at these three additions:

4 + 3 + 7        4 + 3 + 7        4 + 3 + 7
    7  +  7        4  +  10        11  +  3
        14                14                14

Does it matter which order we use to add the numbers?

3 + 6 + 7 + 4 + 2        By spotting pairs of numbers which make 10,
10    10 + 2 = 22        the addition is easier and quicker.

2  Copy and use this method to complete.

a 4+8+6+2+3 =        c 9+7+1+3+5 =        e 6+5+4+5+1 =
b 3+7+9+5+5 =        d 8+7+5+3+2 =        f 9+2+1+8+4 =

3  Write the answer only to the following:

a 5+3+0+5 =        d 2+8+8+2 =        g 3+8+2+4+7 =
b 4+2+6+1 =        e 9+9+1+1 =        h 6+4+9+3 =
c 3+7+4+6 =        f 3+1+7+9 =        i 10+3+4+6 =

Make up some more of your own.

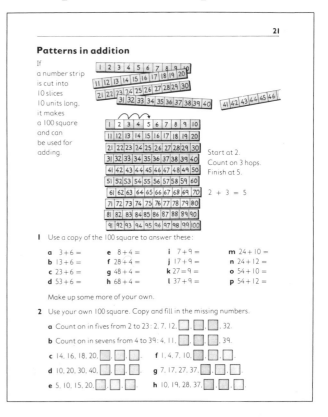

21

### Patterns in addition

If a number strip is cut into 10 slices 10 units long, it makes a 100 square and can be used for adding.

Start at 2.
Count on 3 hops.
Finish at 5.

2 + 3 = 5

1  Use a copy of the 100 square to answer these:

a 3+6 =        e 8+4 =        i 7+9 =        m 24+10 =
b 13+6 =        f 28+4 =        j 17+9 =        n 24+12 =
c 23+6 =        g 48+4 =        k 27+9 =        o 54+10 =
d 53+6 =        h 68+4 =        l 37+9 =        p 54+12 =

Make up some more of your own.

2  Use your own 100 square. Copy and fill in the missing numbers.

a Count on in fives from 2 to 23: 2, 7, 12, ☐, ☐, ☐, 32.

b Count on in sevens from 4 to 39: 4, 11, ☐, ☐, ☐, 39.

c 14, 16, 18, 20, ☐, ☐, ☐.        f 1, 4, 7, 10, ☐, ☐, ☐.

d 10, 20, 30, 40, ☐, ☐, ☐.        g 7, 17, 27, 37, ☐, ☐, ☐.

e 5, 10, 15, 20, ☐, ☐, ☐.        h 10, 19, 28, 37, ☐, ☐, ☐.

## 22

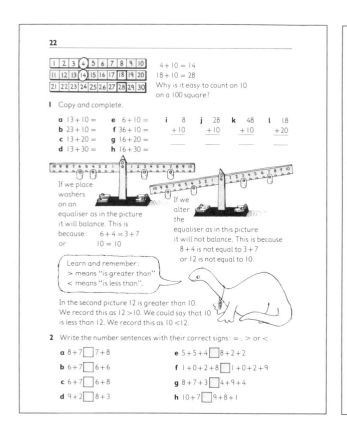

$4 + 10 = 14$
$18 + 10 = 28$
Why is it easy to count on 10 on a 100 square?

**I** Copy and complete.

| | | | | |
|---|---|---|---|---|
| **a** $13+10 =$ | **e** $6+10 =$ | **i** 8 | **j** 28 | **k** 48 **l** 18 |
| **b** $23+10 =$ | **f** $36+10 =$ | $+10$ | $+10$ | $+10$ $+20$ |
| **c** $13+20 =$ | **g** $16+20 =$ | | | |
| **d** $13+30 =$ | **h** $16+30 =$ | | | |

If we place washers on an equaliser as in the picture it will balance. This is because:  $6+4 = 3+7$  or  $10 = 10$

If we alter the equaliser as in this picture it will not balance. This is because $8+4$ is not equal to $3+7$ or 12 is not equal to 10.

Learn and remember:
> means "is greater than"
< means "is less than".

In the second picture 12 is greater than 10. We record this as $12 > 10$. We could say that 10 is less than 12. We record this as $10 < 12$.

**2** Write the number sentences with their correct signs: $=$, $>$ or $<$.

**a** $8+7$ ☐ $7+8$

**b** $6+7$ ☐ $6+6$

**c** $6+7$ ☐ $6+8$

**d** $9+2$ ☐ $8+3$

**e** $5+5+4$ ☐ $8+2+2$

**f** $1+0+2+8$ ☐ $1+0+2+9$

**g** $8+7+3$ ☐ $4+9+4$

**h** $10+7$ ☐ $9+8+1$

## 23

### Magic squares

Why is this number square magic?

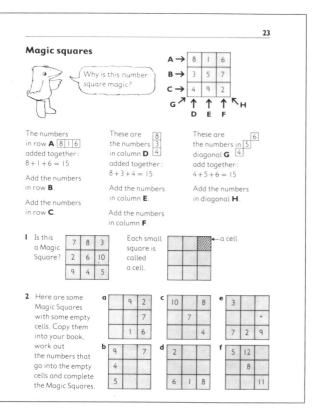

A→ 8 1 6
B→ 3 5 7
C→ 4 9 2
G↗ ↑↑↑ ↖H
D E F

The numbers in row **A** $\boxed{8}\ \boxed{1}\ \boxed{6}$ added together: $8+1+6 = 15$

Add the numbers in row **B**.

Add the numbers in row **C**.

These are the numbers in column **D** $\boxed{8}\ \boxed{3}\ \boxed{4}$ added together: $8+3+4 = 15$

Add the numbers in column **E**.

Add the numbers in column **F**.

These are the numbers in diagonal **G** $\boxed{6}\ \boxed{5}\ \boxed{4}$ add together: $4+5+6 = 15$

Add the numbers in diagonal **H**.

**I** Is this a Magic Square?

| 7 | 8 | 3 |
|---|---|---|
| 2 | 6 | 10 |
| 9 | 4 | 5 |

Each small square is called a cell.

← a cell

**2** Here are some Magic Squares with some empty cells. Copy them into your book, work out the numbers that go into the empty cells and complete the Magic Squares.

**a**
| 9 | 2 | |
|---|---|---|
| | 7 | |
| | 1 | 6 |

**c**
| 10 | | 8 |
|---|---|---|
| | 7 | |
| | | 4 |

**e**
| 3 | | |
|---|---|---|
| | | . |
| 7 | 2 | 9 |

**b**
| 9 | | 7 |
|---|---|---|
| 4 | | |
| 5 | | |

**d**
| 2 | | |
|---|---|---|
| | | |
| 6 | 1 | 8 |

**f**
| 5 | 12 | |
|---|---|---|
| | | 8 |
| | | 11 |

## 24

### The computer

The pointers on the computer say **+3** so it will add 3 to each numeral fed into the machine.

The computer records all the inputs and outputs on a print-out-tape.

| **+3** | | | | | | | | | |
|---|---|---|---|---|---|---|---|---|---|
| Input | 20 | 10 | 0 | 8 | 5 | 2 | 24 | 14 | 4 |
| Output | 23 | 13 | 3 | 11 | 8 | 5 | 27 | 17 | 7 |

Check the tape to see if the computer is working properly.

Copy and complete these tapes:

**I**
| **+6** | | | | | | | | | | |
|---|---|---|---|---|---|---|---|---|---|---|
| Input | 9 | 19 | 29 | 39 | 49 | 0 | 6 | 12 | 18 | 24 |
| Output | 15 | | | | | 6 | | | | |

**2**
| **+10** | | | | | | | | | | |
|---|---|---|---|---|---|---|---|---|---|---|
| Input | 0 | 10 | 30 | 50 | 60 | 3 | 13 | 53 | 23 | 33 |
| Output | | | | | | | | | | |

**3**
| **+9** | | | | | | | | | | |
|---|---|---|---|---|---|---|---|---|---|---|
| Input | 5 | 7 | 8 | 11 | 21 | 31 | 0 | 9 | 18 | 27 |
| Output | | | | | | | | | | |

Make up some more tapes of your own.

### Practice 5
#### Chapter 5: Addition 2

Name _____

| **A** | **B** | **C** |
|---|---|---|
| $10+2 = 12$ | $20+5 = 25$ | $2+8+3+7 = 20$ |
| $10+6 = 16$ | $30+4 = 34$ | $5+1+9+5 = 20$ |
| $10+3 = 13$ | $40+6 = 46$ | $4+2+6+8 = 20$ |
| $10+8 = 18$ | $70+8 = 78$ | $7+2+3+6 = 18$ |
| $10+9 = 19$ | $60+7 = 67$ | $4+3+7+2 = 16$ |
| $10+7 = 17$ | $80+9 = 89$ | $5+8+5+1 = 19$ |

**D**
Fill in the missing numbers:

8, 10, 12, 14, 16, 18.

5, 10, 15, 20, 25, 30.

3, 6, 9, 12, 15, 18, 21.

6, 12, 18, 24, 30, 36.

1, 4, 7, 10, 13, 16, 19.

2, 6, 10, 14, 18, 22.

**E**
Fill in the correct signs:
> or < or =

$8+6 = 6+8$

$6+7 > 6+6$

$3+4 < 4+5$

$34+7 = 7+34$

$21+18 < 19+21$

**F**

| 8 | 18 | 28 | 38 | 26 | 35 | 17 | 40 | 50 | 60 |
|---|---|---|---|---|---|---|---|---|---|
| $+10$ | $+10$ | $+10$ | $+10$ | $+20$ | $+30$ | $+40$ | $+19$ | $+24$ | $+35$ |
| 18 | 28 | 38 | 48 | 46 | 65 | 57 | 59 | 74 | 95 |

**G**

| **+8** | Input | 7 | 4 | 8 | 6 | 5 | 9 |
|---|---|---|---|---|---|---|---|
| | Output | 15 | 12 | 16 | 14 | 13 | 17 |

| **+9** | Input | 6 | 4 | 7 | 20 | 50 | 90 |
|---|---|---|---|---|---|---|---|
| | Output | 15 | 13 | 16 | 29 | 59 | 99 |

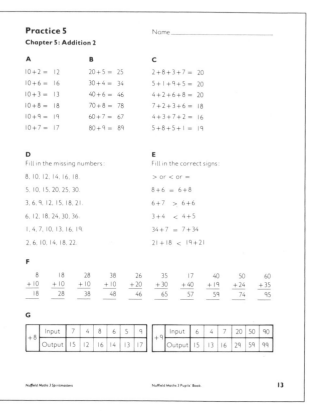

# References and resources

Nuffield Mathematics Teaching Project, *Computation and Structure* ② , Nuffield Teaching Guides, Chambers/Murray 1967. (See Introduction, page xii.)

Shuard, H. and Williams, E., *Primary Mathematics Today* (Chapter 9), Longman Group Ltd 1970

**Number Tracks – points labelled**

*Multilink Number Track, Stern Number Track*, E.S.A.

*Number Strip and Rods* (This has points labelled and can be used to draw number lines), Invicta Plastics

*Number Track*, Metric Aids

*Metlines* (1 metre), Osmiroid

*Graduated paper strips*, Philip & Tacey

*Number Lines*, Taskmaster

**Number Track – space labelled**

*Unifix 100 Track*, Philip & Tacey

**100 Squares**

*One Hundred Board and Number Tablets, Square Roccer Stamp* (to print 100 blank centimetre squares in 10 × 10 block), E. J. Arnold

*Multilink Number Boards and Grid*, E.S.A.

*1–100 Grids (Gridsheets)*, Excitement in Learning

*Hundred Number Board*, Invicta Plastics

*Unifix 1–100 Operational Board, Number Tablets and Window Markers*, Philip & Tacey

*Giant 100 Board and Discs, 100 Square and Number Tablets*, Taskmaster

# Chapter 6

# Money 1

## For the teacher

This chapter is intended to reinforce earlier experience which the child may have had in handling money. It deals mainly with coin recognition and the use of small numbers of coins.

Of all the topics which are taught in mathematics, money is probably the one that is the most familiar to the child. The 'apparatus' needed – money – will have been used and experienced long before it has been introduced in school. Money can be readily related to the child's own experience, and is an area which may have already been partly learnt by the child himself, or may have been taught in an incidental way at home.

What is the role, therefore, of the teacher in the teaching of money? The teacher must:
1 recognise that children may have had different experiences in handling money in their home environment;
2 never under-estimate what the child has already learnt about money through his own experiences;
3 draw to the child's attention certain facts and skills, which are not easily acquired by the day to day handling of money, but without which the child's understanding of our money system will not progress very far.

*Terminology and recording*
It is important to establish the correct terminology from the start. The letter 'p' should follow immediately after the amount recorded – 2p, 3p, etc., and be referred to as 'penny' in 1p or 'pence' in the plural – 3 pence, 5 pence, etc.

*Real coins or imitation coins?*
There is no really satisfactory substitute for handling real money. If, however, teachers feel that money in the classroom is undesirable, then good cardboard or plastic replicas are the next best thing. These should be good facsimiles or reproductions of *real* money, not just discs with a value stamped on them.

Sticky paper coins are useful for recording but may prove expensive. Rubber stamps of coins are now available and these can be used for the preparation of additional exercises and possibly, for recording.

Imitation coins, no matter how realistic in appearance, do not have the same appeal to the sense of touch. The feel of the material, the actual weight of the coin, the sound of the coin falling on to a surface – all have an important part to play in the understanding of money. When children measure we give them real rulers, when children weigh we give them real weights and real scales – we should therefore give them an opportunity in handling real money. Class or group organisation has a part to play here. One table, with an activity requiring use of real money, at which small groups could take it in turns to 'visit' during the lesson could overcome some of the practical problems of using real money with children.

If imitation money is used, try to choose the most realistic and always *limit* the amount that you give to each group. Giving hundreds of coins in a large box only adds to the unrealistic situation created by imitation money. At the beginning of the activity it is suggested that children always check their money box. This is good practice in counting and matching and it indicates whether or not the correct amount of money is in the box before starting. A similar check should be made at the end of the lesson.

Accountability, after all, is one of the skills of handling money.

# Summary of the stages

1   A close look at our coins

2   Analysis of coin values
(Making up the value of a coin)

3   Using coins to make up amounts

4   Finding the missing coin

5   Giving change by counting on

# Vocabulary

Silver, bronze, smooth or plain edge, milled edge, bill.

# Equipment and apparatus

Cardboard, plastic or real coins, sticky paper coins, rubber stamps of coins (but see reference to these in 'For the Teacher').

# Working with the children

### 1   A close look at our coins

By the time the child reaches this stage he can usually recognise the coins in current use. Most children, however, may not have been encouraged to examine the coins in detail and it is by doing this that interest can be re-stimulated.

General points of observation/discussion.

1   All the coins vary in size and thickness.

2   Each coin has a different design.

3   Some coins have milled edges, others have plain or smooth edges.

4   Some are bronze, some are cupro nickel.

5   Each coin shows its value in digital form (for example, 10p coin bears the digits 10 not 10p).

6   1p coins bear the words 'One Penny' (previously 'New Penny') while all other coins bear the words 'New Pence'.

For some years to come, however, pre-decimal coinage will still be in circulation and the child must recognise, by their size, that the old one-shilling and two-shilling coins are equivalent in value to the 5p and the 10p coins.

7   The reverse of the coin bears the reigning monarch's head, name, and the year the coin was minted.

*Sorting coins*

One of the first skills to be acquired when dealing with money is the ability to sort coins into sets of the same kind. This skill runs hand in hand with coin recognition and is a pre-requisite for finding the total value of a number of coins which will be introduced later.

## 2 Analysis of coin values (Making up the value of a coin)

*The 5p coin*
The aim of this activity is to show the relationship of the 5p coin, to the bronze coins – 2p, 1p. It is suggested that the children take the coins in question, draw round them and write their values inside the circles.

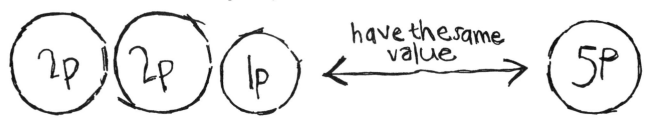

If this is not done the exercise can become one of pure mental addition rather than one of coin experience.

*The 10p coin*
Here the 10p coin is used and its relationship with the 5p coin and bronze coins is developed. It is envisaged that this activity will take the same form as the one dealing with the 5p coin. Again it is important that the children use coins to make up 10p and record by drawing round them and writing the values in the circles.

*The 50p coin*
There are six ways of making 50p using only other 'silver' coins, but if silver and bronze coins are mixed or if bronze coins only are used there are very many ways to make up 50p. Some children may be aware that two 50p coins are worth £1.

## 3 Using coins to make up amounts
Experience is now provided in using coins to make up certain amounts.

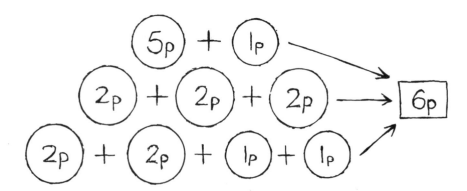

*Nuffield Maths 3 Spiritmasters*, Practice 6. See page 43.
Practice is given in adding bills by matching coins to the prices and using the coins to find the total amount. It is important to stress neat setting out of bills of this kind as shown in the first example.

## 4 Finding the missing coin
This activity helps to develop the skill of 'making up' amounts. In real life we are sometimes short of a certain coin to make up an exact amount.

It is essential that this activity is matched with practical use of coins. Unless this is done it becomes an activity which goes no further than developing addition and subtraction skills.

### 5 Giving change by counting on

In practical situations when change is given, the shopkeeper or bus conductor does not 'take away' to find the change required. He counts on to 'make up' the difference between the cost of the goods or ticket and the value of the coin(s) offered. This method is used countless times a day and yet, because no recorded answer is needed, often the shopkeeper/conductor is not aware of the amount of money given as change – he only knows it is right!

Children need to enact what happens when money is paid and change given, using clearly priced articles and either real or token money. The dialogue involved is very important:

> *Passenger:* A seven-penny ticket, please.
> (He gives the conductor a 10p coin).
> *Conductor:* Thank you. (Gives ticket.)
> Seven – (Counts out change) eight, nine, ten.
> Any more fares?

A 'shorthand' number sentence for what has happened is:

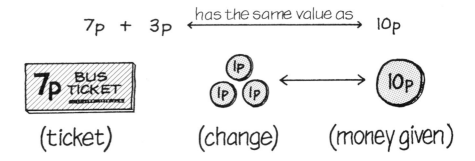

The conductor translates 'What change must I give if tenpence is offered for a sevenpenny ticket?' into 'Start at 7p and count on to 10p.' He is really solving the problem $7 + \square = 10$, but he does not have to 'fill in the box' because the passenger puts the 'answer' in his pocket!

A similar situation arises when comparing two amounts of money in order to find the difference in value. For example, 'Mary has 7p and John has 4p. How much more has Mary than John?' It is misleading to use the phrase 'take away' in this case since a child told to 'take John's 4p away from Mary's 7p' could well answer, 'But please Miss, Mary hasn't got John's 4p so how can I take it away?' Although the process involved is subtraction, it is the *comparative* aspect ('finding the difference') and not the physical removal aspect ('taking away') which is being used.

This example emphasises yet again the importance of language and warns against rushing into the use of symbolism ('– means take away') before the process is understood and described in words.

In real-life situations involving the use of money, the act of either receiving change or giving change is an extremely common occurrence. It is important, therefore, that children are prepared to meet these situations with the necessary skills.

# Pages from the Pupils' Book and Spiritmasters

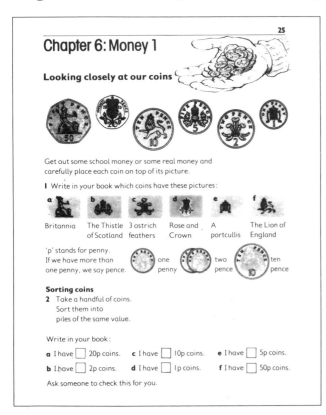

## Chapter 6: Money 1

### Looking closely at our coins

Get out some school money or some real money and carefully place each coin on top of its picture.

**1** Write in your book which coins have these pictures:

- **a** Britannia
- **b** The Thistle of Scotland
- **c** 3 ostrich feathers
- **d** Rose and Crown
- **e** A portcullis
- **f** The Lion of England

'p' stands for penny.
If we have more than one penny, we say pence.

one penny   two pence   ten pence

### Sorting coins

**2** Take a handful of coins.
Sort them into piles of the same value.

Write in your book:

**a** I have ☐ 20p coins.  **c** I have ☐ 10p coins.  **e** I have ☐ 5p coins.

**b** I have ☐ 2p coins.  **d** I have ☐ 1p coins.  **f** I have ☐ 50p coins.

Ask someone to check this for you.

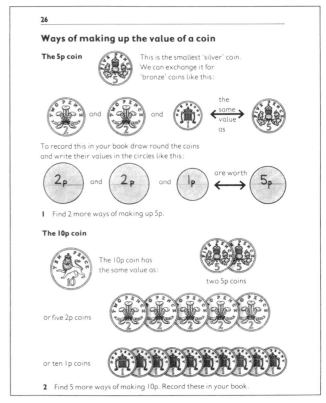

## Ways of making up the value of a coin

**The 5p coin**  This is the smallest 'silver' coin. We can exchange it for 'bronze' coins like this:

and   and   ← the same value as →

To record this in your book draw round the coins and write their values in the circles like this:

2p   and   2p   and   1p   ← are worth →   5p

**1** Find 2 more ways of making up 5p.

**The 10p coin**

The 10p coin has the same value as:

two 5p coins

or five 2p coins

or ten 1p coins

**2** Find 5 more ways of making 10p. Record these in your book.

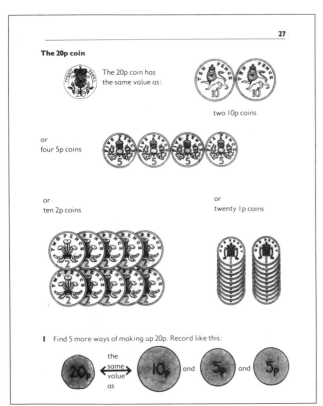

**The 20p coin**

The 20p coin has the same value as:

two 10p coins

or four 5p coins

or ten 2p coins

or twenty 1p coins

**1** Find 5 more ways of making up 20p. Record like this:

20p   ← the same value as →   10p   and   5p   and   5p

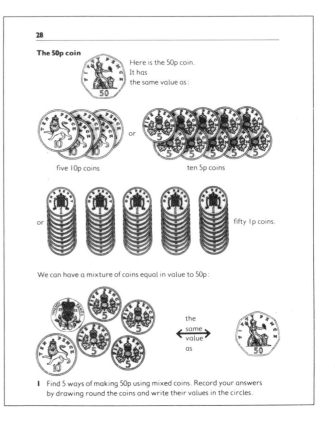

**The 50p coin**

Here is the 50p coin. It has the same value as:

five 10p coins   ten 5p coins

or   fifty 1p coins.

We can have a mixture of coins equal in value to 50p:

← the same value as →   50

**1** Find 5 ways of making 50p using mixed coins. Record your answers by drawing round the coins and write their values in the circles.

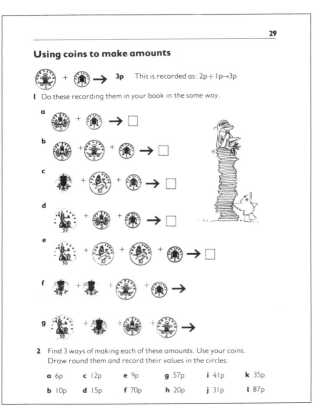

**Using coins to make amounts**

+ → **3p** This is recorded as: 2p+1p→3p

1 Do these recording them in your book in the same way.

a + → □

b + + → □

c + + + → □

d + + + → □

e + + + + → □

f + + + →

g + + + →

2 Find 3 ways of making each of these amounts. Use your coins.
Draw round them and record their values in the circles.

a 6p  c 12p  e 9p  g 57p  i 41p  k 35p
b 10p  d 15p  f 70p  h 20p  j 31p  l 87p

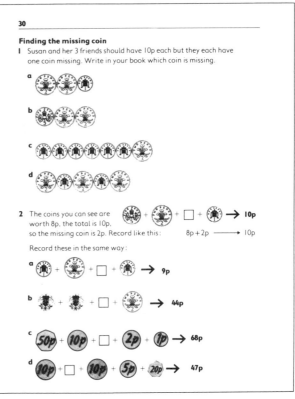

30

**Finding the missing coin**

1 Susan and her 3 friends should have 10p each but they each have
one coin missing. Write in your book which coin is missing.

a

b

c

d

2 The coins you can see are
worth 8p, the total is 10p,
so the missing coin is 2p. Record like this:

+ + □ + → **10p**

8p+2p ⟶ 10p

Record these in the same way:

a + + □ + → **9p**

b + + □ + → **44p**

c 50p + 10p + □ + 2p + 1p → **68p**

d 10p + □ + 10p + 5p + 20p → **47p**

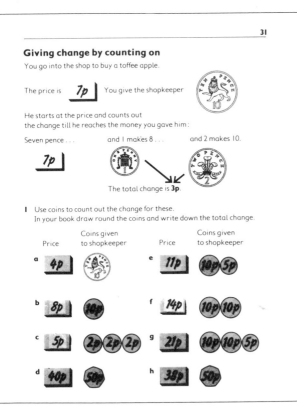

31

**Giving change by counting on**

You go into the shop to buy a toffee apple.

The price is **7p**  You give the shopkeeper

He starts at the price and counts out
the change till he reaches the money you gave him:

Seven pence . . .  and 1 makes 8 . . .  and 2 makes 10.

**7p**

The total change is **3p**.

1 Use coins to count out the change for these.
In your book draw round the coins and write down the total change.

|  | Price | Coins given to shopkeeper |  | Price | Coins given to shopkeeper |
|---|---|---|---|---|---|
| a | 4p |  | e | 11p | 10p 5p |
| b | 8p | 10p | f | 14p | 10p 10p |
| c | 5p | 2p 2p 2p | g | 21p | 10p 10p 5p |
| d | 40p | 50p | h | 38p | 50p |

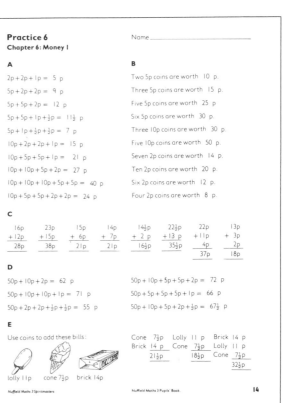

**Practice 6**
**Chapter 6: Money 1**

**A**

2p+2p+1p = 5 p
5p+2p+2p = 9 p
5p+5p+2p = 12 p
5p+5p+1p+$\frac{1}{2}$p = 11$\frac{1}{2}$ p
5p+1p+$\frac{1}{2}$p+$\frac{1}{2}$p = 7 p
10p+2p+2p+1p = 15 p
10p+5p+5p+1p = 21 p
10p+10p+5p+2p = 27 p
10p+10p+10p+5p+5p = 40 p
10p+5p+5p+2p+2p = 24 p

**B**

Two 5p coins are worth 10 p.
Three 5p coins are worth 15 p.
Five 5p coins are worth 25 p.
Six 5p coins are worth 30 p.
Three 10p coins are worth 30 p.
Five 10p coins are worth 50 p.
Seven 2p coins are worth 14 p.
Ten 2p coins are worth 20 p.
Six 2p coins are worth 12 p.
Four 2p coins are worth 8 p.

**C**

| 16p | 23p | 15p | 14p | 14$\frac{1}{2}$p | 22$\frac{1}{2}$p | 22p | 13p |
|---|---|---|---|---|---|---|---|
| +12p | +15p | + 6p | + 7p | + 2 p | +13 p | +11p | + 3p |
| 28p | 38p | 21p | 21p | 16$\frac{1}{2}$p | 35$\frac{1}{2}$p | 4p | 2p |
|  |  |  |  |  |  | 37p | 18p |

**D**

50p+10p+2p = 62 p
50p+10p+10p+1p = 71 p
50p+2p+2p+$\frac{1}{2}$p+$\frac{1}{2}$p = 55 p

50p+10p+5p+5p+2p = 72 p
50p+5p+5p+5p+1p = 66 p
50p+10p+5p+2p+$\frac{1}{2}$p = 67$\frac{1}{2}$ p

**E**

Use coins to add these bills:

lolly 11p  cone 7$\frac{1}{2}$p  brick 14p

| Cone 7$\frac{1}{2}$ p | Lolly 11 p | Brick 14 p |
|---|---|---|
| Brick 14 p | Cone 7$\frac{1}{2}$ p | Lolly 11 p |
| 21$\frac{1}{2}$p | 18$\frac{1}{2}$p | Cone 7$\frac{1}{2}$ p |
|  |  | 32$\frac{1}{2}$p |

# References and resources

*Cardboard token coins, Coin stamps, Gummed Printed Coins, Plastic token coins,* E. J. Arnold

*Our Money Wall Chart, Plastic and Cardboard Coins, Stick-on Decimal Coins,* E.S.A.

*Coin Matching Dominoes, Decimal Coin Rubber Stamps, Plastic and Cardboard Coins, Sorting Trays,* Galt

*Cardboard Coins, Decimal Aid Coin and Symbol Inset Matching Cards, Decimal Aid Money Value Recognition Cards, Decimal Aid Value Matching Cards, Gummed Paper Money, Handy Coin Rubber Stamps, 'How much will it cost?' Rubber Stamps,* Philip & Tacey

# Chapter 7

# Subtraction 1

## For the teacher

This chapter aims at giving children experience of different aspects of subtraction and the ways in which the symbol ' − ' can be interpreted. Particular emphasis is given to the many words and phrases associated with the operation of subtraction: difference between, take away, minus, subtract, remove, compare, make up to, more than, less than, count back, etc.

As many subtraction problems are based upon comparison or 'difference between' rather than physical removal, it is misleading to interpret the symbol ' − ' as always meaning 'take away'. The example quoted in *Nuffield Maths 2 Teachers' Handbook* is worth repeating. 'Mary has 9 pence and John has 4 pence. How much more has Mary than John?' On being told that this is a 'take away' problem and that John's 4p should be taken away from Mary's 9p, it is not surprising that a child is confused for, as he says, 'I can't take it away, she hasn't got it.'

The exercises do not involve regrouping or decomposition and for many children this will be further reinforcement of number facts and techniques with which they are already familiar. It is worth remembering, however, that some children may not have had much practice in using non-expendable materials and will need to be encouraged to set out their computations in a neat and orderly way.

## Summary of the stages

1  Difference

2  Taking away

3  Counting back

## Vocabulary

Difference, more, less, fewer, subtract, take away, remove, minus, how many are left, count back, compare.

## Equipment and apparatus

Rods, interlocking cubes, counters, squared paper, number lines, ten rods and cubes.

## Working with the children

### 1  Difference
Simple examples remind children that when comparing the numbers of objects in sets, the difference can be expressed in a variety of ways:

| | |
|---|---|
| The difference between 9 and 5 is 4 | $9 - 5 = 4$ |
| 9 is 4 more than 5 | $9 = 5 + 4$ |
| 5 is 4 less than 9 | $5 = 9 - 4$ |
| 4 less than 9 is 5 | $9 - 4 = 5$ |

Apart from revising and reinforcing the links between 'subtraction facts' and 'addition facts' the exercises are intended to provide practice at translating from words to symbols – from what we *say* to what we *write*.

The graphing activity revises tallying, drawing block graphs and gives children the opportunity of interpreting a graph to find relationships to be recorded as number sentences. *Nuffield Maths 3 Spiritmasters*, Grid 9.

### 2 Taking away

This section deals with the physical removal or 'take away' aspect of subtraction. The exercises invite the child to, 'Use counters or cubes if you need them.' Although many children will be quite capable of answering the questions without using concrete materials, it is important that some examples are done in which cubes or counters are actually removed. This is to emphasise that, although comparing to find the difference and physical removal both lead to a subtraction process, the situations are dissimilar.

Starting with simple cases involving only numbers up to 20, the exercises progress to subtraction of tens using ten-rods and finally to the subtraction of tens and units which do *not* involve exchange or decomposition. It is important at this stage that great emphasis is placed on neat and careful layout, with columns of figures kept in line.

Question 3 introduces a variation in word order which is often used in everyday speech but tends to cause confusion for some children, for example: 'Take fifty-two from sixty-four.'

Here the numerals are *not* in the order in which they occur in the corresponding sentence $(64 - 52 = \square)$ or would be written in vertical form:

$$\begin{array}{r} 64 \\ -52 \\ \hline \\ \hline \end{array}$$

One way which may help to overcome the confusion caused by two ways of saying the same thing is to re-emphasise the link with concrete materials:

'Take 9 from these 14 counters.'

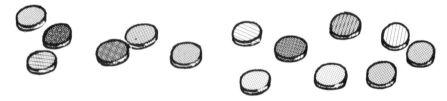

Alternatively, changing the position of two small cards may help:

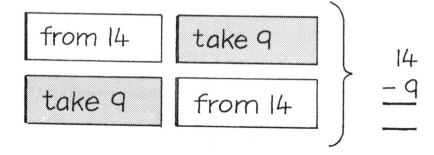

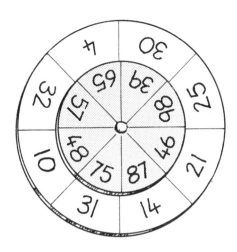

Two circles are cut from stiff card, one with 5 cm diameter the other 8 cm. The circles are divided into eight sectors or 'slices' and fixed together with a brass paper fastener. Numerals are written in the spaces so that when the 'spokes' are lined up, eight subtraction problems are given:

$$39 - 30 =$$
$$98 - 25 =$$
etc.

When the inner circle is moved round, another eight problems appear and so on. The numerals are chosen so that exchanging or 'decomposition' is not involved.

Referring back to the question of word order mentioned previously, it is interesting that some children call the inner circle the 'from' wheel and the outer circle the 'take' wheel.

### 3 Counting back

The use of the number line to show subtraction as counting back or counting down helps to show the connection with addition which is counting on or counting up. A large number line displayed in the classroom is very useful here for demonstration purposes but a 'home-made' number line for each child is necessary for practice. If given a narrow strip of squared paper 'either 1 cm or 2 cm squares) each child can make a number line by writing the numerals from 0 to 20 so that the printed lines go *through* each numeral. (*Nuffield Maths 3 Spiritmasters*, Grid 5.)

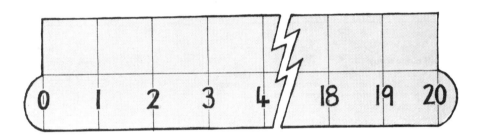

The 'lift' example gives the children experience of a vertical number line (useful for later work on graphs) and further practice in translating words to symbols.

*Speed practices* are provided in *Nuffield Maths 3 Spiritmasters*, Practice 7 (see page 49).

# Pages from the Pupils' Book and Spiritmasters

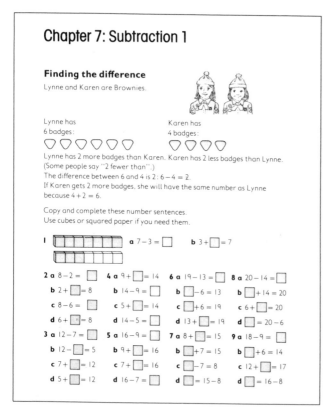

## Chapter 7: Subtraction 1

### Finding the difference

Lynne and Karen are Brownies.

Lynne has
6 badges:

Karen has
4 badges:

Lynne has 2 more badges than Karen. Karen has 2 less badges than Lynne.
(Some people say "2 fewer than".)
The difference between 6 and 4 is 2: $6 - 4 = 2$.
If Karen gets 2 more badges, she will have the same number as Lynne
because $4 + 2 = 6$.

Copy and complete these number sentences.
Use cubes or squared paper if you need them.

1    **a** $7 - 3 = \square$    **b** $3 + \square = 7$

2 **a** $8 - 2 = \square$   4 **a** $9 + \square = 14$   6 **a** $19 - 13 = \square$   8 **a** $20 - 14 = \square$

   **b** $2 + \square = 8$     **b** $14 - 9 = \square$    **b** $\square - 6 = 13$    **b** $\square + 14 = 20$

   **c** $8 - 6 = \square$     **c** $5 + \square = 14$    **c** $\square + 6 = 19$    **c** $6 + \square = 20$

   **d** $6 + \square = 8$     **d** $14 - 5 = \square$    **d** $13 + \square = 19$    **d** $\square = 20 - 6$

3 **a** $12 - 7 = \square$   5 **a** $16 - 9 = \square$   7 **a** $8 + \square = 15$   9 **a** $18 - 9 = \square$

   **b** $12 - \square = 5$    **b** $9 + \square = 16$    **b** $\square + 7 = 15$    **b** $\square + 6 = 14$

   **c** $7 + \square = 12$    **c** $7 + \square = 16$    **c** $\square - 7 = 8$    **c** $12 + \square = 17$

   **d** $5 + \square = 12$    **d** $16 - 7 = \square$    **d** $\square = 15 - 8$    **d** $\square = 16 - 8$

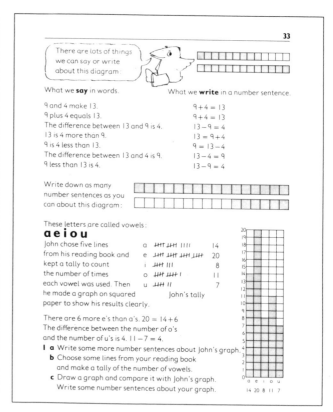

33

There are lots of things
we can say or write
about this diagram:

What we **say** in words.

9 and 4 make 13.
9 plus 4 equals 13.
The difference between 13 and 9 is 4.
13 is 4 more than 9.
9 is 4 less than 13.
The difference between 13 and 4 is 9.
9 less than 13 is 4.

What we **write** in a number sentence.

$9 + 4 = 13$
$9 + 4 = 13$
$13 - 9 = 4$
$13 = 9 + 4$
$9 = 13 - 4$
$13 - 4 = 9$
$13 - 9 = 4$

Write down as many
number sentences as you
can about this diagram:

These letters are called vowels:

**a e i o u**

John chose five lines
from his reading book and
kept a tally to count
the number of times
each vowel was used. Then
he made a graph on squared
paper to show his results clearly.

a   ⊮⊮ ⊮⊮ IIII   14
e   ⊮⊮ ⊮⊮ ⊮⊮ ⊮⊮   20
i   ⊮⊮ III   8
o   ⊮⊮ ⊮⊮ I   11
u   ⊮⊮ II   7

John's tally

There are 6 more e's than a's. $20 = 14 + 6$
The difference between the number of o's
and the number of u's is 4. $11 - 7 = 4$.

1 **a** Write some more number sentences about John's graph.
   **b** Choose some lines from your reading book
     and make a tally of the number of vowels.
   **c** Draw a graph and compare it with John's graph.
     Write some number sentences about your graph.

14 20 8 11 7

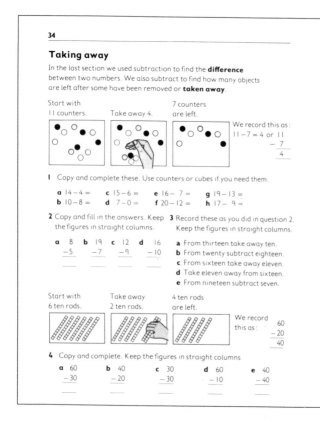

34

### Taking away

In the last section we used subtraction to find the **difference**
between two numbers. We also subtract to find how many objects
are left after some have been removed or **taken away**.

Start with
11 counters.

Take away 4.

7 counters
are left.

We record this as:
$11 - 7 = 4$ or $11$
     $- 7$
     $\overline{\phantom{0}4}$

1 Copy and complete these. Use counters or cubes if you need them.

   **a** $14 - 4 =$    **c** $15 - 6 =$    **e** $16 - 7 =$    **g** $19 - 13 =$

   **b** $10 - 8 =$    **d** $7 - 0 =$    **f** $20 - 12 =$    **h** $17 - 9 =$

2 Copy and fill in the answers. Keep
the figures in straight columns.

   **a** $8$   **b** $19$   **c** $12$   **d** $16$
     $-5$     $-7$     $-9$     $-10$

3 Record these as you did in question 2.
Keep the figures in straight columns.

   **a** From thirteen take away ten.
   **b** From twenty subtract eighteen.
   **c** From sixteen take away eleven.
   **d** Take eleven away from sixteen.
   **e** From nineteen subtract seven.

Start with
6 ten rods.

Take away
2 ten rods.

4 ten rods
are left.

We record
this as:   $60$
      $-20$
      $\overline{40}$

4 Copy and complete. Keep the figures in straight columns

   **a** $60$   **b** $40$   **c** $30$   **d** $60$   **e** $40$
     $-30$    $-20$    $-30$    $-10$    $-40$

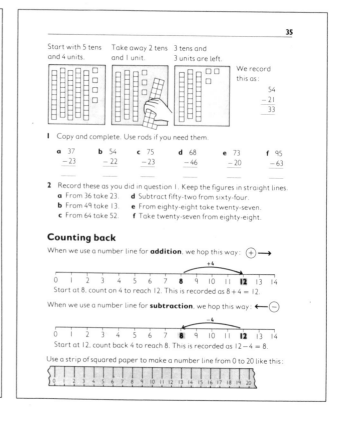

35

Start with 5 tens
and 4 units.

Take away 2 tens
and 1 unit.

3 tens and
3 units are left.

We record
this as:
   $54$
  $-21$
  $\overline{33}$

1 Copy and complete. Use rods if you need them.

   **a** $37$   **b** $54$   **c** $75$   **d** $68$   **e** $73$   **f** $95$
     $-23$    $-22$    $-23$    $-46$    $-20$    $-63$

2 Record these as you did in question 1. Keep the figures in straight lines.
   **a** From 36 take 23.    **d** Subtract fifty-two from sixty-four.
   **b** From 49 take 13.    **e** From eighty-eight take twenty-seven.
   **c** From 64 take 52.    **f** Take twenty-seven from eighty-eight.

### Counting back

When we use a number line for **addition**, we hop this way: $+$ →

Start at 8, count on 4 to reach 12. This is recorded as $8 + 4 = 12$.

When we use a number line for **subtraction**, we hop this way: ← $-$

Start at 12, count back 4 to reach 8. This is recorded as $12 - 4 = 8$.

Use a strip of squared paper to make a number line from 0 to 20 like this:

36

Use your number line to do these.

I  Write the number sentence and put in the missing numeral for ▢

|   | start at | count back | to reach |   | start at | count back | to reach |
|---|---|---|---|---|---|---|---|
| a | 12 | 5 | ▢ | e | 17 | ▢ | 13 |
| b | 19 | 7 | ▢ | f | 14 | 14 | ▢ |
| c | 20 | 12 | ▢ | g | 16 | ▢ | 5 |
| d | 10 | ▢ | 8 | h | 11 | ▢ | 0 |

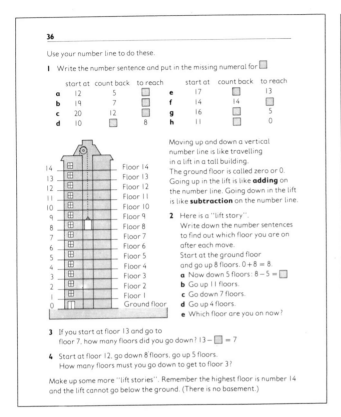

|  |  |
|---|---|
| 14 | Floor 14 |
| 13 | Floor 13 |
| 12 | Floor 12 |
| 11 | Floor 11 |
| 10 | Floor 10 |
| 9 | Floor 9 |
| 8 | Floor 8 |
| 7 | Floor 7 |
| 6 | Floor 6 |
| 5 | Floor 5 |
| 4 | Floor 4 |
| 3 | Floor 3 |
| 2 | Floor 2 |
| 1 | Floor 1 |
| 0 | Ground floor |

Moving up and down a vertical number line is like travelling in a lift in a tall building. The ground floor is called zero or 0. Going up in the lift is like **adding** on the number line. Going down in the lift is like **subtraction** on the number line.

2  Here is a "lift story". Write down the number sentences to find out which floor you are on after each move.
   Start at the ground floor and go up 8 floors. 0 + 8 = 8.
   a  Now down 5 floors: 8 − 5 = ▢
   b  Go up 11 floors.
   c  Go down 7 floors.
   d  Go up 4 floors.
   e  Which floor are you on now?

3  If you start at floor 13 and go to floor 7, how many floors did you go down? 13 − ▢ = 7

4  Start at floor 12, go down 8 floors, go up 5 floors. How many floors must you go down to get to floor 3?

Make up some more "lift stories". Remember the highest floor is number 14 and the lift cannot go below the ground. (There is no basement.)

---

**Practice 7**          Name_____

**Chapter 7: Subtraction I**

| A | | | B | | | C | | | D | | |
|---|---|---|---|---|---|---|---|---|---|---|---|
| 7 − 4 = | | 3 | 6 − 5 = | | 1 | 8 − 3 = | | 5 | 6 − 6 = | | 0 |
| 10 − 3 = | | 7 | 12 − 8 = | | 4 | 11 − 2 = | | 9 | 13 − 11 = | | 2 |
| 14 − 3 = | | 11 | 15 − 6 = | | 9 | 11 − 11 = | | 0 | 20 − 10 = | | 10 |
| 17 − 8 = | | 9 | 16 − 9 = | | 7 | 20 − 12 = | | 8 | 19 − 11 = | | 8 |
| 11 − 0 = | | 11 | 13 − 8 = | | 5 | 15 − 7 = | | 8 | 20 − 9 = | | 11 |
| 14 − 9 = | | 5 | 15 − 9 = | | 6 | 16 − 9 = | | 7 | 17 − 9 = | | 8 |
| 19 − 9 = | | 10 | 19 − 8 = | | 11 | 19 − 7 = | | 12 | 19 − 6 = | | 13 |
| 14 − 5 = | | 9 | 14 − 6 = | | 8 | 14 − 7 = | | 7 | 14 − 8 = | | 6 |
| 13 − 3 = | | 10 | 13 − 2 = | | 11 | 13 − 1 = | | 12 | 13 − 0 = | | 13 |
| 18 − 12 = | | 6 | 18 − 14 = | | 4 | 18 − 16 = | | 2 | 18 − 18 = | | 0 |

E

| 8 | 9 | 7 | 6 | 4 | 10 | 28 | 58 | 69 | 74 |
|---|---|---|---|---|---|---|---|---|---|
| −7 | −6 | −4 | −6 | −0 | −7 | −7 | −17 | −28 | −32 |
| 1 | 3 | 3 | 0 | 4 | 3 | 21 | 41 | 41 | 42 |

F

| 14 | 16 | 15 | 17 | 19 | 18 | 46 | 29 | 37 | 63 |
|---|---|---|---|---|---|---|---|---|---|
| −1 | −2 | −4 | −5 | −6 | −8 | −5 | −18 | −15 | −43 |
| 13 | 14 | 11 | 12 | 13 | 10 | 41 | 11 | 22 | 20 |

G

| 12 | 14 | 17 | 16 | 15 | 18 | 39 | 37 | 54 | 79 |
|---|---|---|---|---|---|---|---|---|---|
| −7 | −6 | −8 | −9 | −7 | −9 | −26 | −17 | −33 | −66 |
| 5 | 8 | 9 | 7 | 8 | 9 | 13 | 20 | 21 | 13 |

*Nuffield Maths 3 Spiritmasters*          *Nuffield Maths 3 Pupils' Book*          15

---

# References and resources

Shuard, H. and Williams, E., *Primary Mathematics Today* (Chapter 9), Longman Group Ltd 1970

Stern, C., *Children Discover Arithmetic*, Harrap 1971

Taverner, N., *Unifix Teachers' Manual*, Philip & Tacey 1970

*Multilink Number Track*, E.S.A.

*Number Strip & Rods, Stern Number Track*, Invicta Plastics

*Centicube, Number Track (Metline)*, Osmiroid

*Unifix Number Track*, Philip & Tacey

*Dial-a-sum*, Triman Classmate

# Chapter 8

# Weight 1

## For the teacher

Of all aspects of measurement, the concept of weight is one of the most difficult to teach, not least because it embraces many skills. Here, as in the teaching of any kind of measurement, it is important to get one's aim right. The target should be to develop the child's idea of weight: how heavy things are in relation to others; the relationships that exist between the size and weight of objects; the gradual realisation of a standard unit of measurement through the child's own experience and through historical development; and finally an informal notion of the principle of conservation of weight. Meanwhile it should not be forgotten that weighing is essentially the simple act of balancing one thing against another.

There are also skills to be learned using scales, balances, and other equipment: establishing the relationships that exist between the standard weights used on these; estimating the weight of objects; selecting the necessary balance weights; and finally counting and recording.

Computation plays a part. Skills learned in specific number work can be reinforced and made more relevant. However, the teaching of computation should never take priority over the development of the child's concept of weight. Practical experience with the materials is absolutely essential.

Much of the work in this chapter is revision of the basic experience that most of the children will have gained earlier. It has been included here because its importance cannot be over-emphasised.

As with earlier work on this topic, the temptation to distinguish mass and weight should be resisted – even though the use of both spring and pan balances might seem to afford a convenient opportunity. At this stage the distinction might well cause confusion, and it is better to stick to the informal term 'weight' throughout. (See page 100 of *Nuffield Maths 2 Teachers' Handbook.*)

One or two points of organisation should be considered because so many different materials can be used – dried peas, stones, bricks, sweets, etc. A corner in the classroom could be allotted for such articles to be displayed. Teachers may wish to give this 'designated area' a name, for example – 'Weight Corner'. Some children may wish to make a collection of empty tins and boxes marked with the metric weights of the contents. All such exhibits add to the atmosphere in the classroom, which should be one of purpose.

There may be problems with the supply of weighing instruments. Ideally no more than two children should be working on a balance or scale at a time if maximum experience is to be gained. To ease the strain on resources teachers may prefer to have more than one activity going on at once, so that some children are doing work not involving the use of scales.

## Summary of the stages

1  Experience of 'heaviness' leading to the simple balance

2  Using a school balance – estimating activities

3  Comparing the weight of materials

4  Towards the concept of conservation

## Vocabulary

Weight, heavy, heavier, light, lighter, balance, comparing, palm, estimate, materials, damp, more, less, than, shape, standard measure, exchange, trader, kilogram.

## Equipment and apparatus

Balances and scales – various types. Simple balance – this could be made from an old ruler, wooden lath, or wire coathanger. Materials and objects to use as standard weights – marbles, bottle tops, sugar cubes, pebbles, rulers, pencils, large balls, small balls, dry sand, damp sand. Containers to hold these – boxes or trays of a standard size and shape make a tidier display. Modelling clay, Plasticine, pieces of solid plastic, wood, expanded polystyrene, upholstery foam or sponge – all cut to the same shape and size. Fresh loaf of bread – unsliced, unwrapped. Two jam jars. Selection of commonplace objects to weigh. Weights: 1 kg, 500 g.

## Working with the children

### 1 Experience of heaviness leading to the simple balance
Before scales are introduced the child should be given the opportunity to use his 'muscle sense'. For the first activity the child should be presented with a variety of objects so that he can arrange them in order of heaviness. Choose objects which will provide as wide a range of weight as possible: from a feather to a piece of iron or brick.

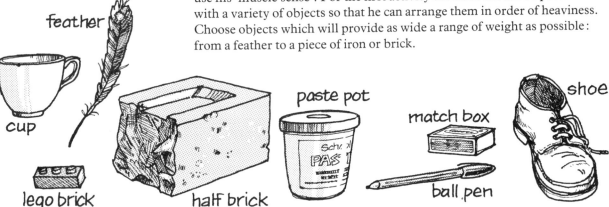

*The balance*

In any weighing activity the question of balance arises. Although for most of the work ready-made commercial balances will be used, children will gain much by retracing the steps of early man and making their own balance. A stick or school ruler suspended by string will do, but if the central suspension point and the strings for attaching weights at the ends are all in a line, the heavier weight will pull the ruler down to a vertical position. One way of avoiding this is by using a wider board on edge, as shown in the drawings. The children could use very stiff card. A wire coathanger with the hook cut off may also be used.

Emphasise the importance of making this simple piece of equipment balance in itself before using it to weigh. All too often, in later stages, children can be found using sophisticated scales which do not balance to begin with!

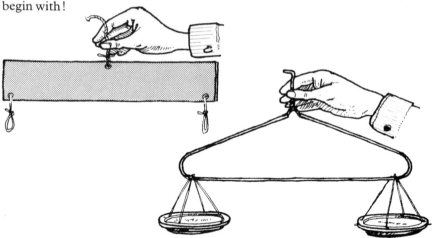

*Heavier and lighter*
This activity is aimed specifically at the use of the terms 'heavier than' and 'lighter than' in relation to the balance. We are assuming that the child has full understanding of these terms through firsthand experience. It is a check to see if the child fully appreciates that the heavier side of the balance will sink lower than the lighter side.

## 2   Using a school balance – estimating activities
Note the point of ensuring that the balance does in fact balance before starting. This checking procedure should be part of every lesson from now onwards. The instructions in weighing are an advance preparation for the next set of activities.

*Estimating weights*
The objectives of these activities are:
1   The making of two balls of plasticine, one large and one small, emphasises the point that it is possible to make your own weights – as was done by early man (though the earliest standard weight was probably a natural 'ready-made' grain of wheat).
2   Each of these two 'weights' will be balanced against a variety of materials, so therefore comparisons will be made.
3   Each weighing is to be preceded by an estimate, so that the child's 'muscle sense' can be used.

## 3   Comparing the weight of materials
*Strange things about the weight of materials*
During the early stages of the development of the concept of weight children sometimes think there is a fixed relationship between the size of an object and its weight: that all large objects must be heavy.

To give the child experience of differing densities, provide four or more pieces of different materials cut as near as possible to the same size. They must not be too large to fit the balance pan.
A suggested line of questioning is:

Pick each one up. Are some of them lighter or heavier than others? If they are, estimate which is lightest. List them all in order of heaviness.

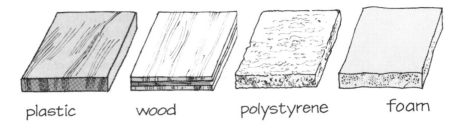

plated        wood        polystyrene        foam

Write down the lightest first.

Now check your estimates on the balance. Write down your results. Are any the same weight? Did you get the order right?

Is it true that all things the same size have the same weight?

Do you know any objects that are very small but very heavy? Record them in your book.

Do you know any objects that are very big but very light? Record these in your book.

*Water in materials*

This work leads up to the concept of conservation of weight. As a loaf of bread dries up and gets lighter, the water is not just disappearing. Children's curiosity may be aroused as to where it is going.

The presence of water accounts for much of the weight of many materials. This can be illustrated quite easily by comparing the weight of dry sand and wet sand.

Food, in particular, contains a very high percentage of water by weight. An interesting experiment to show this requires the use of a very fresh loaf of bread, not sliced or wrapped, weighed against marbles every day for a week. As the water content evaporates so fewer marbles should be needed each day. (The bread need not be wasted – it can be used for bread pudding.) Some teachers may wish their children to show results by means of a block graph.

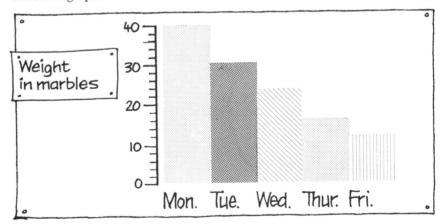

If children show interest in this activity, teachers may wish to set up further 'scientific' experiments involving weighing, for example reconstituting dried foods and changes of weight during cooking.

**4    Towards the concept of conservation**

Some children may think that if the shape of an object is changed then so is its weight. This common misconception among young children is finally resolved in what Piaget calls 'the concept of conservation of weight'.

Before proceeding further the teacher needs to be aware of whether or not the child has reached this stage of his development. Piaget's own experiment, using two balls of modelling clay or Plasticine, provides the child with this experience. A check-up on the invariance of weight is described in Chapter 9 of *Nuffield Maths 2 Teachers' Handbook* and in *Checking Up 2* (Chambers and Murray). (See Introduction page xii.)

## 5    Towards a standardised measure

*Why do we need a standard measure?*

It is important for the child to discover for himself, by retracing some of the experiences of people long ago, that a set of standard weights is necessary.

The children gain a great deal from making their own weights. It is not necessary for them to be of any particular standard weight, but it is important for each child's weights to balance each other. A sensible size of weight would be 2–4 cm in diameter. Once the children have made and balanced their weights they have a chance to use them by weighing objects around the classroom.

The comparison of different sets of weights is a fundamental experience. All children should carry it out. Showing a comparison of results from various children's weights illustrates the problems of using a variety of units and thereby stresses the need to evolve a standard unit of measurement. *Nuffield Maths 3 Spiritmasters*, Grid 10.

## 6    The kilogram and half-kilogram

There is a problem in introducing metric weights to young children. The gram is too small a unit to be of any practical use in itself; while the kilogram, although a useful unit measure, unfortunately is made up of 1000 grams – a number which is outside the counting experience of most young children. One way of overcoming this problem is suggested in the next chapter on weighing where the 100 gram weight or 'hecto' will make its appearance.

The child's first experience with the kilogram weight should be simply to hold it and feel how it reacts with his 'muscle sense'. This activity should now be extended to allow the child to identify objects which are heavier or lighter than 1 kg.

In order to save time when recording the children should be taught the abbreviation kg which stands for kilogram or kilogram*s*, is written in lower case letters (no capitals) and without a full stop – unless it comes at the end of a sentence. The abbreviation for gram(s) is g.

When introducing the 500 g weight, allow the child to discover for himself that two 500 g weights balance 1 kg, and that 500 g is half a kilogram.

Opportunity should now be given for the child to experience using the 500 g weight. This time ask him to identify objects weighing less than 500 g, and objects weighing more than 500 g, but less than 1 kg.

Some children may be capable of sorting objects as shown on the left. This should be done first by 'feel' and then checked on the scales.

Introduce to the child at this point the fact that 1 kg is 1000 g simply as a piece of information, not as a basis for calculation of any kind. As mentioned earlier, it is unlikely that the child has experience of working with or understanding four-digit numbers at this age. But he can get used to the idea that '1000 g' is used as a synonym for '1 kg'.

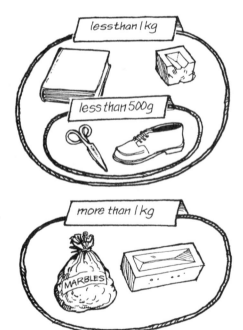

less than 1 kg

less than 500 g

more than 1 kg

MARBLES

# Pages from the Pupils' Book and Spiritmasters

## Chapter 8: Weight 1

### Heaviness

When we measure how heavy
things are, we are really
measuring how easy or difficult
it is to pick things up.

l  Try this with different objects.
Lift each one in turn and put it down.
In your book list them
in order of heaviness.
Write down the lightest object first.

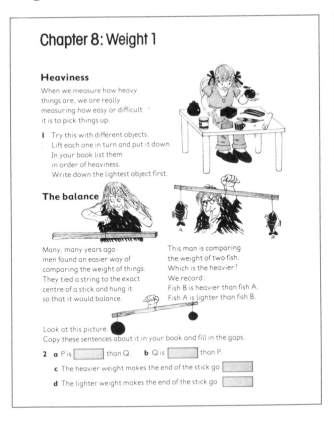

### The balance

Many, many years ago
men found an easier way of
comparing the weight of things.
They tied a string to the exact
centre of a stick and hung it
so that it would balance.

This man is comparing
the weight of two fish.
Which is the heavier?
We record:
Fish B is heavier than fish A.
Fish A is lighter than fish B.

Look at this picture.
Copy these sentences about it in your book and fill in the gaps.

2  a  P is [    ] than Q.     b  Q is [    ] than P.

c  The heavier weight makes the end of the stick go [    ]

d  The lighter weight makes the end of the stick go [    ]

---

**38**

### Using a school balance

It is important that the arrow is
pointing straight down at the mark
before you start to use the balance.

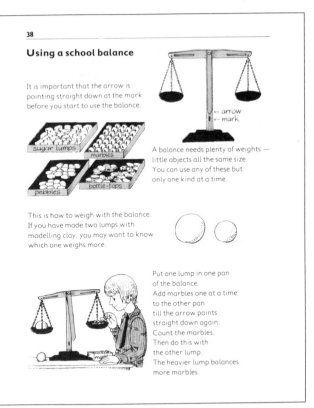

← arrow
← mark

sugar lumps
marbles
pebbles
bottle-tops

A balance needs plenty of weights —
little objects all the same size.
You can use any of these but
only one kind at a time.

This is how to weigh with the balance.
If you have made two lumps with
modelling clay, you may want to know
which one weighs more.

Put one lump in one pan
of the balance.
Add marbles one at a time
to the other pan
till the arrow points
straight down again.
Count the marbles.
Then do this with
the other lump.
The heavier lump balances
more marbles.

---

**39**

### Estimating weights

l  Place a large ball of modelling clay or Plasticine on the palm of
one of your hands. Take a handful of marbles in the other palm.
Do they feel the same weight? If not, add some or take some away.
Use the balance to find how many marbles balance the ball.
Is it the same as your estimate? Write down the number.
Try another estimate using bottle tops, sugar cubes and pebbles.

2  Make a smaller ball of clay and estimate and weigh again.
Record your estimates and what the balance says, like this:

| balances | | estimate | school balance |
|---|---|---|---|
| large ball | marbles | 10 | 12 |
| large ball | bottle tops | | |
| large ball | pebbles | | |

### Water in materials

3  Take two jam jars the same size.
Fill one with dry sand, one with damp sand.
Which jar feels heavier?
Check your estimate on the balance.

4  Take a small loaf of fresh bread.
Weigh it on the balance using marbles.
Record how many marbles it weighs.
Next day weigh it again. Has its weight
altered? Record the weight.

Do this every day for a week.
Record your results like this:

| day | weight in marbles |
|---|---|
| Monday | |
| Tuesday | |
| and so on | |

What is happening to the loaf
of bread? Why is this so?

---

**40**

### Working with modelling clay or Plasticine

Roll out two balls of
modelling clay.
Try to make each ball
the same weight.
Check by using
a balance putting one
ball in each pan.
Add little bits of
clay to the lighter
ball till they
balance each other.

Now take one of
the balls and make it
into something long,
like a snake.
Use the whole ball —
no less, no more.
Weigh your snake
and the ball on
the balance. Does
the snake weigh
more than the ball?

Squash up the snake
and shape it into
something thin and
hollow, like a jug.
Weigh the jug and
the ball. The jug
is thin and empty.
Does it weigh less
than the ball? Does
the shape of something
change its weight?

Make some weights out of modelling clay.
It is important that they all weigh the same.
Use the balance to check this.

l  Use your weights to weigh
objects in the classroom.

Record the weights
like this:

| object | my weights |
|---|---|
| small book | |
| shoe | |
| stone | |

Find some more.

2  Try an experiment. Borrow
your friend's set of weights.
Weigh the same objects again.
Record them next to your own.

What is wrong with every shop
using a different set of weights?

To be fair every shopkeeper
should use standard weights.
This means they should
all be the same.

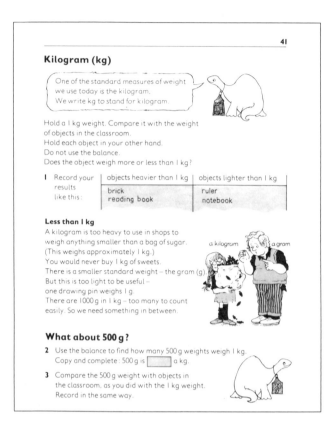

**41**

### Kilogram (kg)

One of the standard measures of weight we use today is the kilogram.
We write kg to stand for kilogram.

Hold a 1 kg weight. Compare it with the weight of objects in the classroom.
Hold each object in your other hand.
Do not use the balance.
Does the object weigh more or less than 1 kg?

**1** Record your results like this:

| objects heavier than 1 kg | objects lighter than 1 kg |
|---|---|
| brick<br>reading book | ruler<br>notebook |

#### Less than 1 kg

A kilogram is too heavy to use in shops to weigh anything smaller than a bag of sugar.
(This weighs approximately 1 kg.)
You would never buy 1 kg of sweets.
There is a smaller standard weight – the gram (g).
But this is too light to be useful –
one drawing pin weighs 1 g.
There are 1000 g in 1 kg – too many to count easily. So we need something in between.

#### What about 500 g?

**2** Use the balance to find how many 500 g weights weigh 1 kg.
Copy and complete: 500 g is [ ] a kg.

**3** Compare the 500 g weight with objects in the classroom, as you did with the 1 kg weight.
Record in the same way.

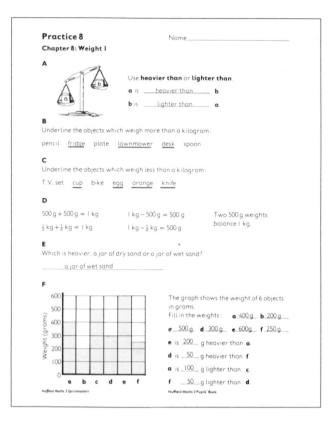

### Practice 8
**Chapter 8: Weight 1**

Name _____

**A**

Use **heavier than** or **lighter than**.

a is ___heavier than___ b.

b is ___lighter than___ a.

**B**
Underline the objects which weigh more than a kilogram:

pencil  <u>fridge</u>  plate  <u>lawnmower</u>  <u>desk</u>  spoon

**C**
Underline the objects which weigh less than a kilogram:

T.V. set  <u>cup</u>  bike  <u>egg</u>  <u>orange</u>  <u>knife</u>

**D**

| | | |
|---|---|---|
| 500 g + 500 g = 1 kg | 1 kg − 500 g = 500 g | Two 500 g weights |
| ½ kg + ½ kg = 1 kg | 1 kg − ½ kg = 500 g | balance 1 kg. |

**E**
Which is heavier, a jar of dry sand or a jar of wet sand?

___a jar of wet sand___

**F**

The graph shows the weight of 6 objects in grams.
Fill in the weights:  **a** 400 g  **b** 200 g
**c** 500 g  **d** 300 g  **e** 600 g  **f** 250 g

**e** is ___200___ g heavier than **a**.

**d** is ___50___ g heavier than **f**.

**a** is ___100___ g lighter than **c**.

**f** ___50___ g lighter than **d**.

Nuffield Maths 3 Spiritmasters

Nuffield Maths 3 Pupils' Book

## References and resources

Chaplin, Sally, *Bakery* (Teaching 5–13 Projects), Macdonald 1974

Nuffield Mathematics Teaching Project, *Beginnings* ▽ , *Checking up* [2], Nuffield Teaching Guides, Chambers/Murray 1967. (See Introduction, page xii.)

Shuard, H. and Williams, E. *Primary Mathematics Today* (Chapter 5), Longman Group Ltd 1970

Williams, M. E., *Come and Measure – Mass*, Macmillan 1975

*Adjusted Metric Weights, Bucket Balance, Compression Scale (10 kg), Cylindrical Weights, Flat Pan Scale (5 kg), Plastic Simple Balance, Simple Balance*, E. J. Arnold

*Primary Balance* (with buckets or pans), E.S.A.

*Rocker Scales, Simple Scales, Weights Board* (age 6–12), Invicta Plastics

*Compression Scales (5 kg), Metric Weights Set, Simple Scales*, Metric-Aids

*Analysis of a Kilogram, Bucket Balance, Compression Scales (10 kg), Equal Pan Balance, Personal Scales, Weighing Set, 100 g Board*, Nicolas Burdett

*Super Beamer Balance*, Osmiroid

*Set of Iron Masses* (Lead adjusted), Philip & Tacey

*Circular Steel Weights, Hexagonal Iron Weights, Personal Scales, Stowaway Scales*, Taskmaster Aids

# Multiplication 1

## For the teacher

This chapter deals with the 'repeated addition' aspect of multiplication and can be used either as an introduction to the subject or as reinforcement to work done previously. Before starting this chapter, children should be able to add up to totals of 30 with confidence since multiplication is developed as a quick and easy way of adding a series of equal numbers.

## Summary of the stages

1   Reinforcing multiplication – multiplication as repeated addition

2   Introducing factors and products

3   Hops of the same size along a number line/track

4   Patterns in multiplication

5   Rows and columns as an introduction to commutativity

## Vocabulary

'sets of', multiplied by, factors, products, pattern, number grid, circle, square, triangle, shade in, row, column, pair.

## Equipment and apparatus

Cubes, counters, pegs, number lines or tracks, 100-squares.

## Working with the children

### 1   Reinforcing multiplication - as repeated addition

A degree of caution should be taken before introducing the mathematical sign ' × '. It should never be assumed that just because a child understands the meaning of ' + ' he will easily understand the meaning of ' × '. It may be easy to teach a child to write down and learn '2 × 4 = 8' but it does not follow that he understands the more difficult concept of multiplication.

If we look at the two equations $2 + 4 = 6$ and $2 \times 4 = 8$, it is not just a question of using a different symbol and arriving at a different answer. In the addition equation, 2, 4 and 6 all represent numbers of *objects* within sets.

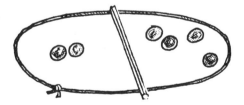

In the multiplication equation, the 2 and the 8 represent numbers of objects but the 4 refers to the *number of sets*.

$2 \times 4 = 8$

To enable the child to understand the true meaning of the equation $4 \times 3 = 12$ it is better to introduce an intermediary form of notation: 3 (4) meaning '3 sets of 4'

In diagram form:

$$
\left.
\begin{array}{ccc}
o & o & o \\
o & o & o \\
o & o & o \\
o & o & o
\end{array}
\right\}
\begin{array}{l}
\longrightarrow 4+4+4 \quad = 12 \\
\text{or} \quad 3 \text{ sets of } 4 = 12 \\
\text{or} \quad 3\,(4) \qquad = 12
\end{array}
$$

The Pupils' Book gives the child experience with this form of notation showing 'Toffo Bars' in packs of 4. This, however, should be supplemented with plenty of practical experience using sets of common objects such as shells, tops, beads, counters, etc.

The child should be encouraged to say to himself, in words, the meanings of the number sentences:

| *In words* | *Number sentences* |
|---|---|
| Five and five and five and five | $5+5+5+5 = 20$ |
| Four sets of five | $4\,(5) = 20$ |

### 2 Introducing factors and products

When the child fully understands the significance of $5(2) = 10$ he can then be introduced to the notation $2 \times 5 = 10$, 'two multiplied by five equals ten'.

$$
\left.
\begin{array}{l}
5 \text{ sets of } 2 \\
5\,(2) \\
2 \times 5 \\
5 \times 2
\end{array}
\right\} \longrightarrow 10
$$

5 and 2 are the *factors* of 10
10 is the *product* of 2 and 5

The terms *product* and *factor* are introduced in order to make it easier to talk about multiplication. *Product* is used instead of 'answer you get when you multiply two numbers'. It is also easier to ask a child 'What are the *factors* of 10?' rather than 'What are the numbers which have to be multiplied together to make 10?'

### 3 Hops of the same size along a number line/track

The number line gives an effective diagrammatic representation of multiplication as repeated addition. To avoid confusing the children, the language used to describe the activity should be chosen carefully. Emphasis should be given to the fact that 'hops of the same size' or 'equal jumps' are being used. *Nuffield Maths 3 Spiritmasters*, Grid 5.

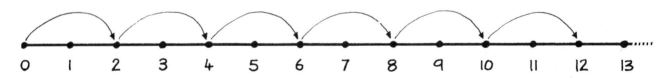

The number line shows: $2+2+2+2+2+2 = 12$

or: 6 jumps of 2　　　　$= 12$

　　　6 (2)　　　　　　$= 12$

or: 'a jump of 2' 6 times$= 12$

　　　$2 \times 6$　　　　　　$= 12$

Alternatively, a cardboard number line and smaller pieces of lengths 2 units, 3 units, 4 units can be used.

$4+4+4 = 12$
$3\,(4) = 12$
$4 \times 3 = 12$

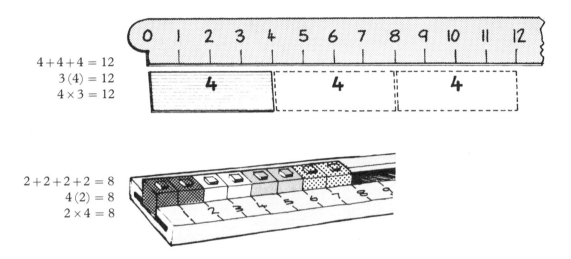

$2+2+2+2 = 8$
$4\,(2) = 8$
$2 \times 4 = 8$

Coloured cubes set out along a number track is a useful variation on the number line.

## 4　Patterns in multiplication

A $10 \times 5$ number grid up to 50, that is half of a 100 square, is used. *Nuffield Maths 3 Spiritmasters*, Grid 3.

| 1 | 2 | ③ | 4 | 5 | ⑥ | 7 | 8 | ⑨ | 10 |
|---|---|---|---|---|---|---|---|---|---|
| 11 | ⑫ | 13 | 14 | ⑮ | 16 | 17 | ⑱ | 19 | 20 |
| ㉑ | 22 | 23 | ㉔ | 25 | 26 | ㉗ | 28 | 29 | ㉚ |
| 31 | 32 | ㉝ | 34 | 35 | ㊱ | 37 | 38 | ㊴ | 40 |
| 41 | ㊷ | 43 | 44 | ㊺ | 46 | 47 | ㊽ | 49 | 50 |

At this stage the aim is to show the patterns which exist in multiplication; that each 'table' has its own pattern. Although the children will gradually become familiar with products up to 50, the acquisition of multiplication facts – 'learning tables' – will be dealt with later.

### 5  Rows and columns as an introduction to commutativity

The order in which two factors are multiplied does not affect the product, $5 \times 2 = 10$ and $2 \times 5 = 10$. This important property of multiplication is illustrated by looking at counters, cubes, etc. arranged in rows and columns.

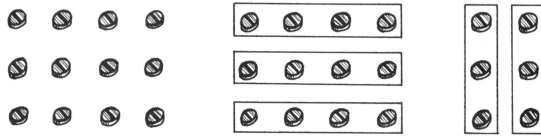
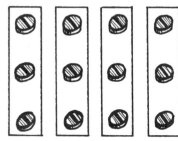

This array can be looked at as:          3 rows of 4    or                    4 columns of 3

In the first instance it is important to establish three teaching points:
1  That the child can differentiate between a row and a column.
2  That the child becomes used to looking at an arrangement of counters in the two ways. At first rulers or pieces of string could be used as partitions.
3  That the child can record in terms of rows or columns.

The children should also be given the chance to explore the different ways in which some products can be split into factors.

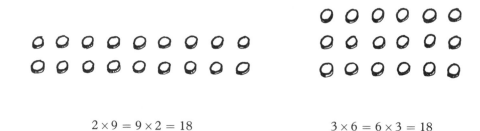

$2 \times 9 = 9 \times 2 = 18$                    $3 \times 6 = 6 \times 3 = 18$

It is important that the idea of 'rows and columns' is dealt with thoroughly because once a child appreciates that multiplication is commutative, the number of table facts to be learned is virtually halved.

# Pages from the Pupils' Book and Spiritmasters

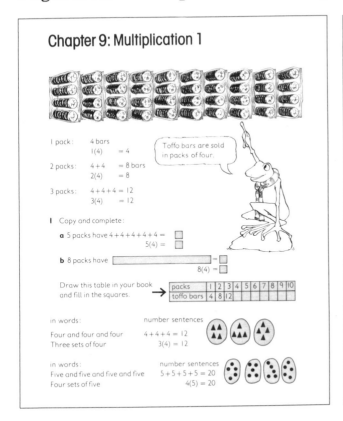

## Chapter 9: Multiplication 1

Toffo bars are sold in packs of four.

1 pack :   4 bars
            1(4)  = 4

2 packs:   4 + 4   = 8 bars
            2(4)  = 8

3 packs:   4 + 4 + 4 = 12
            3(4)  = 12

**1** Copy and complete:

**a** 5 packs have 4 + 4 + 4 + 4 + 4 = ☐
                    5(4) = ☐

**b** 8 packs have ☐ = ☐
                    8(4) = ☐

Draw this table in your book
and fill in the squares. →

| packs | 1 | 2 | 3 | 4 | 5 | 6 | 7 | 8 | 9 | 10 |
|---|---|---|---|---|---|---|---|---|---|---|
| toffo bars | 4 | 8 | 12 | | | | | | | |

in words :                number sentences
Four and four and four    4 + 4 + 4 = 12
Three sets of four        3(4) = 12

in words :                number sentences
Five and five and five and five   5 + 5 + 5 + 5 = 20
Four sets of five         4(5) = 20

---

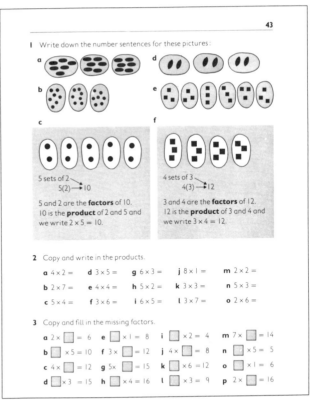

**1** Write down the number sentences for these pictures:

**a**   **d**

**b**   **e**

**c**   **f**

5 sets of 2 → 5(2) → 10

5 and 2 are the **factors** of 10.
10 is the **product** of 2 and 5 and
we write 2 × 5 = 10.

4 sets of 3 → 4(3) → 12

3 and 4 are the **factors** of 12.
12 is the **product** of 3 and 4 and
we write 3 × 4 = 12.

**2** Copy and write in the products.

**a** 4 × 2 =      **d** 3 × 5 =      **g** 6 × 3 =      **j** 8 × 1 =      **m** 2 × 2 =

**b** 2 × 7 =      **e** 4 × 4 =      **h** 5 × 2 =      **k** 3 × 3 =      **n** 5 × 3 =

**c** 5 × 4 =      **f** 3 × 6 =      **i** 6 × 5 =      **l** 3 × 7 =      **o** 2 × 6 =

**3** Copy and fill in the missing factors.

**a** 2 × ☐ = 6      **e** ☐ × 1 = 8      **i** ☐ × 2 = 4      **m** 7 × ☐ = 14

**b** ☐ × 5 = 10     **f** 3 × ☐ = 12     **j** 4 × ☐ = 8      **n** ☐ × 5 = 5

**c** 4 × ☐ = 12     **g** 5 × ☐ = 15     **k** ☐ × 6 = 12     **o** ☐ × 1 = 6

**d** ☐ × 3 = 15     **h** ☐ × 4 = 16     **l** ☐ × 3 = 9      **p** 2 × ☐ = 16

---

### Hops of the same size

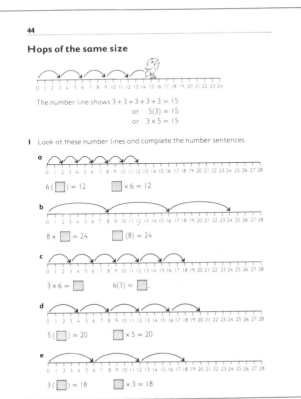

The number line shows 3 + 3 + 3 + 3 + 3 = 15
or   5(3) = 15
or   3 × 5 = 15

**1** Look at these number lines and complete the number sentences.

**a**

6 (☐) = 12      ☐ × 6 = 12

**b**

8 × ☐ = 24      ☐ (8) = 24

**c**

3 × 6 = ☐       6(3) = ☐

**d**

5 (☐) = 20      ☐ × 5 = 20

**e**

3 (☐) = 18      ☐ × 3 = 18

---

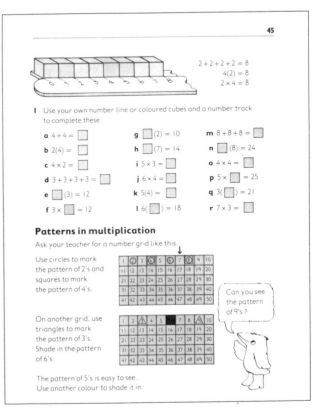

2 + 2 + 2 + 2 = 8
4(2) = 8
2 × 4 = 8

**1** Use your own number line or coloured cubes and a number track
to complete these.

**a** 4 + 4 = ☐        **g** ☐ (2) = 10       **m** 8 + 8 + 8 = ☐

**b** 2(4) = ☐         **h** ☐ (7) = 14       **n** ☐ (8) = 24

**c** 4 × 2 = ☐        **i** 5 × 3 = ☐        **o** 4 × 4 = ☐

**d** 3 + 3 + 3 + 3 = ☐   **j** 6 × 4 = ☐     **p** 5 × ☐ = 25

**e** ☐ (3) = 12       **k** 5(4) = ☐         **q** 3(☐) = 21

**f** 3 × ☐ = 12       **l** 6(☐) = 18        **r** 7 × 3 = ☐

### Patterns in multiplication

Ask your teacher for a number grid like this.

Use circles to mark
the pattern of 2's and
squares to mark
the pattern of 4's.

On another grid, use
triangles to mark
the pattern of 3's.
Shade in the pattern
of 6's.

Can you see
the pattern
of 9's ?

The pattern of 5's is easy to see.
Use another colour to shade it in.

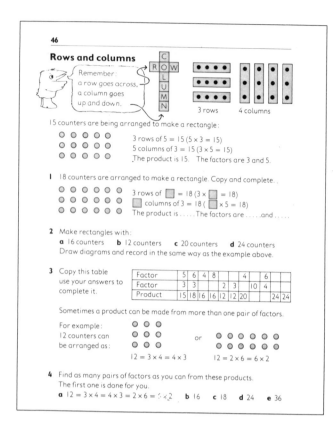

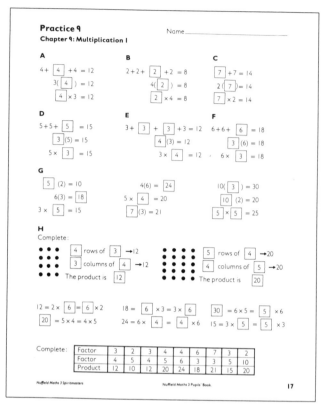

# References and resources

Nuffield Mathematics Teaching Project, *Computation and Structure* ③ , Nuffield Guides, Chambers/Murray 1967. (See Introduction, page xii.)

Shuard, H. and Williams, E., *Primary Mathematics Today* (Chapter 7), Longman Group Ltd 1970

Tavener, N., *Unifix Teachers' Manual*, Philip & Tacey 1970

*Multilink 100 Pegboard, Multilink Number Track, Stern Number Track*, E.S.A.

*Hundred Number Board, Number Strip* and *Rods*, Invicta Plastics

*Centicube Number Track (Metline)*, Osmiroid

*Unifix 100 Board, Unifix Multiplication/Division Markers, Number Tablets* and *Window Markers*, Philip & Tacey

# Time 1

## For the teacher

Ability to measure time is one of the most important of all the basic mathematical skills. This is because it is not just mathematical; it is social. In everyday life you can get away with little or no mathematical ability in most areas. Even counting small sums of money is beyond many people who lead a normal life. But if you cannot tell the time, you are lost.

An adult who has been able to tell the time for years, and who has become used to estimating the passage of time as a result of daily routine, tends to take it for granted that time measurement is easy. But in fact it is more complicated than many other measuring procedures. Instead of the neat, unified decimal system, there is a confusing welter of division into 60, 12 and 5. (To satisfy children who may be bewildered, resentful or just curious about this arrangement, its historical origins are explained in Chapter 20, Time 2.) Furthermore, a clock face has two hands of different sizes, moving at different speeds and around different scales. The numbers 1 to 12 distract attention from the 60 minute divisions, and vice versa. The hour hand does not indicate the hour clearly: at 5.55 it is pointing almost exactly at the 6. Lastly, there is the conventional system of describing times later than half past the hour as 'minutes to' the next hour – a procedure unique to time measurement.

Another problem is that of digital time displays. Many of the children who are doing this work will already have watches, and many of these will be digital. Hands are 'old hat'. Whether this is a passing fashion or not remains to be seen, but the chances are that it is not. More and more indicating instruments, from volt meters to car speedometers, are turning to digital displays; and the advent of micro-processors, which are digital in operation themselves and thus much easier to hook up to a digital display, will probably clinch it. The fact that digital displays are rather illegible does not seem to make any difference.

Many children who have digital watches do not know how to use them. The buttons selecting 'functions' are hard to work. Ask many a proud owner what the time is and you will be told the date. Children are not ready at this stage for the 24-hour time notation system; but in any case a digital wristwatch does not indicate 24-hour time. At 09.30 it says '9.30', leaving the first digit position blank. After noon it indicates p.m. times.

The second chapter on Time in this book (and the accompanying Pupils' Book) includes some work linking digital watch displays (non-24-hour) with hand position on a conventional clock.

Both Time chapters here concentrate mainly on telling the time. Children may well have done work on this earlier. There was some informal practice in Pupils' Worksheets and Teachers' Handbook 2. This is a vital skill which must be reinforced until the time can be told automatically and correctly.

If the teacher feels that this emphasis leads to too little experience in the estimation of the passage of time, it is suggested that the sand, candle and water drip timers described in *Nuffield Maths 2 Teachers' Handbook* should be reintroduced and practice given in calibrating them against a real clock. Using a seconds timer or stopwatch at this stage is probably a mistake: the figures on the face are different; and with hour and minute hands to bother about, the second hand will only tend to complicate matters further.

## Summary of the stages

1   The minute divisions of the clock face

2   Simple fractions of an hour

3   Counting any whole number of minutes

## Equipment and apparatus

Teaching clock face – wood or cardboard, no mechanism, Arabic numerals, minute divisions, removable hour hand (see Appendix 1 for instructions on making your own). 'Interleaved circle' clock face to indicate swept angle of hands (minutes only) (see Appendix 2). Clock face rubber stamp (with numerals 1 to 12) and ink pad. Any or all of the simple timing devices mentioned in *Nuffield Maths 2 Teachers' Handbook*, Chapter 10.

## Vocabulary

Face, hands (of clock), hour, minute (as formal units), pass (of time), later, earlier, real time, sunrise, sunset, daytime and night hours, clockwise, anti-clockwise.

## Working with the children

### 1   The minute divisions of the clock face

The fact that a clock face has to serve for both hours and minutes can cause problems. The suggested method is to 'banish' the hour numbers temporarily to an undiscussed imaginary central area of the clock face. Make sure that all clock faces you are showing to the children do in fact have the hours marked inside the minute marks, and also that the 5-minute marks are noticeably heavier than the other minute marks (which must be present). The Philip & Tacey (12-hour version) and E. J. Arnold clock face rubber stamps are satisfactory in these respects.

It is not a good idea to do this work on minutes either with an 'hourless' clock face or with a stopwatch – type face numbered to 60. The children should get used to the hour figures being there even though they do not indicate the number of minutes directly. However, it would be best to remove the hour hand if possible.

The 'interleaved circle' clock, which is easy to make yourself from the instructions in Appendix 2 will be found most useful as an aid to demonstration. Its display of a period of time as a coloured segment of clock face is a perfect introduction to the segment diagrams at the end of this section. The hour hand should be left off.

Revision may be required in the 5 times table – but what is important here is not the factors, but memorising the sequence '5, 10, 15, 20 . . . 60'.

Make sure that the children grasp that the 60-minute mark also does duty for 0. It should be clear if you explain that there is simply no room to write two figures in the same place.

When the children have had a chance to memorise where the figures are (reinforce this with verbal questions if necessary), they must cover up the marked rubber stamp in their books before going on to the cipher exercise.

The 'secret message' reads: 'Fast horses race at the track.' If the children want to create their own messages, so much the better: it is useful practice provided that they stick to the clock face method.

### 2 Simple fractions of an hour

The children should already have done some work on simple fractions. Revise this if necessary. Although the fact that an hour can be split into thirds should be grasped (as an essential part of getting the 'feel' of the number 60), one-third of an hour is of little use in ordinary timekeeping language. Therefore the point should not be laboured, and any additional practice should be done on halves and quarters.

### 3 Counting any whole number of minutes

Starting to count individual minutes is inevitably rather laborious – but it has to be done some time. The use of a verbal routine is suggested here.

When teaching how to count minutes between two 'small' (non-5-minute) lines, it may seem tempting to point out that, for example, from 12.17 to 12.32 is exactly a quarter of an hour, because both times are 2 minutes along from the 5-minute mark. It would be better not to introduce this until the children have got a thorough grasp of the clumsy but conceptually simple method of counting the single minutes outside the 5-minute marks at both ends. This involves only addition, rather than a mental transposition which they may not be able to visualise.

Make sure that the children really understand the terms 'clockwise' and 'anti-clockwise' and the relationship of forward and back to later and earlier; also that they do not get the idea that counting back involves the clock running backwards.

# Pages from the Pupils' Book and Spiritmasters

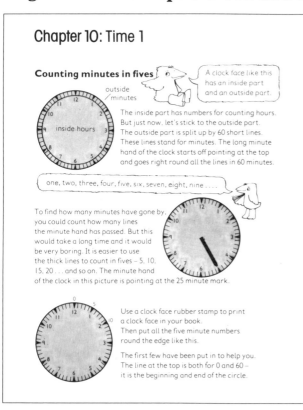

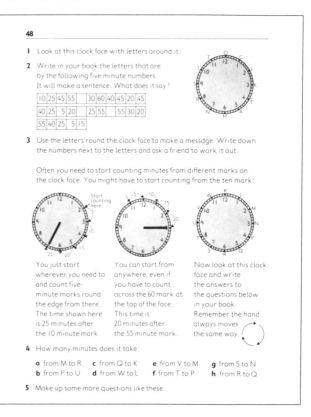

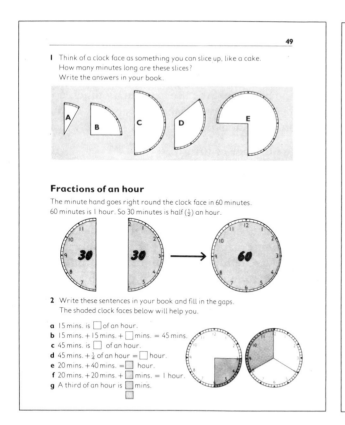

**49**

**1** Think of a clock face as something you can slice up, like a cake.
How many minutes long are these slices?
Write the answers in your book.

### Fractions of an hour

The minute hand goes right round the clock face in 60 minutes.
60 minutes is 1 hour. So 30 minutes is half ($\frac{1}{2}$) an hour.

**2** Write these sentences in your book and fill in the gaps.
The shaded clock faces below will help you.

**a** 15 mins. is ☐ of an hour.
**b** 15 mins. + 15 mins. + ☐ mins. = 45 mins.
**c** 45 mins. is ☐ of an hour.
**d** 45 mins. + $\frac{1}{4}$ of an hour = ☐ hour.
**e** 20 mins. + 40 mins. = ☐ hour.
**f** 20 mins. + 20 mins. + ☐ mins. = 1 hour.
**g** A third of an hour is ☐ mins.

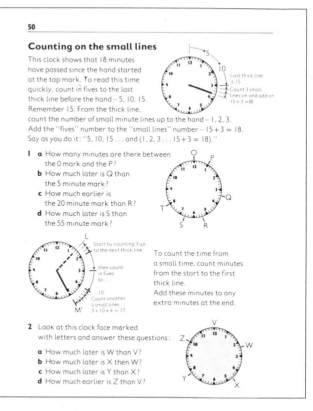

**50**

### Counting on the small lines

This clock shows that 18 minutes
have passed since the hand started
at the top mark. To read this time
quickly, count in fives to the last
thick line before the hand – 5, 10, 15.
Remember 15. From the thick line,
count the number of small minute lines up to the hand – 1, 2, 3.
Add the "fives" number to the "small lines" number – 15 + 3 = 18.
Say as you do it: "5, 10, 15 . . . and (1, 2, 3 . . . 15 + 3 = 18)."

**1 a** How many minutes are there between
the 0 mark and the P?
**b** How much later is Q than
the 5 minute mark?
**c** How much earlier is
the 20 minute mark than R?
**d** How much later is S than
the 55 minute mark?

To count the time from
a small time, count minutes
from the start to the first
thick line.
Add these minutes to any
extra minutes at the end.

**2** Look at this clock face marked
with letters and answer these questions:

**a** How much later is W than V?
**b** How much later is X then W?
**c** How much later is Y than X?
**d** How much earlier is Z than V?

---

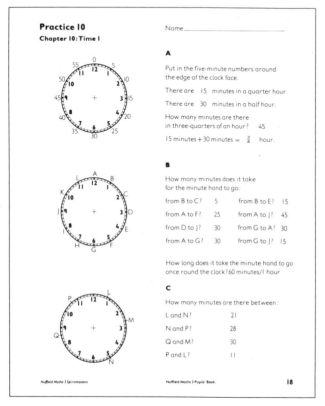

**Practice 10**

**Chapter 10: Time 1**

Name_____

**A**

Put in the five-minute numbers around
the edge of the clock face.

There are  15  minutes in a quarter hour.

There are  30  minutes in a half hour.

How many minutes are there
in three-quarters of an hour?   45

15 minutes + 30 minutes = $\frac{3}{4}$  hour.

**B**

How many minutes does it take
for the minute hand to go:

| | | | |
|---|---|---|---|
| from B to C? | 5 | from B to E? | 15 |
| from A to F? | 25 | from A to J? | 45 |
| from D to J? | 30 | from G to A? | 30 |
| from A to G? | 30 | from G to J? | 15 |

How long does it take the minute hand to go
once round the clock? 60 minutes/1 hour

**C**

How many minutes are there between:

| | |
|---|---|
| L and N? | 21 |
| N and P? | 28 |
| Q and M? | 30 |
| P and L? | 11 |

## References and resources

*Clocks*, Starters Series, Macdonald 1972

*How Much Time?*, *Times Through the Day*
(strips-books), Philip & Tacey

Williams M. E., *Come and Measure – Time*, Macmillan
1975

*Clock Face Rubber Stamp*, *Working Clock*, E. J. Arnold

*Clock Face Tracers*, Invicta Plastics

*Timex Posters* (9 posters and teachers' notes),
Julie Bloomfield Associates, 42 Tavistock Street,
WC2E 7PB

*Wooden Clock Face*
(diam. 35 cm), Metric Aids

*Rotascan Clock*, Osmiroid Educational

*Teach-a-time Clock*, Playcraft Toys

# Appendix 1

### A home-made clock face

In the absence of a large commercially produced clock face, teachers might wish to make their own. (Rubber stamp clock faces are not large enough for demonstration purposes.) It is worth taking a little care in making the first 'prototype' since this can be used as a template for any future versions you may wish to make.

On paper, draw a circle with a radius of at least 10 cm (i.e. 20 cm across). This can be done either by using compasses or by drawing round a circular plate. Cut out the circle and fold it into four. (This will find the centre if you have drawn round a plate, and will also show whether or not the plate was close to a true circle. The folds mark out four positions on the clock face. The other positions may be marked either by using a protractor (angles of 30 degrees at the centre) or by further folding.

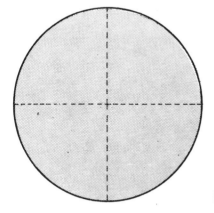

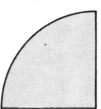

Fold to produce this.

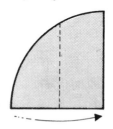 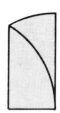

Fold along dotted line.

Open out to this.

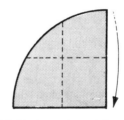 

Fold along dotted line.

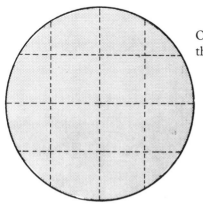

On opening out the paper, the creases appear like this.

Draw lines through the centre to join points where creases cross the circumference, thus dividing it into 12 equal parts.

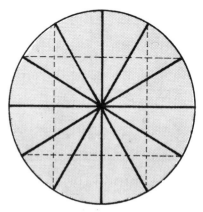

Use the template of the circle divided into 12 equal parts to mark out a clock face on stiff card. The 'hands' can either be cut from card and secured by a brass paper fastener, or can be made from coloured pipe cleaners poked through a small hole at the centre. Bend over at the back of the clock to prevent them slipping through.

# Appendix 2

### Clock face using interleaved circles

Use the template to mark out a clock face on stiff card as before. Cut a straight slit from the centre to the edge of the circle at '12 o'clock'. (Alternatively, cut right to the edge of the card with scissors and then Sellotape across the back just above the 12 mark.)

Now cut out a smaller circle (about 8 cm radius) from card of a different colour. Make a straight cut from the edge to the centre. Draw a 'hand' along one edge of the cut and push the other edge through the slit in the clock face.

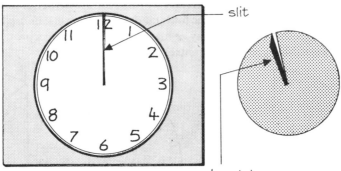

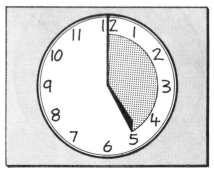

hand drawn on          circles interleaved

To make the hour hand, cut out an even smaller circle of another colour (radius 6 cm). Make a straight cut and draw in a 'hand' as before. Interleave to make a clock with two hands.

If the two circles are made of some clear material, such as overhead projector transparencies, the whole of both hands will be visible.

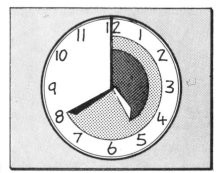

The interleaving circle idea is particularly useful when the children are at the 'minutes past/minutes to' stage. In this case, the back and front of the 'minute hand circle' are coloured to match the numerals of the two halves of the clock face. The circle is slotted into the face one way for 'minutes past'; it is turned over and inserted the other way for 'minutes to'.

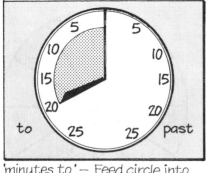

'minutes to' – Feed circle into slot this way.

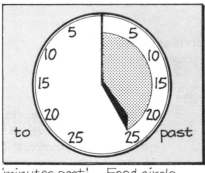

'minutes past' – Feed circle into slot this way.

When the children reach the 'hours and minutes' form (i.e. 7.25, 8.55, etc.), the circle can be slotted into a clock face marked 5, 10, 15, 20 . . . 45, 50, 55.

The advantage of the interleaving circle clock is the visual effect – the angle 'swept out' by the hand (or to be 'swept out' in moving up to the 12 position) is clearly indicated.

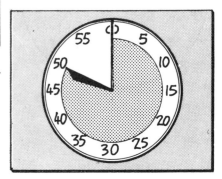

# Capacity 1

## For the teacher

Capacity is a special case of volume: that is the volume of something which can be held by and assumes the shape of the container. 'The capacity of a jug' refers to its internal volume or the volume of material which the jug will hold. Volume implies *space occupied*, whereas capacity implies *space available*. It is in this sense that the seating capacity of a bus indicates how many seats are available not how many seats are occupied.

The measurement of capacity is more than just another form of quantity measurement. True understanding of capacity is far more difficult to achieve than with weight or linear measurement. Several difficulties face the child who is learning about capacity.

The first of these is a problem of intangibility – in the case of linear measurement, a metre can be represented by a metre stick which can be handled by the child and its length compared with familiar objects around the classroom. When dealing with weight, the kilogram can be exemplified by a lump of metal which can be picked up and its weight felt by the child's own 'muscle sense'; and again its weight can be compared with that of familiar objects.

In work on capacity, however, a litre cannot be handled and compared with other familiar amounts. In order for an amount of liquid (or sand) to be assessed, it has to be contained in a vessel of some kind. Containers may be of any shape or size, so estimation or comparison of their contents is a very difficult skill to acquire.

It is important that in all the work in this chapter sufficient equipment is made available for the children. Wherever possible transparent containers should be used. A special corner in the classroom could be set aside to store, display and use capacity equipment.

## Summary of the stages

1   Comparison of capacity of vessels. (Which holds the most?)

2   Measuring capacity using suitable arbitrary measures

3   Development of conservation – using a fixed amount of liquid in varying shaped containers

## Vocabulary

Estimate, container, capacity, measure (noun and verb), eggcupful(s), level, tilt, water line.

## Equipment and apparatus

Drinking cups – different sizes and shapes, shampoo bottles – different sizes and shapes, small cardboard boxes – different sizes and shapes, water, dry sand, egg cups, transparent containers – widely differing shapes, funnels, wax crayons.

# Working with the children

## 1 Comparison of capacity of measures. (Which holds the most?)

The first exercise is intended to establish an informal idea of what the capacity of a container is. The basic skill of comparison of capacity has to be attained to do this, but the concept of units of measurement is not introduced at this stage. It is hoped that the child will invent a method of sorting out the problem. Some children may just pour from one container into another, while others may use a smaller arbitrary measure such as an egg cup. Some egg cups should be made available, but no recommendation should be made as to their use.

The work with shampoo bottles provides an extension of the previous exercise. Children should be encouraged to make collections of unusual shaped containers. Shampoo bottles are ideal because their strange shapes are actually designed to mislead the buyer into believing that they hold much more than they actually do. *Nuffield Maths 3 Spiritmasters*, Grid 11.

Avoid giving children the idea that only water can be used in work on capacity. You could hold a discussion to see how many liquids the children can think of – see the section on 'liquids'. Dry sand is also a useful substance for developing the concept of capacity, especially when using cardboard containers.

### *Liquids*

The basic work here on capacity could well be extended to include some simple science. The suggested collection of liquids could be arranged to form a display. Apart from the variety of colours other work could include some properties of liquids (smell, taste, drinkable?) as well as evaporation, dilution, etc. Great care, however, should be taken to avoid exposure to intoxicating, poisonous, flammable, or staining liquids. (See DES *Safety in Science Laboratories*, New Edition, HMSO 1978.)

If the children bring in a variety of liquid containers, preferably with labels showing their capacity in litres or millilitres, these can be used in future exercises.

## 2 Measuring capacity using suitable arbitrary measures

Initial activities should have established the fact that we are concerned with measuring how much containers hold. Before introducing standard measures it is important for the child to appreciate that the activity is to do with measuring and not playing around with water or sand.

As with all quantity work, measuring should start with arbitrary measures, thus developing a realisation for the need for a standard measure. Egg cups have been suggested for this activity. If various egg cups of different sizes are available the children will be able to compare results.

### *Choosing a suitable measure*

The need to choose a sensible measure is an important aspect of any measuring activity. It is hoped that discussion between teacher and child could develop from this exercise.

## 3 Development of conservation – using a fixed amount of liquid in varying shaped containers

Piaget laid great importance on the development of the concept of conservation. Conservation of volume is far more difficult to grasp than that of mass or weight.

After pouring one cupful of water, using a funnel if necessary, into each of four different shaped transparent containers, the child is asked if each now contains the same amount.

If possible, this work should be carried out with individual children. A brief discussion with each will help establish whether or not the child has in fact reached this stage of conceptual development.

Some children also have difficulty in appreciating that water level always remains horizontal irrespective of how the container is tilted.

# Pages from the Pupils' Book and Spiritmasters

## Chapter 11: Capacity 1

### Which holds the most?

Greedy Sam does not know which cup to take so that he will get the most orange drink. How can he find which cup holds the most? Is it the tallest or the widest?

1 Take four cups that look different. Fill them with water to find which is really largest. How will you compare them? In your book list them in order, starting with the largest.

2 Some shampoo comes in trick bottles. They are all tall and wide to make you think that they hold a lot. Bring some empty shampoo bottles to school. Fill them with water to see which one holds the most. In your book list them in order starting with the one which holds the most.

3 You can compare boxes too. Water would make them soggy so use sand instead.

First try to estimate which box is largest and which is second largest, third largest and smallest. List your estimates in your book. Fill the boxes with sand and compare them. Were you right? Record the results.

52

### Measuring capacity

To measure the capacity of a container, you put liquid, dry sand or rice into it. Capacity is how much a container holds.

You may have noticed that just because a container is tall it does not mean that it holds more than a short one.

Use the cups, bottles and boxes you had before. Find an egg cup to use as a measure.

1 List your containers and your findings like this:

| container | estimate (eggcupfuls) | measure (eggcupfuls) |
|-----------|----------------------|----------------------|
| cup 1     | 10                   |                      |
| cup 2     | 8                    |                      |

Fill the eggcup with water and use it to fill the cups.

Fill the shampoo bottle and see how many times it will fill the eggcup.

Use sand for the box. Level off each eggcupful with your finger, then pour it into the box.

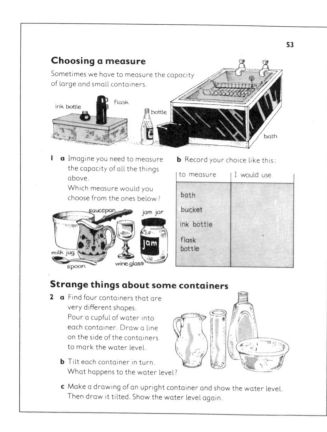

**53**

### Choosing a measure

Sometimes we have to measure the capacity of large and small containers.

ink bottle · flask · bottle · bath

**1 a** Imagine you need to measure the capacity of all the things above.
Which measure would you choose from the ones below?

saucepan · jam jar · milk jug · wine glass · spoon

**b** Record your choice like this:

| to measure | I would use |
|---|---|
| bath | |
| bucket | |
| ink bottle | |
| flask | |
| bottle | |

### Strange things about some containers

**2 a** Find four containers that are very different shapes.
Pour a cupful of water into each container. Draw a line on the side of the containers to mark the water level.

**b** Tilt each container in turn. What happens to the water level?

**c** Make a drawing of an upright container and show the water level. Then draw it tilted. Show the water level again.

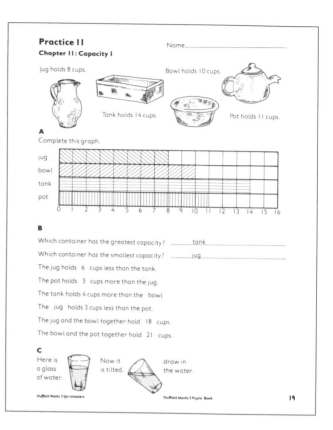

### Practice 11
**Chapter 11: Capacity 1**

Name _____

Jug holds 8 cups. · Bowl holds 10 cups. · Tank holds 14 cups. · Pot holds 11 cups.

**A**
Complete this graph.

|  | 0 1 2 3 4 5 6 7 8 9 10 11 12 13 14 15 16 |
|---|---|
| jug | |
| bowl | |
| tank | |
| pot | |

**B**

Which container has the greatest capacity? _____ tank _____

Which container has the smallest capacity? _____ jug _____

The jug holds 6 cups less than the tank.

The pot holds 3 cups more than the jug.

The tank holds 4 cups more than the bowl.

The jug holds 3 cups less than the pot.

The jug and the bowl together hold 18 cups.

The bowl and the pot together hold 21 cups.

**C**

Here is a glass of water. · Now it is tilted. · draw in the water.

*Nuffield Maths 3 Spiritmasters* · *Nuffield Maths 3 Pupils' Book* · **19**

# References and resources

Matthews, G. and J. *Water*, Early Mathematical Experiences, Addison-Wesley 1978

Nuffield Mathematics Teaching Project, *Beginnings* $\triangledown$, Nuffield Guide, Chambers/Murray 1967. (See Introduction, page xii.)

Williams, M. E., *Come and Measure – Capacity* (pages 1–13), Macmillan 1975

*Set of Plastic Funnels, Sand Play Set, Water Play Set*, E. J. Arnold

*Capacity Measures*, Invicta Plastics

*Set of 3 Funnels*, Nicolas Burdett

*Spoon and Cup Measure*, Osmiroid

*Odd Bottle Set*, Six to Twelve

# Chapter 12

# Division 1

## For the teacher

Some children may have had practical experience of division (*Nuffield Maths 2 Teachers' Handbook*, Chapter 6). This chapter may be used to reinforce these experiences or as an introduction to division. Two aspects of division – sharing and repeated subtraction – are dealt with separately for, although the same symbol ÷ is used for both aspects, the moving and rearrangement of objects, counters, etc. is quite different in each case. The following example indicates the differences.

'Ten divided by two'
$10 \div 2$

**Sharing**
Sometimes called 'partition'.

**Repeated subtraction**
Sometimes called 'quotition', 'grouping' or the 'measuring aspect'.

Ten sweets

Ten sweets

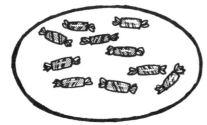

shared out between 2 children.

2 sweets given to each child.

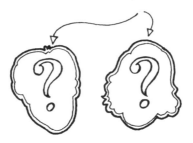

How many *sweets* for each child?
This is usually done by children *sharing* out the sweets on a 'one for you, one for me' basis.
We know how many 'customers' (subsets) there are. What is the share for each?

How many *children* receive sweets?
This is done by repeatedly subtracting 2 sweets as each child 'comes to the head of the queue'.
We know what the quota or ration is.
How many 'customers' can we serve?
'Sharing' is not appropriate here as we do not know how many 'shareholders' there are.

In this case, $10 \div 2 = 5$ comes from 'If 10 sweets are shared equally between 2 children, each child received 5 *sweets*.'

In this case, $10 \div 2 = 5$ comes from 'If 10 sweets are given out 2 per child, there are enough for 5 *children*.'

For both these aspects, 'Ten divided by two' or '10 ÷ 2' is correct whereas if the word 'share' is used for the operation as in, 'Ten shared by two' it is not correct for repeated subtraction since the 10 sweets are then *shared by* 5 children although 10 has been *divided by* 2.

## Summary of the stages

**1** Division by sharing

**2** Division by repeated subtraction

## Vocabulary

The reading associated with the exercises and problems in the text may have to be adjusted according to the ability of the children but the following words are those considered important for an understanding of this chapter on division.

Share, equally, *between, divide, division, divided by, sets, subsets, column, row.

## Equipment and apparatus

Collections of objects such as shells, beads, marbles, buttons, counters, etc. Apparatus for use with sets such as hoops, cake tins or trays. Structural apparatus – rods, interlocking cubes, number lines, number tracks.

## Working with the children

### 1   Division by sharing

Lots of practical activities should precede the more formal work. Ideally the activity illustrated in the Pupils' Book, sharing 12 cakes equally between 4 plates, should be 'acted out' by a group of children with appropriate language being injected by the teacher.

Further practical examples might be similar to:

'Share these 18 marbles between 6 children. How many marbles does each child get?'

'Put these 15 counters in 3 equal subsets. How many counters in each subset?'

'Arrange these 20 pegs in 5 equal rows. How many pegs in each row?'

* 'Between and among. The Oxford English Dictionary gives a warning against the superstition that *between* can be used only of the relationship *between* two things, and that if there are more *among* is the right preposition. 'In all senses *between* has been, from its earliest appearance, extended to more than two. . . . It is still the only word available to express the relation of a thing to many surrounding things severally and individually; *among* expresses a relation to them collectively and vaguely. We should not say the space lying among the three points or a treaty among three Powers.'

*Dictionary of Modern English Usage*, H. W. Fowler, O.U.P., 1965

The results of these activities should be recorded first in words:

'20 pegs in 5 equal rows. 4 pegs in each row.'

and then in a number sentence:

$20 \div 5 = 4$

with the symbol ÷ read as 'divided by'.

It is important that children are allowed to use counters, pegs, cubes, bottle tops, etc. until they have built up sufficient confidence to dispense with aids.

In all cases of division by *sharing*, the 'answer' is always the same sort of thing or in the same units as the original set.

## 2 Division by repeated subtraction

Again it is important that the examples illustrated in the Pupil's Book are 'performed' with real objects while the teacher 'talks through' the process. Division as repeated subtraction is shown as the inverse of multiplication as repeated addition.

```
    18              6
  -  6            +  6
  ────               6
    12            ─────
  -  6              18
  ────
     6          6 is added 3 times
  -  6          to make 18
  ────             6 × 3 = 18
     0
```

6 is subtracted 3 times
from 18.
$18 \div 6 = 3$

When real objects are used for division by *repeated subtraction*, the 'answer' is the number of subsets or whatever is used to represent the subset. For example:

8 straws are used to make squares.

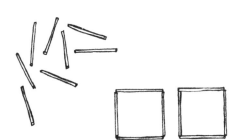

In this case there are 2 subsets of 4 which are called 'squares'.

The repeated subtraction aspect of division is also shown by 'hops back on the number line'. *Nuffield Maths 3 Spiritmasters*, Grid 5.

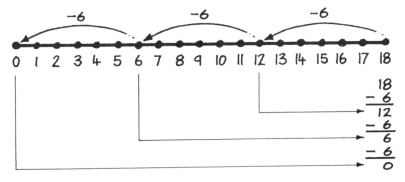

Starting at 18 and hopping back in sixes, it takes 3 hops to reach zero.

$18 \div 6 = 3$

The word 'measuring' becomes more appropriate for this aspect of division when structural apparatus is used.

How many 2-rods do you need to make a 10-rod? $\Box(2) = 10$

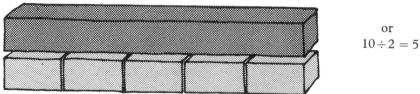

or
$10 \div 2 = 5$

Here, the 2-rod is used as a 'measure' in the same way that a hand span may be used to measure the length of a table.

In the case of interlocking cubes such as Centicubes, Multilink, Unifix, etc. colour may be used to show, for example, the number of sets of 2 in 8:

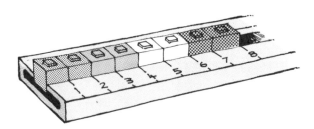

Unifix Multiplication/Division Markers show 8 divided into 4 sets of 2:

Most written methods of division depend upon repeated subtraction. Hand calculators and computers also have the dividend (the number to be divided) in the store and repeatedly subtract the division until the store is emptied.

*A word of warning.* The language used in posing questions involving repeated subtraction must be chosen very carefully. A boy was once asked, 'How many times can you subtract 4 from 20?' He was busy for some time filling a whole page of his book:

$$
\begin{array}{ccc}
20 & 20 & 20 \\
-\ 4 & -\ 4 & -\ 4 \\
\hline
16 & 16 & 16 \quad \ldots
\end{array}
$$

Finally he returned with the answer, 'I've subtracted 4 from 20 over 60 times and it keeps coming to 16!'

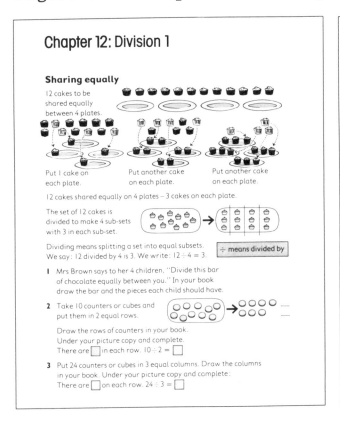
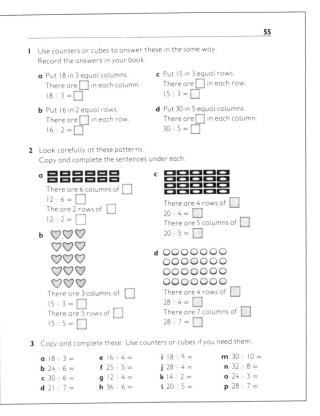
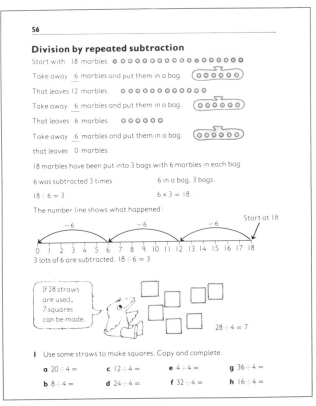
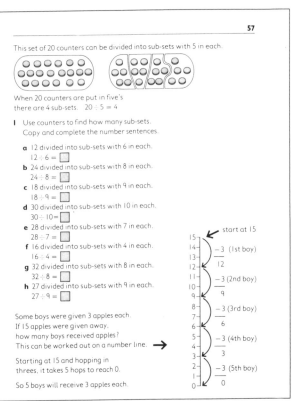

# Pages from the Pupils' Book and Spiritmasters

## Chapter 12: Division 1

### Sharing equally

12 cakes to be shared equally between 4 plates.

Put 1 cake on each plate.

Put another cake on each plate.

Put another cake on each plate.

12 cakes shared equally on 4 plates – 3 cakes on each plate.

The set of 12 cakes is divided to make 4 sub-sets with 3 in each sub-set.

Dividing means splitting a set into equal subsets. We say: 12 divided by 4 is 3. We write: $12 \div 4 = 3$.

$\div$ means divided by

1 Mrs Brown says to her 4 children, "Divide this bar of chocolate equally between you." In your book draw the bar and the pieces each child should have.

2 Take 10 counters or cubes and put them in 2 equal rows.

Draw the rows of counters in your book. Under your picture copy and complete. There are ☐ in each row. $10 \div 2 = $ ☐

3 Put 24 counters or cubes in 3 equal columns. Draw the columns in your book. Under your picture copy and complete: There are ☐ on each row. $24 \div 3 = $ ☐

---

55

1 Use counters or cubes to answer these in the same way. Record the answers in your book.

a Put 18 in 3 equal columns.
There are ☐ in each column.
$18 \div 3 = $ ☐

b Put 16 in 2 equal rows.
There are ☐ in each row.
$16 \div 2 = $ ☐

c Put 15 in 3 equal rows.
There are ☐ in each row.
$15 \div 3 = $ ☐

d Put 30 in 5 equal columns.
There are ☐ in each column.
$30 \div 5 = $ ☐

2 Look carefully at these patterns. Copy and complete the sentences under each.

a There are 6 columns of ☐
$12 \div 6 = $ ☐
The are 2 rows of ☐
$12 \div 2 = $ ☐

b There are 3 columns of ☐
$15 \div 3 = $ ☐
There are 5 rows of ☐
$15 \div 5 = $ ☐

c There are 4 rows of ☐
$20 \div 4 = $ ☐
There are 5 columns of ☐
$20 \div 5 = $ ☐

d There are 4 rows of ☐
$28 \div 4 = $ ☐
There are 7 columns of ☐
$28 \div 7 = $ ☐

3 Copy and complete these. Use counters or cubes if you need them.

a $18 \div 3 = $
b $24 \div 6 = $
c $30 \div 6 = $
d $21 \div 7 = $
e $16 \div 4 = $
f $25 \div 5 = $
g $12 \div 4 = $
h $36 \div 6 = $
i $18 \div 9 = $
j $28 \div 4 = $
k $14 \div 2 = $
l $20 \div 5 = $
m $30 \div 10 = $
n $32 \div 8 = $
o $24 \div 3 = $
p $28 \div 7 = $

---

56

### Division by repeated subtraction

Start with 18 marbles. ○○○○○○○○○○○○○○○○○○

Take away 6 marbles and put them in a bag.

That leaves 12 marbles. ○○○○○○○○○○○○

Take away 6 marbles and put them in a bag.

That leaves 6 marbles. ○○○○○○

Take away 6 marbles and put them in a bag.

that leaves 0 marbles.

18 marbles have been put into 3 bags with 6 marbles in each bag

6 was subtracted 3 times
$18 \div 6 = 3$

6 in a bag, 3 bags.
$6 \times 3 = 18$.

The number line shows what happened:

3 lots of 6 are subtracted. $18 \div 6 = 3$

If 28 straws are used, 7 squares can be made.

$28 \div 4 = 7$

1 Use some straws to make squares. Copy and complete.

a $20 \div 4 = $
b $8 \div 4 = $
c $12 \div 4 = $
d $24 \div 4 = $
e $4 \div 4 = $
f $32 \div 4 = $
g $36 \div 4 = $
h $16 \div 4 = $

---

57

This set of 20 counters can be divided into sub-sets with 5 in each.

When 20 counters are put in five's there are 4 sub-sets. $20 \div 5 = 4$

1 Use counters to find how many sub-sets. Copy and complete the number sentences.

a 12 divided into sub-sets with 6 in each.
$12 \div 6 = $ ☐

b 24 divided into sub-sets with 8 in each.
$24 \div 8 = $ ☐

c 18 divided into sub-sets with 9 in each.
$18 \div 9 = $ ☐

d 30 divided into sub-sets with 10 in each.
$30 \div 10 = $ ☐

e 28 divided into sub-sets with 7 in each.
$28 \div 7 = $ ☐

f 16 divided into sub-sets with 4 in each.
$16 \div 4 = $ ☐

g 32 divided into sub-sets with 8 in each.
$32 \div 8 = $ ☐

h 27 divided into sub-sets with 9 in each.
$27 \div 9 = $ ☐

Some boys were given 3 apples each. If 15 apples were given away, how many boys received apples? This can be worked out on a number line. →

Starting at 15 and hopping in threes, it takes 5 hops to reach 0.

So 5 boys will receive 3 apples each.

start at 15
$-3$ (1st boy)
12
$-3$ (2nd boy)
9
$-3$ (3rd boy)
6
$-3$ (4th boy)
3
$-3$ (5th boy)
0

## 58

**1** Use your number line for these:

**a** $30 \div 10 = \boxed{\phantom{0}}$    **c** $24 \div 6 = \boxed{\phantom{0}}$    **e** $18 \div 3 = \boxed{\phantom{0}}$

**b** $27 \div 3 = \boxed{\phantom{0}}$    **d** $28 \div 7 = \boxed{\phantom{0}}$    **f** $36 \div 6 = \boxed{\phantom{0}}$

**2** Use the number line to work out the answers to these
word problems. Make the hops along the number line
with your finger – do not mark the book.

**a** If a coat has 6 buttons, how many coats will have been
made when 30 buttons have been used?

**b** Bags of crisps cost 7p each. How many can be bought
for 35p?

**c** Mother gave each of her children £5, if she gave away
£25 how many children has she?

**d** There are 4 children to each table in the dining hall,
if 32 children stayed to lunch how many tables were used?

**e** How many pieces of ribbon each 8 centimetres long
can be cut from a length of 24 centimetres?

**f** There are 18 children working in pairs on a project.
How many pairs are there?

**g** For a concert, 36 chairs are put into rows with 9 in a row.
How many rows will there be?

**h** How many chocolate bars at 5p each can you buy for 30p?

**i** How many 2 kilogram weights will balance a parcel
which weighs 12 kg?

**j** Chairs are stacked in 6's.
How many stacks will 24 chairs make?

**k** A medicine spoon holds 5 millilitres.
How many spoonfuls can be poured from 35 millilitres?

**l** To make a square, 4 of these $\triangledown$ triangles are fitted
together $\boxtimes$.
How many squares can be made from 36 triangles?

**m** John takes 9 seconds to sharpen a pencil.
How many can he sharpen in 27 seconds?

```
36
35
34
33
32
31
30
29
28
27
26
25
24
23
22
21
20
19
18
17
16
15
14
13
12
11
10
9
8
7
6
5
4
3
2
1
0
```

---

**Practice 12**        Name_____

**Chapter 12: Division 1**

**A**

Complete the sentences under these patterns.

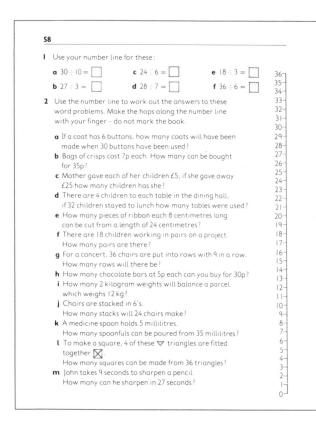

There are 6 columns of   3       There are 8 columns of   4

$18 \div 6 =$   3              $32 \div 8 =$   4

There are 3 rows of   6       There are 4 rows of   8

$18 \div 3 =$   6              $32 \div 4 =$   8

**B**

Write these multiplication statements as division statements.
Use the same three numbers. There are two answers to each.

| $4 \times 7 = 28$ | $7 \times 3 = 21$ | $5 \times 8 = 40$ | $6 \times 4 = 24$ |
|---|---|---|---|
| $28 \div 4 = 7$ | $21 \div 7 = 3$ | $40 \div 5 = 8$ | $24 \div 6 = 4$ |
| $28 \div 7 = 4$ | $21 \div 3 = 7$ | $40 \div 8 = 5$ | $24 \div 4 = 6$ |

**C**

A bag of apples weighs 6 kg.
How many bags can be filled from 42 kg?   \_\_\_7\_\_\_

1 pencil costs 9p.   5   cost 45p.

Share 33p equally between three children. They each have   11p

How many children can be given   4   biscuits each
from a box of 28 biscuits?   \_\_\_7\_\_\_

How many 7p chocolate bars can be bought with 21p?   \_\_\_3\_\_\_

*Nuffield Maths 3 Spiritmasters*       *Nuffield Maths 3 Pupils' Book*      **20**

---

# References and resources

Shuard, H. and Williams, E., *Primary Mathematics Today* (Chapter 17),
Longman Group Ltd 1970

*Multilink Number Track, Stern Number Track*, E.S.A.

*Number Strips* and *Rods*, Invicta Plastics

*Centicube Number Track (Metline)*, Osmiroid

*Unifix Multiplication/Division Markers*, Philip & Tacey

# Chapter 13

# Addresses on a grid

## For the teacher

The children will already have had experience of grids made up of squares when filling in numbers on addition and multiplication charts. This chapter introduces the idea of naming a square by indicating first which column and then which row it is in. The 'ordered pair' of numbers giving this information may be called the 'address' of the square or region on the grid.

There is an agreed convention for grids of this type. Starting at the bottom left-hand corner, the first number indicates how far to go *across* to the foot of the correct column and the second number indicates how far to go *up* to the correct row.

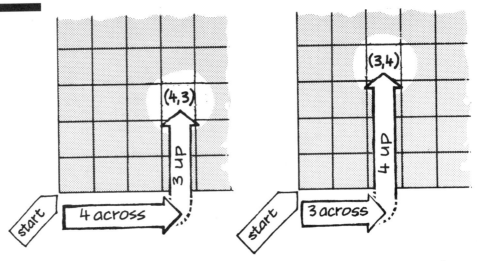

Using this convention ensures that there is a one-to-one correspondence between the set of ordered pairs or 'addresses' and the set of squares or regions on the grid.

This chapter lays the foundation for future work on the use of ordered pairs as co-ordinates identifying points on a plane, which is fundamental to the drawing and interpretation of graphs.

## Summary of the stages

1   Addresses by counting across and up

2   Naming squares on a map

3   Codes

## Vocabulary

Across, up, column, row, address, position, order, diagonal, code, decode.

## Equipment and apparatus

Squared paper (1 cm and 2 cm), a street guide, two different coloured dice.

| | | |
|---|---|---|
| (1,3) | (2,3) | (3,3) |
| (1,2) | (2,2) | (3,2) |
| (1,1) | (2,1) | (3,1) |

# Working with the children

## 1 Addresses by counting across and up

Using a simple grid to represent a block of lockers, the method for indicating a particular locker is introduced. It is important to stress that to do this everyone must agree:

a  to start at the bottom left-hand corner,

b  to count *across* first,

c  then to count *up*.

At this stage the columns and rows are not labelled as some children find this confusing and in any case the concentration is on the move from the starting point.

The two numbers counted are written in the correct order with a comma between them. Because this pair of numbers forms one 'address', brackets are put round them to keep them together. The importance of the *order* is stressed by pointing out that the address of Fred's locker is (4, 3) but Mary's is (3, 4).

If there is a block of lockers in the room, these could be labelled with the 'address' and the name of the owner.

Most children have played the game 'Noughts and Crosses' so this is used as a further example of a grid on which each square has an address.

## 2 Naming squares on a map

Once the idea of counting across and then up from an agreed starting point is established, the labelling of columns and rows on a map divided into squares by grid lines is introduced.

When children make their own maps, paper ruled in squares of 2 cm or larger should be used. Some children may be able to make up additional questions about the map such as 'Which squares does the railway run through?' At this point teachers may wish to show how useful the 'ordered pair' idea is for finding a place on a street guide. Most street guides use letters across the bottom to label columns and numbers down the side to label rows. Unfortunately, in some street guides the rows are numbered from top to bottom. In the case of a town plan on one sheet, however, this could be altered.

It should be explained to the children that, in the Birmingham guide for example, *Ebury Road D4 83* means that Ebury Road is in square D4 on page 83.

Some children may know how to play 'Battleships' but at this stage this may be too complicated. A simpler game can be played on a square grid with columns and rows labelled 1 to 6. Two dice of different colours, for example red for 'across' and blue for 'up', are thrown by each player in turn. If the address rolled by a player is empty, he puts his initial and the address in the square. If the square has already been claimed, he must wait for his next turn to try for an empty one. When every square is filled, the player with the most squares wins. Of course, any player who writes in the wrong address loses the square!

The final pattern of the addresses in a completed grid makes it easy to spot an incorrect address.

| blue | | | | | | |
|---|---|---|---|---|---|---|
| 6 | A (1,6) | C (2,6) | A (3,6) | B (4,6) | B (5,6) | A (6,6) |
| 5 | B (1,5) | A (2,5) | B (3,5) | C (4,5) | C (5,5) | C (6,5) |
| 4 | A (1,4) | C (2,4) | C (3,4) | B (4,4) | A (5,4) | B (6,4) |
| 3 | B (1,3) | B (2,3) | B (3,3) | C (4,3) | A (5,3) | A (6,3) |
| 2 | A (1,2) | B (2,2) | A (3,2) | C (4,2) | B (5,2) | A (6,2) |
| 1 | A (1,1) | C (2,1) | B (3,1) | A (4,1) | A (5,1) | C (6,1) |
| | 1 | 2 | 3 | 4 | 5 | 6 |

— red —

## 3 Codes

Children are fascinated by secret codes and this simple 5 × 5 grid gives lots of extra practice in using ordered pairs or addresses when both writing and decoding messages.

# Pages from the Pupils' Book and Spiritmasters

## Chapter 13: Addresses

This picture shows the lockers in a classroom

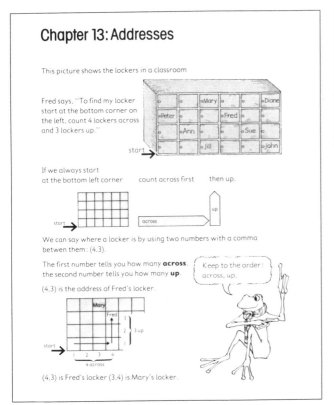

Fred says, "To find my locker start at the bottom corner on the left, count 4 lockers across and 3 lockers up."

If we always start at the bottom left corner     count across first     then up.

We can say where a locker is by using two numbers with a comma between them: (4,3).

The first number tells you how many **across**, the second number tells you how many **up**.

*Keep to the order: across, up.*

(4,3) is the address of Fred's locker.

(4,3) is Fred's locker (3,4) is Mary's locker.

---

**60**

1  Write in your book the address of:

  **a** Jill's locker    **d** Peter's locker    **g** the locker underneath Sue's

  **b** Ann's locker    **e** John's locker    **h** The locker next to Diane's.

  **c** Sue's locker    **f** Diane's locker

2  Draw a block of lockers on a piece of squared paper. Mark the bottom left corner of the lockers as START. Write the names of your friends on the lockers. Make a list of the names and addresses of each friend's locker.

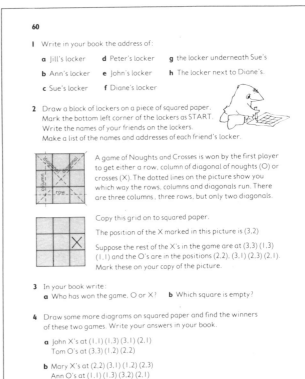

A game of Noughts and Crosses is won by the first player to get either a row, column of diagonal of noughts (O) or crosses (X). The dotted lines on the picture show you which way the rows, columns and diagonals run. There are three columns, three rows, but only two diagonals.

Copy this grid on to squared paper.

The position of the X marked in this picture is (3,2)

Suppose the rest of the X's in the game are at (3,3) (1,3) (1,1) and the O's are in the positions (2,2), (3,1) (2,3) (2,1). Mark these on your copy of the picture.

3  In your book write:
  **a** Who has won the game, O or X?    **b** Which square is empty?

4  Draw some more diagrams on squared paper and find the winners of these two games. Write your answers in your book.

  **a** John X's at (1,1) (1,3) (3,1) (2,1)
    Tom O's at (3,3) (1,2) (2,2)

  **b** Mary X's at (2,2) (3,1) (1,2) (2,3)
    Ann O's at (1,1) (1,3) (3,2) (2,1)

---

**61**

### Naming squares on a map

This is a map of a village. The columns and rows are numbered so that we can give the address of each place on the map.

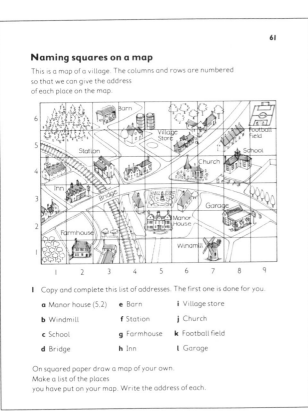

1  Copy and complete this list of addresses. The first one is done for you.

  **a** Manor house (5,2)    **e** Barn    **i** Village store

  **b** Windmill    **f** Station    **j** Church

  **c** School    **g** Farmhouse    **k** Football field

  **d** Bridge    **h** Inn    **l** Garage

On squared paper draw a map of your own. Make a list of the places you have put on your map. Write the address of each.

---

**62**

### Codes

We can use the addresses of squares to write messages in a secret code.

F is in square (1,4)

O is in square (5,3)

X is in square (4,1)

So "FOX" is written in code as (1,4) (5,3) (4,1)

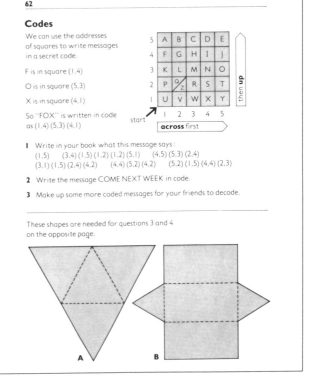

1  Write in your book what this message says:
  (1,5)    (3,4) (1,5) (1,2) (1,2) (5,1)    (4,5) (5,3) (2,4)
  (3,1) (1,5) (2,4) (4,2)    (4,4) (5,2) (4,2)    (5,2) (1,5) (4,4) (2,3)

2  Write the message COME NEXT WEEK in code.

3  Make up some more coded messages for your friends to decode.

These shapes are needed for questions 3 and 4 on the opposite page.

A    B

---

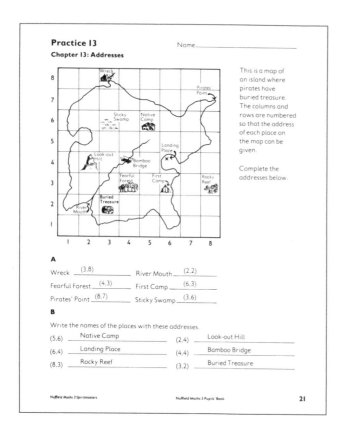

**Practice 13**

**Chapter 13: Addresses**

Name_____

8

7

6

5

4

3

2

1

   1   2   3   4   5   6   7   8

This is a map of an island where pirates have buried treasure. The columns and rows are numbered so that the address of each place on the map can be given.

Complete the addresses below.

**A**

Wreck ___(3,8)___          River Mouth ___(2,2)___

Fearful Forest ___(4,3)___          First Camp ___(6,3)___

Pirates' Point ___(8,7)___          Sticky Swamp ___(3,6)___

**B**

Write the names of the places with these addresses.

(5,6) ___Native Camp___          (2,4) ___Look-out Hill___

(6,4) ___Landing Place___          (4,4) ___Bamboo Bridge___

(8,3) ___Rocky Reef___          (3,2) ___Buried Treasure___

Nuffield Maths 3 Spiritmasters          Nuffield Maths 3 Pupils' Book          **21**

# References and resources

Nuffield Mathematics Teaching Project, *Graphs Leading to Algebra* ②, Nuffield Guide, Chambers/Murray 1969. (See Introduction page xii.)

# Chapter 14

# Shape 2

## For the teacher

This chapter is concerned with activities involving three dimensional (3D) shapes, and their surfaces, faces, edges and corners. By handling and discussing the shapes an appropriate language can be developed. Teachers may start a collection of three-dimensional shapes and display them on a 'Shapes Table'. This collection might include items brought from home such as cereal boxes – rectangular prisms (cuboids); tea packets – square based prisms; fruit tins – circular prisms (cylinders); Toblerone chocolate boxes – triangular based prisms; various pencils and biscuit tins – hexagonal prisms.

Rectangular prism
Base – a rectangle

Square prism
Base – a square

Circular prism or cylinder
Base – a circle

Triangular prism
Base – a triangle

Hexagonal prism
Base – hexagon

An Appendix (reprinted from *Nuffield Maths 1 Teachers' Handbook*) giving the names of the more common solids and dealing with the problem of depicting three-dimensional figures on paper is at the end of this chapter.

If several plane shapes of the same shape and size are made, the idea of a prism can be illustrated by piling or aligning them to make a solid. At this stage, the prism can be thought of as a solid which could be cut into slices all the same shape and size. This cannot be done in the case of a sphere, a cone, or a 'cottage loaf'.

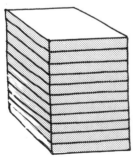

Rectangular prism
or cuboid

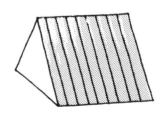

Triangular prism.

Hexagonal prism.

## Summary of the stages

1  Experiences with three dimensional objects – curved and flat surfaces – edges, faces and corners

2  Counting faces, edges and corners

3  Fitting solids together

## Vocabulary

Solid, face, edge, corner, surface, flat, straight, curved, base, rectangular, triangular.

## Equipment and apparatus

Wooden or plastic cubes, cuboids, prisms and pyramids, etc., such as Poleidoblocs Set G; collection of boxes and containers from various sources – cereal boxes, tea packets, Toblerone cartons, toilet roll centres, cheese cartons, tetrahedron milk packs, etc. Plasticine or modelling clay, straws and pipe cleaners.

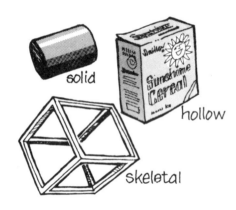

solid

hollow

skeletal

## Working with the children

**1  Experiences with three-dimensional objects – curved and flat surfaces – edges, faces and corners**

Through handling three-dimensional objects such as bricks, boxes, balls, cones, etc., the child will have begun to experience the difference between flat and curved surfaces. There are three types of three-dimensional model which the children may have handled. See illustration on left.

When wishing to draw attention to *faces*, obviously the solid or hollow models are more appropriate. Skeletal models have the advantages of emphasising edges and corners and of showing the space inside.

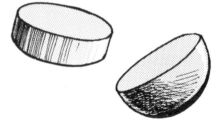

Some shapes have no edges or corners.

Other shapes have edges but no corners.

The surface or 'skin' of a solid may be broken up into faces, flat or curved, by edges so that an edge is crossed when moving the finger from one face to another. It may be easier to see an edge as the boundary between two faces if different colours are used for the faces. Corners occur where two or more edges meet. Before proceeding to the more formal work, examples from the environment should be used to reinforce this

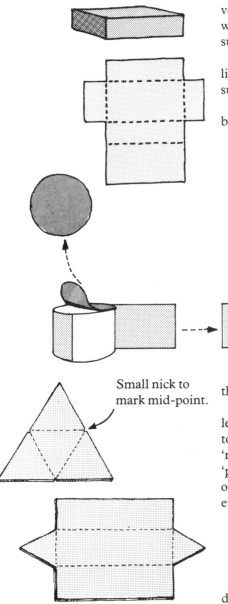

Small nick to mark mid-point.

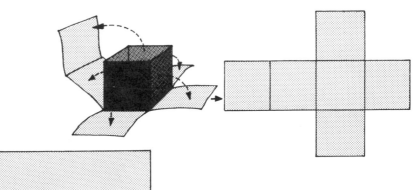

vocabulary. The children should be asked to collect or make lists of shapes which, for example, have no edges or corners; edges but no corners; flat surfaces only, and so on.

Cutting along the edges of cardboard containers to see what they look like when 'flattened out' will help children to appreciate how the total surface of a solid is separated into faces.

It is also helpful if a child is allowed to 'peel off' a paper 'skin' which has been loosely affixed to a solid.

These activities will also provide opportunities to remind the children of the names of plane shapes.

Apart from handling and looking at three-dimensional shapes, children learn even more by making them. Plasticine or modelling clay can be used to make solid models. When attempting to construct hollow models from 'nets' the children should first be reminded of the 'flattening out' and 'peeling off' activities mentioned previously. The provision by the teacher of templates cut from stiff card will allow children to attempt these models even if they are not very good at copying diagrams or measuring.

The construction of skeletal models requires a little patience and dexterity. Some children may need help in cutting the straws to the required length and fitting in the pipe cleaners which should be cut into lengths of about 3 cm in preparation for this activity. Skeletal models can also be made from commercially produced construction kits (see 'References and Resources' section at the end of this chapter).

## 2  Counting faces, edges and corners

The first exercise uses pictures of some of the more common environmental shapes which have curved or curved and flat faces. Most children are able to interpret pictures of 3-D shapes but it is advisable to use real objects first so that the children can handle them, running their hands over surfaces and fingers along edges. It is often helpful to use chalk to number faces as the solid is turned so that children do not lose count.

The nets of solids are also useful for counting faces but they should not be used for counting edges or corners because flattening out the net leads to some edges being shown twice and some corners three times!

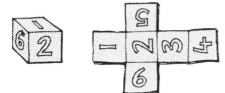

For the next exercise the children complete a table after counting the faces, edges and corners of 'transparent' solids. If 3-D models of these shapes are available the children should be allowed to use them if they need to. *Nuffield Maths 3 Spiritmasters*, Grid 12.

The pictures for the next exercise have been drawn 'solid' deliberately. The children are required to try to imagine the faces, edges and corners which are not visible in the pictures. Children who find this too difficult should be given 3-D models corresponding to the pictures.

### 3    Fitting solids together

Another property of 3-D shapes is how well they fit together without spaces in between – what might be called their 'packability'. Packing bricks into boxes will lead children to see that some shapes are better 'space fitters' than others. The supermarket provides good examples of how sugar cubes and cuboid soap packets fit into cartons compared with cylindrical tins, eggs or oranges.

This experience is important because it is the basis of future work on volume where the cube is used as a convenient unit.

# Pages from the Pupils' Book and Spiritmasters

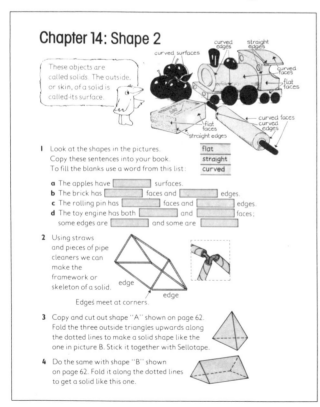

**Chapter 14: Shape 2**

These objects are called solids. The outside, or skin, of a solid is called its surface.

I   Look at the shapes in the pictures.
Copy these sentences into your book.
To fill the blanks use a word from this list:

| flat |
| straight |
| curved |

**a** The apples have [ ] surfaces.
**b** The brick has [ ] faces and [ ] edges.
**c** The rolling pin has [ ] faces and [ ] edges.
**d** The toy engine has both [ ] and [ ] faces; some edges are [ ] and some are [ ]

2   Using straws and pieces of pipe cleaners we can make the framework or skeleton of a solid.
Edges meet at corners.

3   Copy and cut out shape "A" shown on page 62. Fold the three outside triangles upwards along the dotted lines to make a solid shape like the one in picture B. Stick it together with Sellotape.

4   Do the same with shape "B" shown on page 62. Fold it along the dotted lines to get a solid like this one.

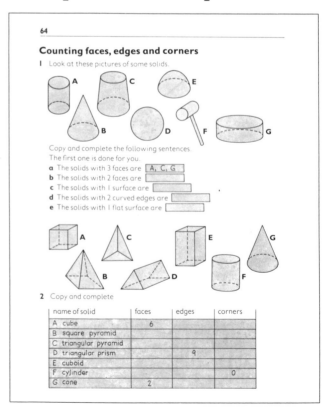

64

**Counting faces, edges and corners**

I   Look at these pictures of some solids.

Copy and complete the following sentences.
The first one is done for you.
**a** The solids with 3 faces are [ A, C, G ]
**b** The solids with 2 faces are [ ]
**c** The solids with 1 surface are [ ]
**d** The solids with 2 curved edges are [ ]
**e** The solids with 1 flat surface are [ ]

2   Copy and complete

| name of solid | faces | edges | corners |
|---|---|---|---|
| A  cube | 6 | | |
| B  square pyramid | | | |
| C  triangular pyramid | | | |
| D  triangular prism | | 9 | |
| E  cuboid | | | |
| F  cylinder | | | 0 |
| G  cone | 2 | | |

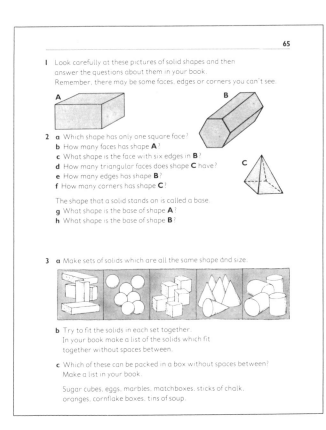

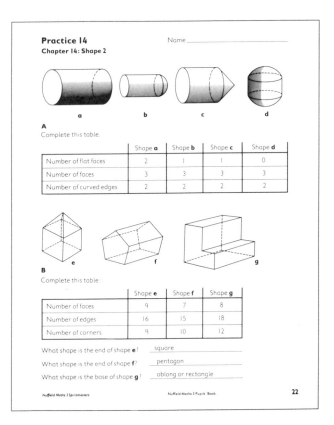

# References and resources

Nuffield Mathematics Teaching Project, *Environmental Geometry, Shape and Size* ▽, Nuffield Guides, Chambers/Murray 1967. (See Introductory page xii.)

Shuard, H. and Williams, E., *Primary Mathematics Today* (Chapters 11 and 12), Longman Group Ltd 1970

*Constructa-straw, Orbit Materials*, Cochranes of Oxford

*Construct-o-Straws*, E. J. Arnold

*Geometry Models, Orbit Mathematics Set, Poleidoblocs* (Margaret Lowenfeld), E.S.A.

*Geometry Models, Kubic Bubbles*, Nicolas Burdett

*Centicubes*, Osmiroid

*3-D Geometry Rubber Stamps*, Philip & Tacey

*Geometrical Models*, Taskmaster

# Appendix

These diagrams are to help teachers overcome the problem of depicting three-dimensional figures on paper.

They are *not* intended as exercises for young children.

**Cube**—a prism with six square faces all of the same size.

1 Draw one square face.

2 Draw another square, slightly smaller, to one side and higher.

3 Join up corresponding corners to make a 'glass' cube.

4 Erase unwanted lines and shade to give a 'solid' appearance.

**Cuboid**—a prism with six rectangular faces, opposite faces being of the same shape and size. (Sometimes called a rectangular prism.)

 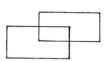 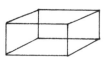

1          2          3          4

**Triangular prism**—a solid with equal, parallel triangular ends of the same shape and rectangular lateral faces.

1          2          3          4

**Prism**—a solid with parallel ends of the same shape and size, and rectangular lateral faces.

Example : Square prism

1          2          3          4

Example : Hexagonal prism

  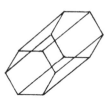 

1          2          3          4

**Cylinder**—a solid with a circular face and two equal, parallel circular ends. A cylinder could be thought of as a circular prism.

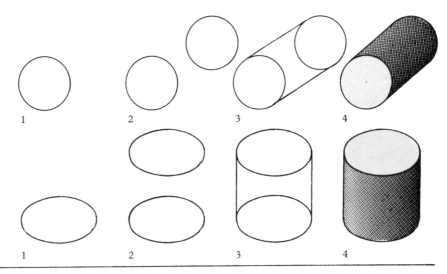

**Pyramid**—a solid with a straight-edged base and sloping triangular faces meeting a point (the apex).

Example: A square pyramid

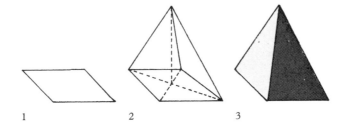

**Cone**—a solid with a flat circular base and a curved surface coming to a point (the apex). A cone could be thought of as a circular pyramid.

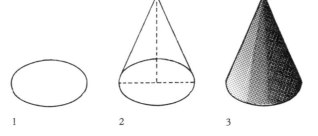

**Sphere**—a solid with a surface on which every point is the same distance from the centre of the solid.

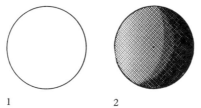

# Chapter 15

# Subtraction 2

## For the teacher

This chapter takes the development of subtraction further by using patterns and by building on previous 'missing number' or 'making up to' experiences. This gives the children a method for dealing with the subtraction of 2-digit numbers without using re-grouping or decomposition.

Reference is made to odd and even numbers and simple word problems involving subtraction are introduced.

## Summary of the stages

1 Patterns in subtraction

2 Complementary addition ('making up the difference')

3 Word problems

## Vocabulary

row, column difference, odd, even, minus, subtract, input, output, 'make up to', counting on, change, take away, cheaper, dearer, heavier, lighter, farther, longer, shorter, more, less, fewer, slower, faster.

## Equipment and apparatus

Squared paper, counters, rods, interlocking cubs, 100 squares.

## Working with the children

### 1 Patterns in subtraction

The subtraction square gives further reinforcement of 'subtraction facts' up to 20 and provides the opportunity for finding patterns – particularly if the children are encouraged to look at diagonal lines. Diagonals in this direction ⟋⟋⟋⟋ each consist of the same number; diagonals in this direction ⟍⟍⟍⟍ show alternate sequences of odd and even numbers.

Children who have difficulty in following columns and rows may be helped by an ⌐-shaped piece of card acting as a guide.

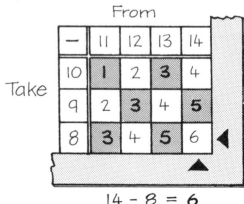

A more visual approach to odd and even numbers can be made without reference to division by two or remainders:

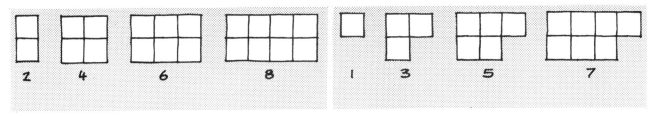

even numbers                                                          odd numbers

The 'computer' which was introduced in 'Addition 2' is used again to provide motivation, practice and the opportunity to investigate patterns. The 'print-out tapes' also provide results which can be used to test the odd/even rules. Some children may wish to use the computer print-outs to investigate patterns obtained by repeated subtraction, using each 'output' as the next 'input'. *Nuffield Maths 3 Spiritmasters*, Grid 2.

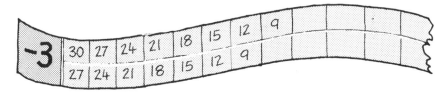

## 2 Complementary addition ('making up the difference')

In the early stages of subtraction children are introduced to the idea of complementary addition, that is adding on to the smaller number to make it up to the larger. This is often demonstrated using rods or interlocking cubes:

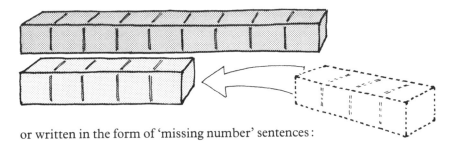

or written in the form of 'missing number' sentences:

$$5 + \square = 9$$

'What must be added to 5 to make a total of 9?' or '5 and what make 9?'

These are sometimes referred to by the children as 'adding sums with holes in' or 'gazuptas'. ('What do I have to put on to the 5 block so that it gazupta the 9 block?') This way of tackling subtraction is used everyday in shops to give 'change' – that is the *difference* between the price and the money offered – but it becomes the 'Cinderella' method in schools once larger numbers are involved. This may be because there is no concise form of recording it. This is a pity because 'making up' is very practical, is easily understood and helps to show the strong connection between subtraction and addition.

Once children have been reminded that a 'difference' question
($9 - 5 = \square$) can be rewritten as a 'missing number' question ($5 + \square = 9$),
the idea of 'making up to' can be demonstrated by using coins for a suitable
example such as $28 + \square = 50$, 'It costs 28p, I gave the shopkeeper 50p,
what change does he count out?' Usually the price is made up to the next
10p above,

$$28p + 2p \longrightarrow 30p$$

and then the counting on continues in 10's

$$\boxed{28p} \longrightarrow 30 \longrightarrow 40 \longrightarrow 50p$$
$$\quad +2 \quad\quad +10 \quad +10$$

To record the answer (this is not usual in the process of giving change)
the 10's are put together and the units added below:

$$2p \quad + \quad 10p \quad + \quad 10p$$
$$20$$
$$+\ \ 2$$
$$\overline{22p}$$

So that 22 is added to 28 to make 50: $28 + \boxed{22} = 50$,
or the *difference* between 50 and 28 is 22: $50 - 28 = \boxed{22}$

When progressing to examples where the larger number is not a
multiple of 10, an extra figure has to be included in the final addition. For
example:

$$37 + \square = 66$$

$$37 \longrightarrow 40 \longrightarrow 50 \longrightarrow 60 \longrightarrow 66$$
$$\ +3 \quad\quad +10 \quad +10 \quad\quad +6$$
$$20$$
$$9$$
$$\overline{29}$$

If a vertical arrangement is preferred, this zig-zig layout may be used:

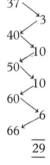

This method enables children to find the difference between two 2-digit
numbers using only the skills of counting on and addition.

Both 'making up' and counting back can be shown on the 100 square
which is really a number strip arranged to occupy less space and to make
patterns more obvious.

△ Start

○ Finish

Each hop this way adds on 1.

Each hop this way adds on 10.

| 1 | 2 | 3 | 4 | △5 | 6 | 7 | 8 | ⑨ | 10 |
|---|---|---|---|---|---|---|---|---|---|
| 11 | 12 | ⑬ | 14 | 15 | 16 | 17 | 18 | 19 | 20 |
| 21 | 22 | 23 | 24 | 25 | 26 | 27 | 28 | 29 | 30 |
| 31 | 32 | 33 | 34 | 35 | 36 | 37 | 38 | 39 | 40 |
| 41 | 42 | ㊸ | 44 | 45 | 46 | 47 | 48 | 49 | 50 |
| 51 | 52 | 53 | 54 | 55 | 56 | 57 | 58 | 59 | 60 |
| 61 | 62 | 63 | 64 | 65 | △66 | 67 | 68 | 69 | 70 |
| 71 | 72 | 73 | 74 | 75 | 76 | 77 | 78 | 79 | 80 |
| 81 | 82 | 83 | 84 | 85 | 86 | 87 | 88 | 89 | ⑨⓪ |
| 91 | 92 | 93 | 94 | 95 | 96 | 97 | 98 | 99 | 100 |

See *Nuffield Maths 3 Spiritmasters*, Grid 3

A large 100 square displayed in the classroom is very useful –
particularly if it is covered by clear adhesive plastic such as *Contact*.
Water-based felt-tip pens can then be used to make marks which can easily
be wiped off.

For example, a red triangle might be used to mark the 'start' and a blue
circle the 'finish'.

'Making up to' problems can now be illustrated on the 100 square,
starting with 'unit hops' only, then 'ten hops' only and, finally,
combinations of the 'unit hops' and 'ten hops'.

In examples such as $18 + \square = 43$, the 'moves' are:

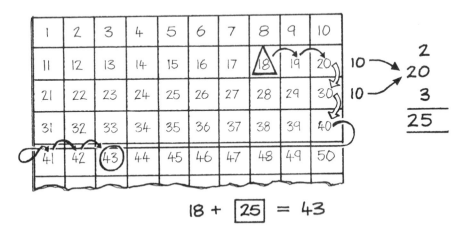

$$18 + \boxed{25} = 43$$

The children may need to be reminded that the move from the right-hand
end of one row to the left-hand end of the next is one 'unit hop'.
The 100-square can be used to illustrate 'taking away' or counting back.

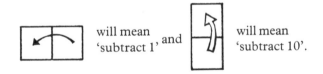

will mean 'subtract 1', and will mean 'subtract 10'.

However, some teachers may prefer not to introduce this idea just as children are gaining confidence with 'making up'. The reversal of the direction of the 'hops' may cause confusion – especially in cases where 'unit hops' involve moving from the left-hand end of one row to the right-hand end of the row above as in 43 − 5 for example.

### 3  Word problems

Many children reach the stage at which they can read with some fluency and can cope with computation either with or without concrete materials. Although they may be competent in each of these skills, they often find it difficult to combine them in order to deal with word problems.

Earlier, children may have had some experience with 'picture problems'. (*Nuffield Maths 2 Teachers' Handbook*, Chapters 2 and 4.) The translation from word problems into number sentences will be made easier if counters, pictures or diagrams are used to help children see the numbers, relationships and operations involved. Discussion between teacher and child, possibly 'acting out' the story, plays an essential part in learning to 'comb the mathematics out of the words'. For example:

Question 3.   Susan wants to save up 45p to buy a book. So far she has saved 32p. How much more does she need?

Susan has 32p.          She needs 45p.        32p + □p = 45p

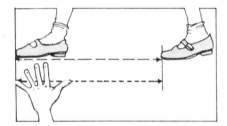

Question 9.   Carol's pace is 50 centimetres long, her handspan is 16 centimetres. How much longer is her pace than her handspan?

| | |
|---|---|
| Pace | 50 cm |
| Handspan | − 16 cm |
| How much longer? | cm |

The children need as much experience as possible in interpreting and using the many words and phrases which imply subtraction. Here are some examples, but the lists are by no means exhaustive:

a) *Physical removal*, take away, lost, fell off, gave away, flew away, ate, stole, etc.

b) *Comparison or difference* – more, less, fewer, longer, shorter, heavier, lighter, dearer, cheaper, faster, slower, etc.

c) *Complementary addition* – make up to, how many more are needed, what must be added to, change, etc.

[*Nuffield Maths 3 Spiritmasters*, Practice 15 (see page 96.)]

# Pages from the Pupils' Book and Spiritmasters

## Chapter 15: Subtraction 2

### Subtraction patterns

In this table, the difference between
a number in the top row and a number
in the left hand column is in the square
where the row and column cross each other.

| − | 11 | 12 | 13 | 14 | 15 | 16 | 17 | 18 | 19 | 20 |
|----|----|----|----|----|----|----|----|----|----|----|
| 10 | 1 | 2 | 3 | 4 | 5 | 6 | 7 | 8 | 9 | 10 |
| 9 | 2 | 3 | 4 | 5 | 6 | 7 | 8 | 9 | 10 | 11 |
| 8 | 3 | 4 | 5 | 6 | 7 | 8 | 9 | 10 | 11 | 12 |
| 7 | 4 | 5 | 6 | 7 | 8 | 9 | 10 | 11 | 12 | 13 |
| 6 | 5 | 6 | 7 | 8 | 9 | 10 | 11 | 12 | 13 | 14 |
| 5 | 6 | 7 | 8 | 9 | 10 | 11 | 12 | 13 | 14 | 15 |
| 4 | 7 | 8 | 9 | 10 | 11 | 12 | 13 | 14 | 15 | 16 |
| 3 | 8 | 9 | 10 | 11 | 12 | 13 | 14 | 15 | 16 | 17 |
| 2 | 9 | 10 | 11 | 12 | 13 | 14 | 15 | 16 | 17 | 18 |
| 1 | 10 | 11 | 12 | 13 | 14 | 15 | 16 | 17 | 18 | 19 |

For example: $14 - 8 = \square$

Look down the 14 column
till you reach the 8 row.
The number in
the square where
the 14 column
crosses the 8 row
is 6, so
$14 - 8 = 6.$

| − | 11 | 12 | 13 | 14 |
|----|----|----|----|----|
| 10 | 1 | 2 | 3 | 4 |
| 9 | 2 | 3 | 4 | 5 |
| 8 | 3 | 4 | 5 | 6 |

I   Use this table to answer these:

| **a** $14-6$ | **b** $17-9$ | **c** $16-7$ | **d** $19-8$ |
|---|---|---|---|
| $16-4$ | $15-7$ | $18-5$ | $15-6$ |
| $18-10$ | $19-5$ | $14-3$ | $11-10$ |
| $20-2$ | $13-9$ | $12-9$ | $19-2$ |

Look for patterns in the subtraction table.

**Even numbers** can all be divided by 2 without a remainder:
2, 4, 6, 8, 10, 12, 14, 16, 18, 20, 22, ....
**Odd numbers** have a remainder of 1 when divided by 2:
3, 5, 7, 9, 11, 13, 15, 17, 19, 21, 23, ....
What do you notice about the answers in a?
What about the answers in b, c and d?

---

**The computer**
The pointers
on the computer
say $-3$
so it will subtract 3
from each number
fed into the input

The computer records all the inputs and outputs on
a print-out tape:

| $-3$ | | 13 | 9 | 20 | 14 | 12 | 10 | |
|------|---|----|----|----|----|----|----|---|
| **Input** | 7 | 11 | 19 | | 10 | 6 | 17 | 11 | 9 | 7 |
| **Output** | 4 | 8 | 16 | | | | | | | |

Check the tape to see if the computer is working properly.
As an odd number is being subtracted, check that odd − odd = even
and even − odd = odd.

I   Copy and complete these tapes:

a | $-6$ | 9 | 19 | 29 | 39 | 49 | 12 | 22 | 32 | 42 | 52 |

b | $-8$ | 10 | 20 | 30 | 40 | 50 | 13 | 23 | 33 | 43 | 53 |

c | $-9$ | 14 | 24 | 34 | 15 | 25 | 35 | 16 | 26 | 36 | 46 |

d | $-13$ | 20 | 30 | 40 | 50 | 60 | 70 | 80 | 90 |

e | $-5$ | 13 | 18 | 23 | 28 | 35 | 38 | 43 | 48 |

**2**   Make up some more tapes of your own.

---

### Making up the difference

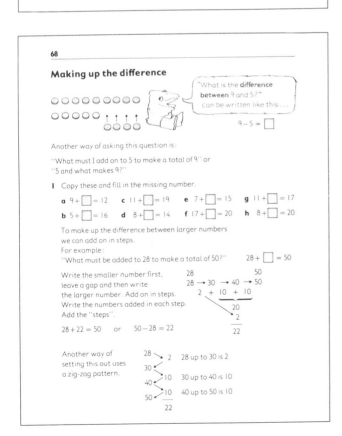

"What is the **difference**
between 9 and 5?"
can be written like this....

$9 - 5 = \square$

Another way of asking this question is:

"What must I add on to 5 to make a total of 9" or
"5 and what makes 9?"

I   Copy these and fill in the missing number.

**a** $9 + \square = 12$   **c** $11 + \square = 19$   **e** $7 + \square = 15$   **g** $11 + \square = 17$

**b** $5 + \square = 16$   **d** $8 + \square = 14$   **f** $17 + \square = 20$   **h** $8 + \square = 20$

To make up the difference between larger numbers
we can add on in steps.
For example:
"What must be added to 28 to make a total of 50?"   $28 + \square = 50$

Write the smaller number first,
leave a gap and then write
the larger number. Add on in steps.
Write the numbers added in each step.
Add the "steps".

$$28 \qquad\qquad 50$$
$$28 \rightarrow 30 \rightarrow 40 \rightarrow 50$$
$$2 + \underline{10 + 10}$$
$$\underline{\quad 20 \quad}$$
$$\underline{\quad\; 2 \quad}$$
$$22$$

$28 + 22 = 50$   or   $50 - 28 = 22$

Another way of
setting this out uses
a zig-zag pattern.

28 → 2   28 up to 30 is 2
30 → 10   30 up to 40 is 10
40 → 10   40 up to 50 is 10
50
   $\underline{\quad}$
   22

---

This method is like giving change
for 50p when sweets costing 28p
are bought:

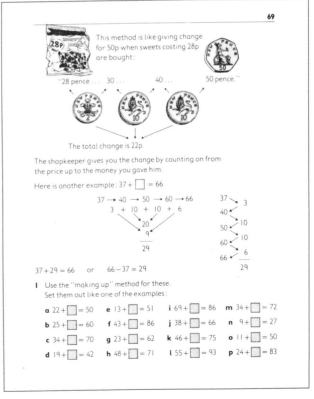

"28 pence ... 30 ...   40 ...   50 pence."

The total change is 22p.

The shopkeeper gives you the change by counting on from
the price up to the money you gave him.

Here is another example: $37 + \square = 66$

$$37 \rightarrow 40 \rightarrow 50 \rightarrow 60 \rightarrow 66$$
$$3 + 10 + 10 + 6$$
$$9$$
$$\underline{\quad 29 \quad}$$

37 → 3
40 → 10
50 → 10
60 → 6
66
   $\underline{\quad}$
   29

$37 + 29 = 66$   or   $66 - 37 = 29$

I   Use the "making up" method for these.
Set them out like one of the examples:

**a** $22 + \square = 50$   **e** $13 + \square = 51$   **i** $69 + \square = 86$   **m** $34 + \square = 72$

**b** $25 + \square = 60$   **f** $43 + \square = 86$   **j** $38 + \square = 66$   **n** $9 + \square = 27$

**c** $34 + \square = 70$   **g** $23 + \square = 62$   **k** $46 + \square = 75$   **o** $11 + \square = 50$

**d** $19 + \square = 42$   **h** $48 + \square = 71$   **l** $55 + \square = 93$   **p** $24 + \square = 83$

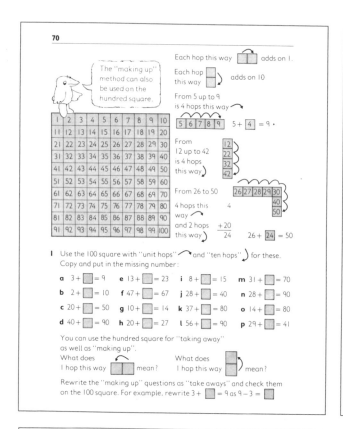

**70**

The "making up" method can also be used on the hundred square.

Each hop this way adds on 1.

Each hop this way adds on 10.

From 5 up to 9 is 4 hops this way

| 5 | 6 | 7 | 8 | 9 |

$5 + \boxed{4} = 9$.

From 12 up to 42 is 4 hops this way

| 12 |
| 22 |
| 32 |
| 42 |

From 26 to 50
4 hops this way ......... 4
and 2 hops this way ... +20
                         24

| 26 | 27 | 28 | 29 | 30 |
| 40 |
| 50 |

$26 + \boxed{24} = 50$

**1** Use the 100 square with "unit hops" and "ten hops" for these.
Copy and put in the missing number:

a  $3 + \boxed{\phantom{0}} = 9$
b  $2 + \boxed{\phantom{0}} = 10$
c  $20 + \boxed{\phantom{0}} = 50$
d  $40 + \boxed{\phantom{0}} = 90$

e  $13 + \boxed{\phantom{0}} = 23$
f  $47 + \boxed{\phantom{0}} = 67$
g  $10 + \boxed{\phantom{0}} = 14$
h  $20 + \boxed{\phantom{0}} = 27$

i  $8 + \boxed{\phantom{0}} = 15$
j  $28 + \boxed{\phantom{0}} = 40$
k  $37 + \boxed{\phantom{0}} = 80$
l  $56 + \boxed{\phantom{0}} = 90$

m  $31 + \boxed{\phantom{0}} = 70$
n  $28 + \boxed{\phantom{0}} = 90$
o  $14 + \boxed{\phantom{0}} = 80$
p  $29 + \boxed{\phantom{0}} = 41$

You can use the hundred square for "taking away" as well as "making up".

What does 1 hop this way mean?

What does 1 hop this way mean?

Rewrite the "making up" questions as "take aways" and check them on the 100 square. For example, rewrite $3 + \boxed{\phantom{0}} = 9$ as $9 - 3 = \boxed{\phantom{0}}$.

---

**71**

## Word problems

Word problems are like stories which have to be changed into number sentences.

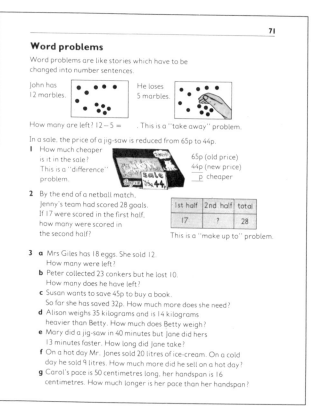

John has 12 marbles.

He loses 5 marbles.

How many are left? $12 - 5 = \boxed{\phantom{0}}$ . This is a "take away" problem.

In a sale, the price of a jig-saw is reduced from 65p to 44p.

**1** How much cheaper is it in the sale? This is a "difference" problem.

65p (old price)
44p (new price)
____ p cheaper

**2** By the end of a netball match, Jenny's team had scored 28 goals. If 17 were scored in the first half, how many were scored in the second half?

| 1st half | 2nd half | total |
|----------|----------|-------|
| 17 | ? | 28 |

This is a "make up to" problem.

**3 a** Mrs Giles has 18 eggs. She sold 12. How many were left?

**b** Peter collected 23 conkers but he lost 10. How many does he have left?

**c** Susan wants to save 45p to buy a book. So far she has saved 32p. How much more does she need?

**d** Alison weighs 35 kilograms and is 14 kilograms heavier than Betty. How much does Betty weigh?

**e** Mary did a jig-saw in 40 minutes but Jane did hers 13 minutes faster. How long did Jane take?

**f** On a hot day Mr. Jones sold 20 litres of ice-cream. On a cold day he sold 9 litres. How much more did he sell on a hot day?

**g** Carol's pace is 50 centimetres long, her handspan is 16 centimetres. How much longer is her pace than her handspan?

---

**Practice 15**

**Chapter 15: Subtraction 2**

Name _____

**A**

Complete these making up problems. The first is done for you.

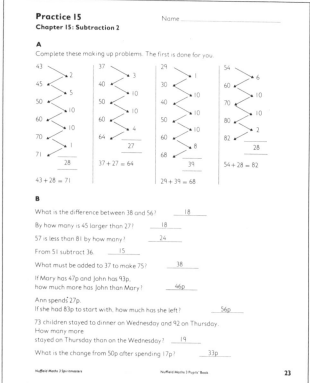

$43 + 28 = 71$

$37 + 27 = 64$

$29 + 39 = 68$

$54 + 28 = 82$

**B**

What is the difference between 38 and 56?     18

By how many is 45 larger than 27?     18

57 is less than 81 by how many?     24

From 51 subtract 36.     15

What must be added to 37 to make 75?     38

If Mary has 47p and John has 93p, how much more has John than Mary?     46p

Ann spends 27p. If she had 83p to start with, how much has she left?     56p

73 children stayed to dinner on Wednesday and 92 on Thursday. How many more stayed on Thursday than on the Wednesday?     19

What is the change from 50p after spending 17p?     33p

*Nuffield Maths 3 Spiritmasters*          *Nuffield Maths 3 Pupils' Book*          **23**

---

# References and resources

Shuard, H. and Williams, E., *Primary Mathematics Today* (Chapter 9), Longman Group Ltd 1970

## 100 Squares

*One Hundred Board* and *Number Tablets, Square Roccer Stamp* (to print 100 blank centimetre squares in $10 \times 10$ block), E. J. Arnold

*Multilink Number Boards* and *Grid*, E.S.A.

*1–100 Grids* (Gridsheets), Excitement in Learning

*Hundred Number Board*, Invicta Plastics

*Unifix 1–100 Operational Board, Number Tablets* and *Window Markers*, Philip & Tacey

*100 Square* and *Number Tablets, Giant 100 Board* and *Discs*, Taskmaster

*Dial-a-sum*, Triman Classmate

# Chapter 16

# Money 2

## For the teacher

A large part of this chapter deals with counting amounts. It is appreciated that children have been doing this for some time but we are now concerned with improving the efficiency of the skills and techniques used in counting money. As the child progresses through he will acquire:

a) *Skills*: for example, counting in 5's.

b) *Techniques*: for example, grouping 5p coins in pairs so as to count in 10's.

## Summary of the stages

1 Counting up amounts – 5p coins. Counting amounts of mixed coins

2 Going shopping – some vocabulary used when buying and selling Bills and simple multiplication and division examples

3 Payment and change.
   a) Giving change by counting on
   b) Selecting coins and receiving change
   c) Checking your change

## Vocabulary

Sequence, in pairs, order of value, cheaper, cheapest, expensive, least, most, dearer, dearest, save, approximate, amount, change, connect, share equally, each, afford, total change.

## Apparatus and equipment

Cardboard, plastic or real coins, classroom shop or class catalogue, card for price labels.

### 1 Counting up amounts of coins

This is an activity that is enjoyable for the child and at the same time can reinforce counting experience in pure number work. Before a child finds the total value of a collection of mixed coins, it is important to make sure that he is fairly confident at dealing with several coins of the same value. The example in the pupils' book involves 5p coins but finding the total value of a collection of 2p coins or of 10p coins are also useful exercises.

*Counting the amount of 5p coins*
Before presenting the child with a situation where there is a mixture of coins it is necessary to ensure that the child is confident in counting on in fives.

*Counting the total value of mixed coins*
When finding the total value of mixed coins it is important that the child understands the need to put them in *order of value* first. If this is appreciated and adequate experience with 'counting on' has been provided, then finding the total value of a number of mixed coins should be relatively easy.

The first set of exercises deals only with 'counting on' – starting with the coin of greatest value. Once again, it is essential that either real or imitation coins are used in order to fulfil the experience.

The ultimate aim is that the child should be capable of transferring these acquired skills to real, everyday situations using money.

The next exercise is similar to the previous one but the child is expected to select coins to match the ones in each example, arrange them in *order of value* himself and then find their total value.

Drawing round coins at this stage should not be necessary, but the child should be expected to record sub-totals and totals as shown in the example.

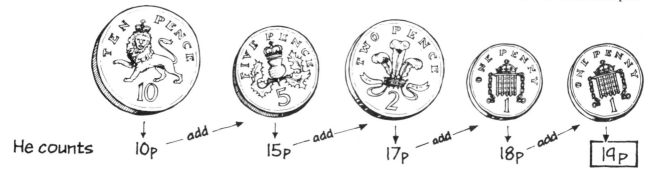

He records this as : 10p, 15p, 17p, 18p, 19p.

## 2  Going shopping

The development of the concept of money with young children goes far beyond the skills of recognising coins, counting, adding up bills, etc. The world of money has a language of its own. Prices such as '8p' need to be related to actual items which can be purchased for that price. With ever rising prices, it is important that, even at this stage, real prices are used and up-dated when necessary. As soon as this is done, the concept of value is introduced. Vocabulary such as expensive, cheap, saving, bargain is commonplace in the world of shopping and children should be encouraged to use these words.

The questions relating to the picture are examples of the language which can develop from shopping. The teacher should spend time discussing the picture with a group of children in order to extend their vocabulary and understanding of shopping. For example:

'Why do you think ice-cream is sold at 3 prices?'
'Why do you think home-made toffee is more expensive than ordinary toffee?'
'If you wanted to buy your friend a present and had 20p to spend what sort of things would you buy and why would you buy them?'

*A class shop*
A common feature of many lower junior classrooms is the class shop. However, a shop worth having is a shop worth thinking about. Besides making it attractive the teacher needs to consider:

1  What opportunities the class shop presents;
2  What skills the children can acquire by using the shop;
3  When the 'situations' provided by the shop should change as the children acquire new skills;
4  How far the class shop is used to develop the children's use of language.

*Class catalogue*

If space does not allow the setting up of a class shop a class catalogue may be used instead. Pictures of items from mail-order catalogues, etc., with prices clearly marked, can be mounted on sugar paper to make a useful and permanent catalogue. This can be used in the same way as the shop for discussion, practical activities and written work.

This activity involves relating a price to each of the items and then adding a simple bill. Where possible children should be encouraged to add the two or three items on the bill mentally.

The children are then asked to select the coins needed to make the total. The children should be encouraged to select the coins of highest value first – working down to the smaller value coins later. Using the method of recording shown in the text will help the child to do this.

It must be emphasised that there is no real substitute for practical situations such as a class-shop for the development of this aspect of money.

The last two exercises involve revision of simple multiplication and division. Ideally, children should use mental calculations for these but some may still need to do them practically using coins.

### 3 Payment and change

There are three aspects to the skill of giving or receiving change:
a) Giving change by counting on;
b) Selecting the appropriate coins to give when the exact coins needed for the price are not available;
c) Working out or checking the price charged from the coins received in the change.

The pupils' exercises give practice in each of these aspects. It is essential that the work is done practically and that answers are not derived from a formal subtraction exercise.

### a) Giving change by counting on

This is a similar activity to that given in Money 1, stage 5. (See page 41.)

### b) Selecting coins offered and receiving change

In real life situations we need the skill of selecting what coins to offer for items. This too requires practical experience in coin selection and receiving change before coming to the worked examples. The class shop can provide this and careful planning is required to ensure that the prices and the coins children are given do not allow correct amounts to be tendered in payment.

### c) Checking your change

This activity will almost certainly require the children to use coins. Again the practical applications and the work done in the class-shop cannot be over-emphasised. This is a most important aspect in the everyday use of money but one that is often overlooked in school.

*Finding the cost of household goods*

It is essential that any new work done in school is made relevant to the child's real world at home. The aim of this activity is to make such a point of contact. It is also intended to make children more aware of the prices of household goods.

The word 'approximate' can be introduced at this stage and discussion could develop as to why there is a diversity in prices recorded.

# Pages from the Pupils' Book and Spiritmasters

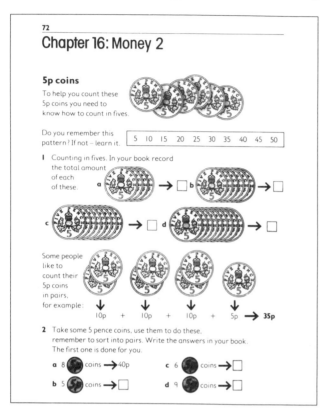

72

## Chapter 16: Money 2

### 5p coins

To help you count these
5p coins you need to
know how to count in fives.

Do you remember this
pattern? If not – learn it. | 5 | 10 | 15 | 20 | 25 | 30 | 35 | 40 | 45 | 50 |

1   Counting in fives. In your book record
the total amount
of each
of these.

a → □   b → □

c → □   d → □

Some people
like to
count their
5p coins
in pairs,
for example:

↓        ↓        ↓        ↓
10p   +   10p   +   10p   +   5p   → **35p**

2   Take some 5 pence coins, use them to do these,
remember to sort into pairs. Write the answers in your book.
The first one is done for you.

a  8 coins → 40p        c  6 coins → □

b  5 coins → □          d  9 coins → □

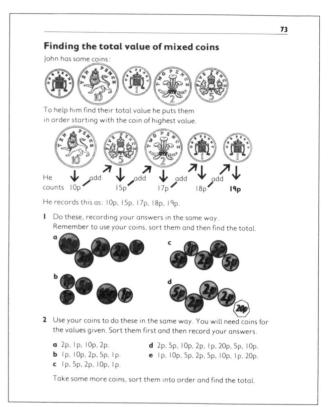

73

### Finding the total value of mixed coins

John has some coins:

To help him find their total value he puts them
in order starting with the coin of highest value.

He
counts   10p   15p   17p   18p   **19p**

add   add   add   add

He records this as: 10p, 15p, 17p, 18p, 19p.

1   Do these, recording your answers in the same way.
Remember to use your coins, sort them and then find the total.

a          c

b          d

2   Use your coins to do these in the same way. You will need coins for
the values given. Sort them first and then record your answers.

a  2p, 1p, 10p, 2p.           d  2p, 5p, 10p, 2p, 1p, 20p, 5p, 10p.
b  1p, 10p, 2p, 5p, 1p.       e  1p, 10p, 5p, 2p, 5p, 10p, 1p, 20p.
c  1p, 5p, 2p, 10p, 1p.

Take some more coins, sort them into order and find the total.

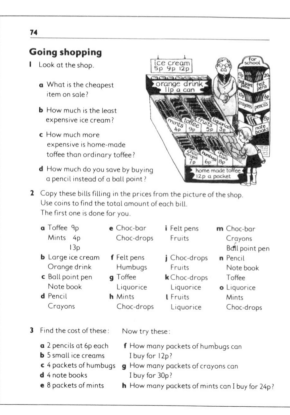

74

### Going shopping

1   Look at the shop.

a  What is the cheapest
item on sale?

b  How much is the least
expensive ice cream?

c  How much more
expensive is home-made
toffee than ordinary toffee?

d  How much do you save by buying
a pencil instead of a ball point?

2   Copy these bills filling in the prices from the picture of the shop.
Use coins to find the total amount of each bill.
The first one is done for you.

a  Toffee  9p      e  Choc-bar       i  Felt pens     m  Choc-bar
Mints   4p         Choc-drops        Fruits           Crayons
         13p                                          Ball point pen
b  Large ice cream  f  Felt pens     j  Choc-drops    n  Pencil
Orange drink        Humbugs          Fruits           Note book
c  Ball point pen   g  Toffee        k Choc-drops     Toffee
Note book           Liquorice        Liquorice       o  Liquorice
d  Pencil           h  Mints         l  Fruits        Mints
Crayons             Choc-drops       Liquorice        Choc-drops

3   Find the cost of these :       Now try these :

a  2 pencils at 6p each      f  How many packets of humbugs can
b  5 small ice creams           I buy for 12p?
c  4 packets of humbugs      g  How many packets of crayons can
d  4 note books                 I buy for 30p?
e  8 packets of mints        h  How many packets of mints can I buy for 24p?

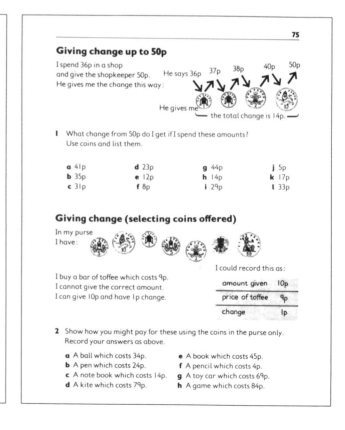

75

### Giving change up to 50p

I spend 36p in a shop
and give the shopkeeper 50p.
He says 36p   37p   38p   40p   50p
He gives me the change this way:

He gives me ——— the total change is 14p. ———

1   What change from 50p do I get if I spend these amounts?
Use coins and list them.

a  41p       d  23p       g  44p       j  5p
b  35p       e  12p       h  14p       k  17p
c  31p       f  8p        i  29p       l  33p

### Giving change (selecting coins offered)

In my purse
I have :

I buy a bar of toffee which costs 9p.
I cannot give the correct amount.
I can give 10p and have 1p change.

I could record this as:

| amount given | 10p |
| --- | --- |
| price of toffee | 9p |
| change | 1p |

2   Show how you might pay for these using the coins in the purse only.
Record your answers as above.

a  A ball which costs 34p.         e  A book which costs 45p.
b  A pen which costs 24p.          f  A pencil which costs 4p.
c  A note book which costs 14p.    g  A toy car which costs 69p.
d  A kite which costs 79p.         h  A game which costs 84p.

**76**

## Looking at change given

1 You go to a shop with 20p.    You are given 2p change.    How much did you spend?

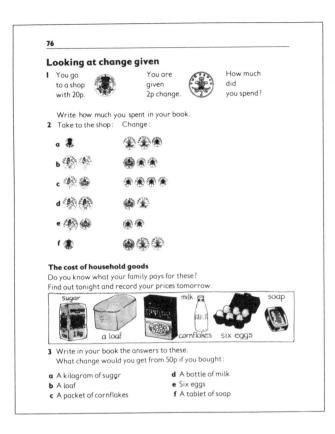

Write how much you spent in your book.

2 Take to the shop:    Change:

a

b

c

d

e

f

### The cost of household goods

Do you know what your family pays for these?
Find out tonight and record your prices tomorrow.

sugar    a loaf    milk    cornflakes    six eggs    soap
1 kg

3 Write in your book the answers to these.
What change would you get from 50p if you bought:

a A kilogram of sugar          d A bottle of milk
b A loaf                        e Six eggs
c A packet of cornflakes        f A tablet of soap

---

**A**

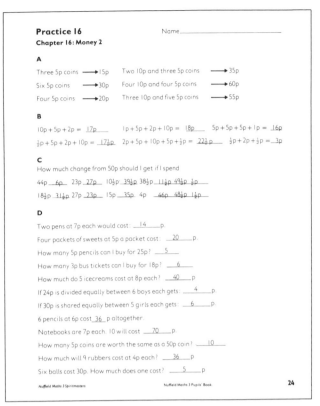

Three 5p coins ⟶ 15p     Two 10p and three 5p coins ⟶ 35p
Six 5p coins ⟶ 30p       Four 10p and four 5p coins ⟶ 60p
Four 5p coins ⟶ 20p      Three 10p and five 5p coins ⟶ 55p

**B**

$10p + 5p + 2p = \underline{17p}$     $1p + 5p + 2p + 10p = \underline{18p}$     $5p + 5p + 5p + 1p = \underline{16p}$

$\frac{1}{2}p + 5p + 2p + 10p = \underline{17\frac{1}{2}p}$     $2p + 5p + 10p + 5p + \frac{1}{2}p = \underline{22\frac{1}{2}p}$     $\frac{1}{2}p + 2p + \frac{1}{2}p = \underline{3p}$

**C**

How much change from 50p should I get if I spend

44p $\underline{6p}$  23p $\underline{27p}$  10½p $\underline{39\frac{1}{2}p}$  38½p $\underline{11\frac{1}{2}p}$  49½p $\underline{\frac{1}{2}p}$

18½p $\underline{31\frac{1}{2}p}$  27p $\underline{23p}$  15p $\underline{35p}$  4p $\underline{46p}$  48½p $\underline{1\frac{1}{2}p}$

**D**

Two pens at 7p each would cost: $\underline{14}$ p.

Four packets of sweets at 5p a packet cost: $\underline{20}$ p.

How many 5p pencils can I buy for 25p? $\underline{5}$

How many 3p bus tickets can I buy for 18p? $\underline{6}$

How much do 5 icecreams cost at 8p each? $\underline{40}$ p

If 24p is divided equally between 6 boys each gets: $\underline{4}$ p.

If 30p is shared equally between 5 girls each gets: $\underline{6}$ p.

6 pencils at 6p cost $\underline{36}$ p altogether.

Notebooks are 7p each. 10 will cost $\underline{70}$ p.

How many 5p coins are worth the same as a 50p coin? $\underline{10}$

How much will 9 rubbers cost at 4p each? $\underline{36}$ p

Six balls cost 30p. How much does one cost? $\underline{5}$ p

---

# References and resources

*Cardboard token coins, Coin stamps, Gummed Printed Coins, Plastic token coins*, E. J. Arnold

*Our Money Wall Chart, Plastic and Cardboard Coins, Stick-on Decimal Coins*, E.S.A.

*Decimal Coin Rubber Stamps, Plastic and Cardboard Coins*, Galt

*Cardboard Coins, Gummed Paper Money, Handy Coin Rubber Stamps, 'How much will it cost?' Rubber Stamps*, Philip & Tacey

# Chapter 17

# Multiplication 2

## For the teacher

This chapter builds on the work done in Chapter 9 by using rows and columns to peinforce the commutative property of multiplication and to introduce square numbers. Activities are suggested which will help children to learn the first block of multiplication facts.

## Summary of the stages

1  More rows and columns – commutativity

2  Square numbers

3  Learning multiplication tables – making a start

4  Vertical layout of multiplication

5  Magic squares

## Vocabulary

Row, column, factor, product, square, diagonal, doubling.

## Equipment and apparatus

Geoboard, pegs, counters, rulers (to make partitions), squared paper, $6 \times 6$ multiplication square, dice, card for dominoes.

## Working with the children

### 1  More rows and columns – commutativity

Before starting the exercises in the Pupils' Book, the children should be given ample opportunity to make rectangular arrays of counters, cubes, pegs, etc., possibly using colours to emphasise the difference between rows and columns.

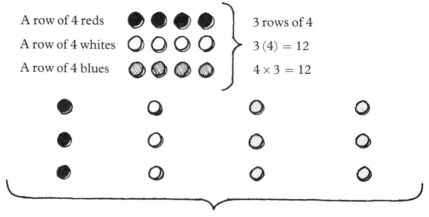

A row of 4 reds
A row of 4 whites
A row of 4 blues

3 rows of 4
$3\,(4) = 12$
$4 \times 3 = 12$

A column of 3 blacks    A column of 3 whites    A column of 3 reds    A column of 3 yellows

4 columns of 3

$4\,(3) = 12$        $3 \times 4 = 12$

The use of the words *factor* and *product* should be encouraged as part of normal vocabulary. The commutative property of multiplication can be stated without using the word commutative by saying: 'Two factors multiplied in any order give the same product.'

*Other ways of demonstrating that multiplication is commutative*
a) Using the 'equaliser' or mathematical balance:

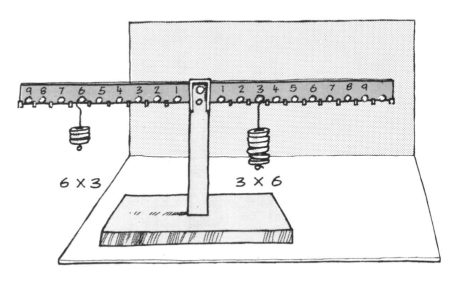

3 washers on hook 6 on one side can be balanced with 6 washers on hook 3 on the other side.
b) Using blocks from the Stern, Colour Factor or Cuisenaire apparatus:

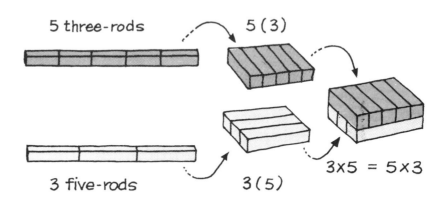

c) Using the number line or number track and rods:

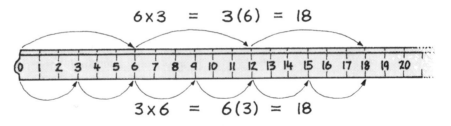

## 2  Square numbers

Special attention is given to arrays in which the number of rows and the number of columns is the same – the so-called square numbers. For example:

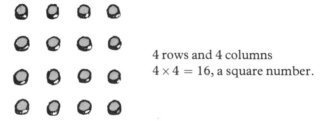

4 rows and 4 columns
$4 \times 4 = 16$, a square number.

It is important for the child to make these arrangements for himself by using counters, pegs, geoboards and elastic bands, or by colouring in on squared paper to investigate square numbers.

Most children are intrigued by this connection between numbers and shape, especially if they build up the squares and look at the pattern of differences.

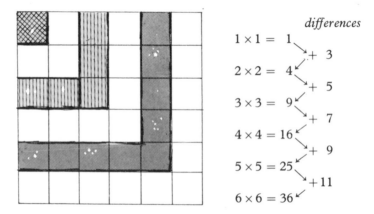

*differences*

$1 \times 1 = 1$

$+ 3$

$2 \times 2 = 4$

$+ 5$

$3 \times 3 = 9$

$+ 7$

$4 \times 4 = 16$

$+ 9$

$5 \times 5 = 25$

$+ 11$

$6 \times 6 = 36$

Activities like this will help motivate children to commit to memory the first six square numbers. This is a good introduction to the learning of multiplication tables.

## 3  Learning multiplication tables – making a start

The following extract is from Chapter 5 of *Nuffield Maths 2 Teachers' Handbook*:

> It is frustrating for a child to realise that he requires multiplication in order to solve a problem but then have to stop and ponder about $3 \times 7$. On the other hand, it must be just as frustrating to have learned table facts by rote and then not be sure how to apply them.
>
> It need not be a question of choice between:
>   'I can't remember the facts I need'
> and 'I know the facts but can't use them.'
>
> The gathering and remembering of multiplication facts should be a gradual process based on a variety of activities carefully planned to promote understanding, bolster confidence and facilitate memorisation.
>
> It is essential that practical experience of multiplication using counters, blocks, arrays, number lines, etc. comes *before* the learning of tables and not the other way round and that the learning process does not depend

*solely* on mindless, parrot-like repetition. Some children may like chanting tables but others find it a chore. As one little boy said, 'I know the tune but I can never remember the words.'

Traditionally children have been taught the '3 times' table before 'progressing' to the '4 times', and so on. This need not be the best way, because it implies that $9 \times 3 = 27$ should be learnt before $5 \times 4 = 20$. Moreover, how often in everyday life are we required to 'recite' a complete table?

Giving a child confidence in his ability to remember multiplication facts is best achieved by convincing him that really there are not all that many facts to learn. The diagrams in the pupils' book show that by starting with a $6 \times 6$ multiplication square, putting in the square numbers and using the child's understanding that multiplication works backwards and forwards (commutative law), there are only 15 facts to learn. If we take out the table of 1's which is easy and the table of 2's which involves a doubling process, there are only 6 facts left! This system of splitting the full range of required facts into sections or 'zones' will be developed further in later chapters.

However systematic the approach by the teacher, 'instant recall' of multiplication facts still requires regular practice by the children. Some practice is provided in *Nuffield Maths 3 Spiritmasters*, Practices 9 and 17 and Grid 4.

Graphs showing a regular 'table staircase' will help children to remember what tables 'look' like as well as what they 'sound' like.

$$3 \times 1 = 3 \quad 3 \times 2 = 6 \quad 3 \times 3 = 9 \quad 3 \times 4 = 12 \quad 3 \times 5 = 15 \quad 3 \times 6 = 18$$

$$4 \times 1 = 4 \quad 4 \times 2 = 8 \quad 4 \times 3 = 12 \quad 4 \times 4 = 16 \quad 4 \times 5 = 20 \quad 4 \times 6 = 24$$

There are many games which encourage the learning of multiplication facts. Here are a few examples:

a) *Table dominoes*
These should be copied onto cards measuring about 10 cm by 5 cm. This game can be played by up to 4 players starting with 4 dominoes each. It is

similar to the usual game of dominoes – when a player 'cannot go' he takes an extra domino from those left face down in the middle of the table. The winner is the first player to use all his dominoes.

 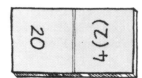 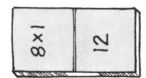 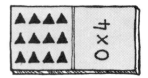

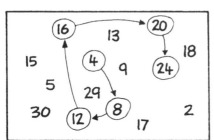

The set of dominoes may also be used by a single player for 'domino patience'.

b) *'Join the family'*
The family of 4:
The members of the family of 4 are ringed and joined in order.
It is a good exercise for children to make up these for their friends.

| 1 | 2 | 3 | 4 | 5 | 6 |
|---|---|---|---|---|---|
| 8 | 9 | 10 | 12 | 15 | 16 |
| 18 | 20 | 24 | 25 | 30 | 36 |

c) *Games using two standard dice*
Multiplication only:
Each player in turn rolls two dice, works out the product of the numbers obtained and covers the corresponding square on his card with a counter. E.g. If he rolls [dice] $3 \times 4 = 12$ so he covers 12.

The player who covers his card first wins.

| 1 | 2 | 3 | 4 | 5 |
|---|---|---|---|---|
| 6 | 7 | 8 | 9 | 10 |
| 11 | 12 | 15 | 16 | 18 |
| 20 | 24 | 25 | 30 | 36 |

Product, Difference and Sum:
This time the player may cover the product, difference and sum of the two numbers obtained on the dice. E.g. if he rolls [dice] $5 \times 3 = 15, 5 - 3 = 2$ and $5 + 3 = 8$, so he covers 15, 2 and 8. The object of this game is to try to get children to think of multiplication as a way of combining two numbers as well as by adding them or finding their difference.

## 4   Vertical layout of multiplication
Whilst still using numbers within the children's experience, this alternative layout is introduced in preparation for later work.
It is important to leave a space between the × sign and the 4 and to remind the children that the digits in the product must be placed in the correct columns.

$$\begin{array}{r} 6 \\ \times\ 4 \\ \hline 24 \end{array}$$

## 5   Magic squares
Magic squares have already been introduced in previous chapters on addition. An interesting point to learn about magic squares is that if the number in each small square or cell is multiplied by a common factor, another magic square is formed. After each new magic square has been made the child can check the accuracy of his multiplication by adding the rows, columns and diagonals to see if he still has a magic square.

# Pages from the Pupils' Book and Spiritmasters

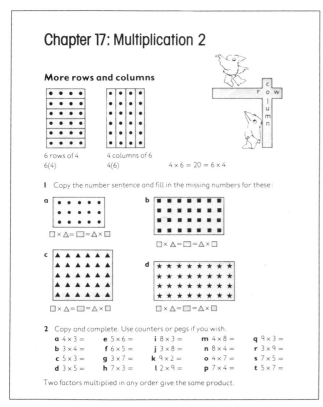

## Chapter 17: Multiplication 2

### More rows and columns

6 rows of 4
6(4)

4 columns of 6
4(6)

$4 \times 6 = 20 = 6 \times 4$

1 Copy the number sentence and fill in the missing numbers for these:

a

$\square \times \triangle = \square = \triangle \times \square$

b

$\square \times \triangle = \square = \triangle \times \square$

c

$\square \times \triangle = \square = \triangle \times \square$

d

$\square \times \triangle = \square = \triangle \times \square$

2 Copy and complete. Use counters or pegs if you wish.

a $4 \times 3 =$    e $5 \times 6 =$    i $8 \times 3 =$    m $4 \times 8 =$    q $9 \times 3 =$
b $3 \times 4 =$    f $6 \times 5 =$    j $3 \times 8 =$    n $8 \times 4 =$    r $3 \times 9 =$
c $5 \times 3 =$    g $3 \times 7 =$    k $9 \times 2 =$    o $4 \times 7 =$    s $7 \times 5 =$
d $3 \times 5 =$    h $7 \times 3 =$    l $2 \times 9 =$    p $7 \times 4 =$    t $5 \times 7 =$

Two factors multiplied in any order give the same product.

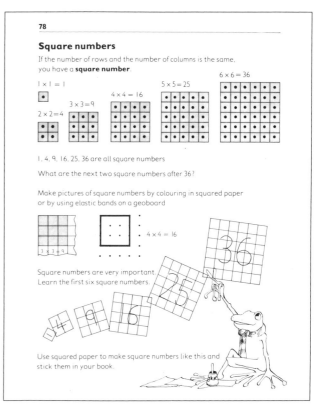

### Square numbers

If the number of rows and the number of columns is the same, you have a **square number**.

$1 \times 1 = 1$

$2 \times 2 = 4$

$3 \times 3 = 9$

$4 \times 4 = 16$

$5 \times 5 = 25$

$6 \times 6 = 36$

1, 4, 9, 16, 25, 36 are all square numbers

What are the next two square numbers after 36?

Make pictures of square numbers by colouring in squared paper or by using elastic bands on a geoboard

$4 \times 4 = 16$

Square numbers are very important. Learn the first six square numbers.

Use squared paper to make square numbers like this and stick them in your book.

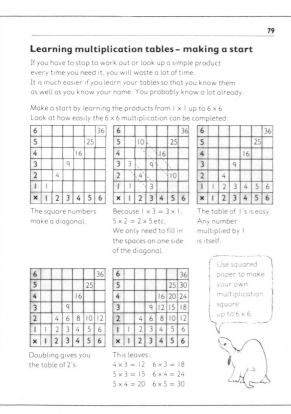

### Learning multiplication tables – making a start

If you have to stop to work out or look up a simple product every time you need it, you will waste a lot of time.
It is much easier if you learn your tables so that you know them as well as you know your name. You probably know a lot already.

Make a start by learning the products from $1 \times 1$ up to $6 \times 6$.
Look at how easily the $6 \times 6$ multiplication can be completed:

The square numbers make a diagonal.

Because $1 \times 3 = 3 \times 1$,
$5 \times 2 = 2 \times 5$ etc.
We only need to fill in the spaces on one side of the diagonal.

The table of 1's is easy.
Any number multiplied by 1 is itself.

Use squared paper to make your own multiplication square up to $6 \times 6$.

Doubling gives you the table of 2's.

This leaves:

$4 \times 3 = 12$    $6 \times 3 = 18$
$5 \times 3 = 15$    $6 \times 4 = 24$
$5 \times 4 = 20$    $6 \times 5 = 30$

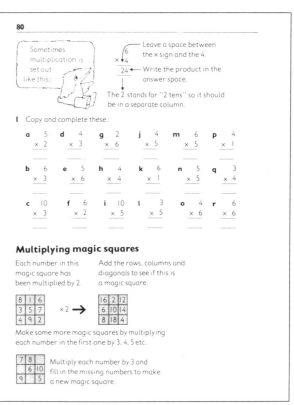

Sometimes multiplication is set out like this:

Leave a space between the $\times$ sign and the 4.

Write the product in the answer space.

The 2 stands for "2 tens" so it should be in a separate column.

1 Copy and complete these:

a  5     d  4     g  2     j  4     m  6     p  4
 $\times 2$    $\times 3$    $\times 6$    $\times 5$    $\times 5$    $\times 1$

b  6     e  5     h  4     k  6     n  5     q  3
 $\times 3$    $\times 6$    $\times 4$    $\times 1$    $\times 5$    $\times 4$

c 10     f  6     i 10     l  3     o  4     r  4
 $\times 3$    $\times 2$    $\times 5$    $\times 5$    $\times 6$    $\times 6$

### Multiplying magic squares

Each number in this magic square has been multiplied by 2.

Add the rows, columns and diagonals to see if this is a magic square.

| 8 | 1 | 6 |
| 3 | 5 | 7 |
| 4 | 9 | 2 |

$\times 2 \rightarrow$

| 16 | 2 | 12 |
| 6 | 10 | 14 |
| 8 | 18 | 4 |

Make some more magic squares by multiplying each number in the first one by 3, 4, 5 etc.

| 7 | 8 | |
| | 6 | 10 |
| 9 | | 5 |

Multiply each number by 3 and fill in the missing numbers to make a new magic square.

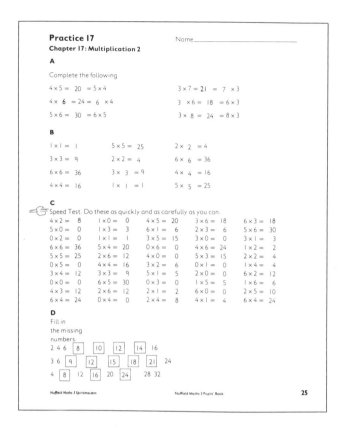

## References and resources

Nuffield Mathematics Teaching Project, *Computation and Structure* ③, Nuffield Guides, Chambers/Murray 1967. (See Introduction, page xii.)

Shuard, H. and Williams, E., *Primary Mathematics Today* (Chapter 7), Longman Group Ltd 1970

Tavener, N., *Unifix Teachers' Manual*, Philip & Tacey 1970

*Multilink Number Track, Multilink 100 pegboard, Stern Number Track*, E.S.A.

*Hundred Number Board, Number Strip and Rods*, Invicta Ed. Aids

*Centicube Number Track (Metline)*, Osmiroid

*Unifix Multiplication/Division Markers, Unifix 100 Board, Window Markers* and *Number Tablets*, Philip & Tacey

# Length 2

## For the teacher

Previous work on Length (Chapter 4) involved measurement in metres and decimetres (10-cm rods). This chapter leads the children to more accurate measurement in centimetres.

Successful acquisition of the skills described in this chapter depends upon the careful build-up of a routine or technique. It is advisable, therefore, to start the activities with a few children at a time in order to ensure maximum supervision and individual guidance.

Many of the activities involving measurement in centimetres reinforce number work in the range 0–100.

## Summary of the stages

1  Measuring lines in centimetres

2  Drawing lines the correct length

3  Measuring distances and curved lines

4  Measuring lengths up to 100 cm
   a) using a metre rule,
   b) using a shorter ruler

5  Addition and subtraction of centimetres

## Vocabulary

centimetre, ruler, 'dead length', 'waste end', zero mark, length, distance.

## Equipment and apparatus

At least one metre rule calibrated in cm, rulers marked in cm up to 20, 25 or 30 cm – either 'dead length' or with 'waste end', string, rods based on 1 cm unit, variety of objects suitable for measuring (0–100 cm range), lines with clearly defined ends and up to 100 cm in length drawn on larger sheets of paper.

## Working with the children

**1  Measuring lines in centimetres**

To establish the relationship between the centimetre and the metre, the child should be shown and allowed to handle a metre rule clearly divided into 100 centimetres. Words such as *cent* (100 to the dollar), *century* (100 years or 100 runs), *centurion* (in charge of 100 men), *centigrade* (100 degrees) can be used to emphasise the connection with a hundred. The abbreviation cm should be introduced at this stage with the reminder that cm stands for centimetre or centimetres and is only followed by a full stop if it comes at the end of a sentence.

A close inspection of the children's own rulers should follow. Suppliers' catalogues suggest that three lengths (20 cm, 25 cm and 30 cm) and two types ('dead length' and 'waste end') are in common use.

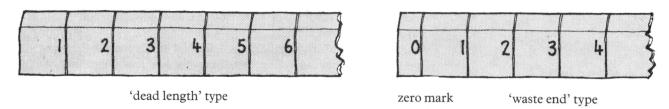

'dead length' type                    zero mark    'waste end' type

The children are likely to meet both types so the techniques for using both types are described. In the first instance, however, it is advisable to concentrate on only one type. Children using the 'waste end' type of ruler will often need to be reminded that the 'zero mark' is the point from which measurement must start.

Whichever type of ruler is used, it is most important that the numerals are printed as close as possible to the corresponding marks. Large numerals in the spaces between marks cause confusion when reading off a length.

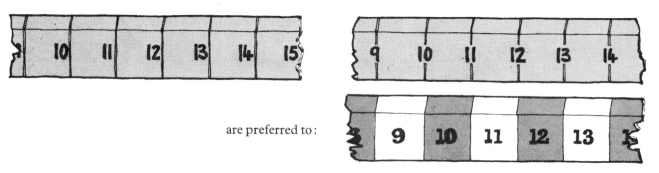

are preferred to:

When the children start measuring, it is useful to emphasise these points:
a) Use the ruler with the numerals reading from left to right.
b) Make sure that the left-hand end of the ruler, or the zero mark, is level with the left-hand end of the line.
c) Count along the ruler to the end of the line. (In the first instance use lines with lengths in whole centimetres.)
d) Read off the numeral level with the right-hand end of the line. This is the length of the line in centimetres.
e) Write down the length. (Many children become so engrossed in the measuring that they forget to record.)

Children need plenty of practice in using a calibrated ruler – measuring lines, Cuisenaire or Colour Factor rods, strips of card, sticks, the edges of boxes, etc. Some children will omit stage (c) and read off without counting along. *Nuffield Maths 3 Spiritmasters*, Practice 18 (see page 114).

## 2 Drawing lines the correct length
This time the 'routine' is:
a) Place the ruler with the numerals reading from left to right.
b) Hold the ruler firmly by spreading the fingers and look along the ruler to where the line will finish. (Some children may like to mark the paper to indicate how far to draw the line.)

c) Start to draw the line from the end of the ruler or the zero mark★ –
preferably 'pulling' the pencil rather than 'pushing' it.

d) Check that the line is the correct length before taking away the ruler.

### 3 Measuring distances and curved lines

After measuring lines, rods or other solid objects, measuring a *distance*
between two points represents a new stage since some children may think
you cannot measure what is not there!

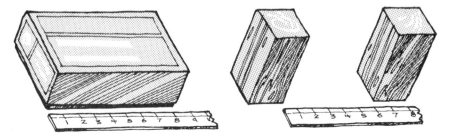

Length of box is 8 cm.   Distance between bricks is 6 cm.

In the first instance it may help if a piece of thin string is stretched
between the points. The string is then measured using the technique
described below.

Measuring curved lengths involves the use of an intermediate measure –
a piece of string. The children first lay the string carefully on the curved
line (again, ensuring that the starting ends are level) and nip the string with
their finger nails level with the other end of the line. They then transfer the
string, carefully gripping the 'nip', to a ruler in order to read off the
measurement. *Nuffield Maths 3 Spiritmasters*, Grid 13 and Practice 18 (see
page 114).

At this point estimating before measuring is encouraged. Children are
often intrigued by the way in which lines of the same length can be made to
look different by slanting or curving them:

All these lines are 10 cm long:

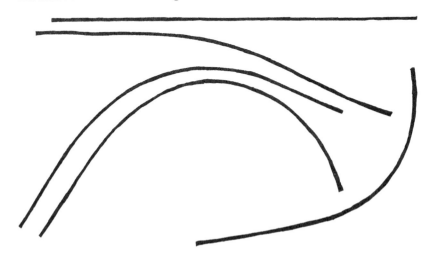

★ Some left-handed children may prefer to draw the line from right to left; so that
in drawing a line 9 cm long for instance they start at the 9 cm mark and finish the
line at the zero mark.

Using string to measure curved lines requires some dexterity. Children may work better in pairs, making use of more fingers. The degree of accuracy achieved may not be high but it is the experience and practice of the technique which is important at this stage. Alternatively, a plastic flexible curve, which can be moulded to fit the curve and then straightened out, makes the task easier.

For measuring curved objects a tape measure or calibrated paper strip makes the use of string as an intermediate measure unnecessary.

## 4   Measuring lengths up to 100 cm

*a) Using a metre rule*
As the children gain confidence they can go on to measure longer lengths and distances up to 100 cm using the steps mentioned previously except that step (c) will involve counting in tens first and then the odd units at the end:

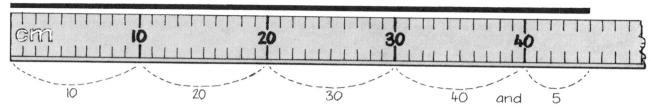

The line is 45 cm long

This activity will help to establish the relationship between the centimetre and the metre whilst providing additional experience with numbers up to 100 with the metre rule acting as a number line. The six objects suggested for measuring in the Pupils' Book can be supplemented by other objects or by lines drawn on a large sheet of paper.

*b) Using a shorter ruler*
Further experience in measuring up to 100 cm can be gained by using the child's own ruler. First the child makes a copy of the table which corresponds to his own ruler length. The longer line is then measured by 'stepping' the ruler along the length, being sure to make a mark level with the last centimetre which becomes the starting point for the next 'ruler length'.

The total length is measured in 'ruler lengths' and centimetres so that, for example, using a 25 cm ruler, the measurement of 79 cm would be recorded like this:

| | | |
|---|---|---|
| 3 ruler lengths | 75 cm | (From appropriate table) |
| extra part | 4 cm | |
| Length of line is | 79 cm | |

Measuring the line again using a metre rule or tape measure serves as a check on the accuracy of the measurement and of the addition.

## 5   Addition and subtraction of centimetres
Further opportunities for using the ruler both for measuring and as a number line lead to simple calculations involving centimetres which provide practice and reinforcement of number skills.

# Pages from the Pupils' Book and Spiritmasters

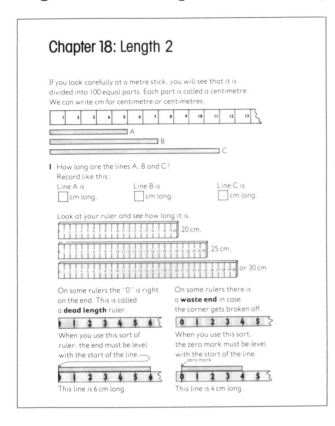

## Chapter 18: Length 2

If you look carefully at a metre stick, you will see that it is divided into 100 equal parts. Each part is called a centimetre. We can write cm for centimetre or centimetres.

A
B
C

1  How long are the lines A, B and C?
Record like this:

Line A is  ☐ cm long.    Line B is  ☐ cm long.    Line C is  ☐ cm long.

Look at your ruler and see how long it is.

20 cm,
25 cm,
or 30 cm

On some rulers the "0" is right on the end. This is called a **dead length** ruler.

On some rulers there is a **waste end** in case the corner gets broken off.

When you use this sort of ruler, the end must be level with the start of the line.

When you use this sort, the zero mark must be level with the start of the line.

This line is 6 cm long.    This line is 4 cm long.

---

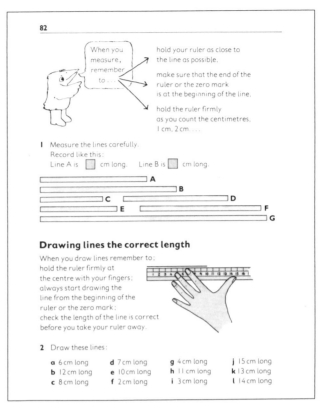

82

When you measure, remember to . . .

→ hold your ruler as close to the line as possible.

→ make sure that the end of the ruler or the zero mark is at the beginning of the line.

→ hold the ruler firmly as you count the centimetres. 1 cm, 2 cm. . . .

1  Measure the lines carefully.
Record like this:
Line A is  ☐ cm long.    Line B is  ☐ cm long.

A
B
C    D
E    F
G

### Drawing lines the correct length

When you draw lines remember to;
hold the ruler firmly at the centre with your fingers;
always start drawing the line from the beginning of the ruler or the zero mark;
check the length of the line is correct before you take your ruler away.

2  Draw these lines:

| a | 6 cm long | d | 7 cm long | g | 4 cm long | j | 15 cm long |
| b | 12 cm long | e | 10 cm long | h | 11 cm long | k | 13 cm long |
| c | 8 cm long | f | 2 cm long | i | 3 cm long | l | 14 cm long |

---

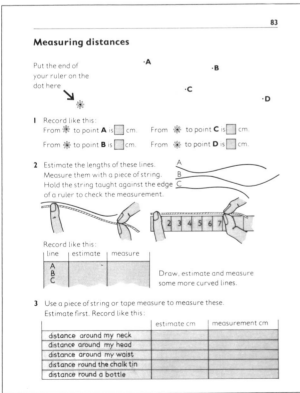

83

### Measuring distances

Put the end of your ruler on the dot here ↓

·A
·B
·C
·D

1  Record like this:
From ✳ to point **A** is ☐ cm.    From ✳ to point **C** is ☐ cm.
From ✳ to point **B** is ☐ cm.    From ✳ to point **D** is ☐ cm.

2  Estimate the lengths of these lines.
Measure them with a piece of string.
Hold the string taught against the edge of a ruler to check the measurement.

A
B
C

Record like this:

| line | estimate | measure |
|---|---|---|
| A | | |
| B | | |
| C | | |

Draw, estimate and measure some more curved lines.

3  Use a piece of string or tape measure to measure these.
Estimate first. Record like this:

| | estimate cm | measurement cm |
|---|---|---|
| distance around my neck | | |
| distance around my head | | |
| distance around my waist | | |
| distance round the chalk tin | | |
| distance round a bottle | | |

---

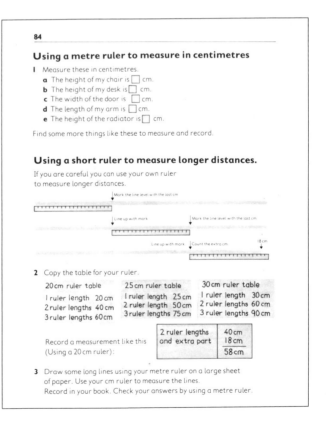

84

### Using a metre ruler to measure in centimetres

1  Measure these in centimetres.
a  The height of my chair is ☐ cm.
b  The height of my desk is ☐ cm.
c  The width of the door is ☐ cm.
d  The length of my arm is ☐ cm.
e  The height of the radiator is ☐ cm.

Find some more things like these to measure and record.

### Using a short ruler to measure longer distances.

If you are careful you can use your own ruler to measure longer distances.

Mark the line level with the last cm
Line up with mark    Mark the line level with the last cm
Line up with mark    Count the extra cm    18 cm

2  Copy the table for your ruler.

| 20 cm ruler table | 25 cm ruler table | 30 cm ruler table |
|---|---|---|
| 1 ruler length  20 cm | 1 ruler length  25 cm | 1 ruler length  30 cm |
| 2 ruler lengths  40 cm | 2 ruler lengths  50 cm | 2 ruler lengths  60 cm |
| 3 ruler lengths  60 cm | 3 ruler lengths  75 cm | 3 ruler lengths  90 cm |

Record a measurement like this
(Using a 20 cm ruler):

| 2 ruler lengths and extra part | 40 cm |
| | 18 cm |
| | 58 cm |

3  Draw some long lines using your metre ruler on a large sheet of paper. Use your cm ruler to measure the lines.
Record in your book. Check your answers by using a metre ruler.

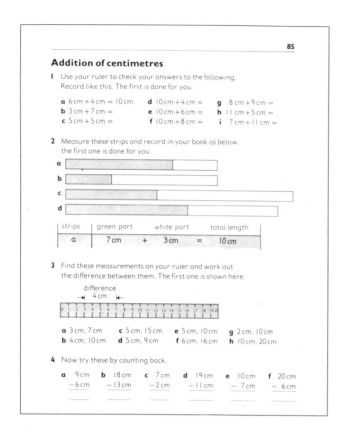

**Addition of centimetres** 85

I Use your ruler to check your answers to the following.
Record like this. The first is done for you.

**a** 6 cm + 4 cm = 10 cm.   **d** 10 cm + 4 cm =   **g** 8 cm + 9 cm =
**b** 3 cm + 7 cm =   **e** 10 cm + 6 cm =   **h** 11 cm + 5 cm =
**c** 5 cm + 5 cm =   **f** 10 cm + 8 cm =   **i** 7 cm + 11 cm =

2 Measure these strips and record in your book as below.
the first one is done for you.

a
b
c
d

| strips | green part | white part | total length |
|--------|-----------|-----------|--------------|
| a | 7 cm + | 3 cm = | 10 cm |

3 Find these measurements on your ruler and work out
the difference between them. The first is shown here.

difference
4 cm

**a** 3 cm, 7 cm   **c** 5 cm, 15 cm   **e** 5 cm, 10 cm   **g** 2 cm, 10 cm
**b** 4 cm, 10 cm   **d** 5 cm, 9 cm   **f** 6 cm, 16 cm   **h** 10 cm, 20 cm

4 Now try these by counting back.

**a** 9 cm   **b** 18 cm   **c** 7 cm   **d** 19 cm   **e** 10 cm   **f** 20 cm
  − 6 cm    − 13 cm    − 2 cm    − 11 cm    − 7 cm    − 6 cm

---

**Practice 18**   Name _____
Chapter 18: Length 2

**A**
Measure these lines and record your answers.

_____ 6 cm      _____ 8 cm
_____ 4 cm      _____ 11 cm
_____ 12 cm _____ 3 cm
_____ 14 cm ____ 1 cm
_____ 13 cm _____ 2 cm

**B**
Draw lines of the following lengths on this sheet.

4 cm _____      8 cm _____
7 cm _____      6 cm _____
2 cm ____      12 cm _____
10 cm _____      5 cm ____
9 cm _____      3 cm ____

**C**
Complete the table for the lengths of these lines.

a        b        c

d

|        | Estimate in cm | Measurement in cm |
|--------|----------------|-------------------|
| Line a |                | 9 cm              |
| Line b |                | 7 cm              |
| Line c |                | 10 cm             |
| Line d |                | 8 cm              |

Nuffield Maths 3 Spiritsmasters        Nuffield Maths 3 Pupils' Book        26

---

# References and resources

Nuffield Mathematics Teaching Project, *Computation and Structure* ②,
  Nuffield Guide, Chambers/Murray 1967. (See Introduction, page xii.)

Shuard, H. and Williams, E., *Primary Mathematics Today* (Chapter 6),
  Longman Group Limited 1970

*100 cm Rule, Roll-up Height Measure, Set of Metre Sticks*, E. J. Arnold

*First Metre Rod*, E.S.A.

*Metristick*, Invicta Plastics

*Flexible Height Measure, Height fi ure and Floor Stand, Measure Tapes, Set
  of Metre Sticks*, Nicolas Burdett

*Depth Gauge, Metline Number Track*, Osmiroid

*1 Metre Graduated Paper Strips, Metre Measuring and Comparison Rods
  Set, Metre Measuring Tapes, Metric-Aid Metre Tape*, Philip & Tacey

*Flexible 1 m Measures, Measuring Tapes, Metre Rules*, Taskmaster

# Introducing fractions 1

## For the teacher

It has been said that 'fractions' have been responsible for putting more people off mathematics than any other single topic. In fact the very word *fraction* has been known to make strong men wince!

This antipathy is probably the result of the confusion caused by introducing fractions too rapidly. The headlong rush into computation with fractions, using such mumbo-jumbo as 'add the tops but not the bottoms' or 'turn it upside down and multiply', has often been attempted before the idea of a fraction or fractional notation has been fully understood.

The use of common or vulgar fractions is likely to continue despite decimalisation and metrication. The Americans, for example, still use 'quarter' for 25 cents and fashion writers are unlikely to refer to dresses with .75 sleeves!

This chapter provides a gentle introduction to common or vulgar fractions by limiting examples to *unit* fractions ($\frac{1}{2}, \frac{1}{3}, \frac{1}{4}, \frac{1}{5}, \frac{1}{10}$). These are illustrated first by symmetrical shapes, then by measures and finally by sets of countable objects. Language and notation are developed side by side so that at this stage, for example:

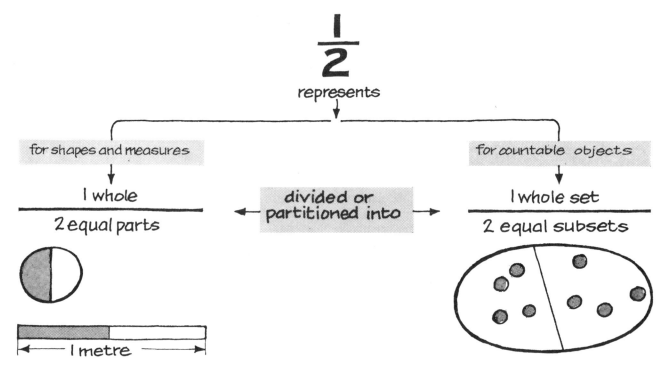

There are several difficulties in the use of language concerning fractions. Some everyday expressions are likely to cause confusion. A 'quarter of tea' or a 'half of butter' both look like *whole* packets and rarely, if ever, do we see the 'whole' from which these fractions are derived. We use what sound like ordinal numerals such as third, fifth and tenth as the name of a fractional part but we depart from this usage for half (not 'second') and quarter – although fourth is used occasionally. This confusion was highlighted by a little girl who overheard adults discussing 'a third of the human race' and asked who came first and second.

115

When writing common fractions it is advisable to insist upon $\frac{1}{2}$ rather than $^1/_2$ since $\frac{1}{2}$ may remind the children that this is a shortened version of $1 \div 2$ and $^1/_2$ can easily degenerate into $1/2$, and hence 112. The relative sizes of the numerals used for common fractions is also important especially as in later stages 'mixed numbers' such as $3\frac{1}{3}$ will consist of whole numbers and fractional parts side by side.

## Summary of the stages

1   Dividing shapes into equal parts

2   Fractions of measures

3   Fractions from sets

## Vocabulary

Equal parts, half, halves, thirds, quarters, fifths, tenths, divided, whole, fraction, kite.

## Apparatus and equipment

Paper shapes, pinboards, elastic bands, Plasticine, string, paper strips, centimetre squared paper, counters, cubes, buttons, marbles, bottle tops, coloured cards, etc.

## Working with the children

### 1   Dividing shapes into equal parts

It is important to emphasise that a half, for example, is one of two *equal* parts into which a whole shape has been divided. (Children often talk about having 'the biggest half'!)

In the case of halves and quarters, much can be done by folding paper along lines of symmetry but it should be remembered that it is not always necessary or even possible to fold along an axis of symmetry so that the two halves fit one on the other. For example:

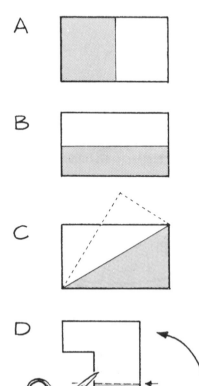

In A and B folding along an axis of symmetry produces 2 halves, one half fitting on to the other.

In C, the diagonal does divide the shape into 2 halves but it is not an axis of symmetry and one half does not fit on to the other by folding.

In D folding does not fit one half on to the other but cutting and rotating does.

Children need plenty of practical experience of shading, folding and cutting paper shapes or dividing up shapes made on a pinboard. Discussion and display should place great emphasis on *equal* parts.

The example of the kite being divided into 2 parts which are NOT HALVES reinforces this point and can be followed by other similar cases involving thirds, quarters, etc.

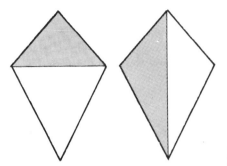 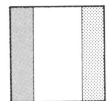 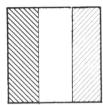 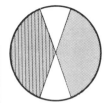 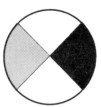

Having divided a whole into fractional parts, the children should be given opportunities to reverse the process by building up a whole from parts. Stiff card or floor tiles, cut and appropriately marked, are more suitable than paper shapes and can be used as templates for recording.

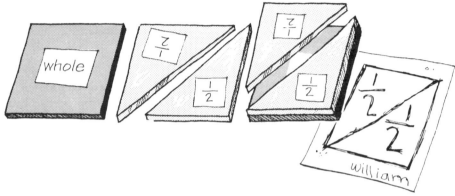

A very useful and more permanent piece of apparatus the fraction board. This consists of thick coloured cards which slide into a board rather like those used to display hymn numbers in church.

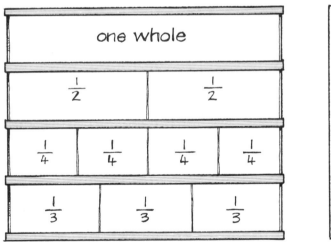
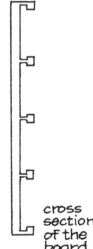

Alternatively pieces of magnetic strip are glued to the backs of the cards which are then displayed on a magnetic board. A flannel graph is another alternative.

Once the board has been made, a wide assortment of cards can be built up. Later, sets of cards showing decimal fractions, percentage fractions, etc., can be added to the collection.

A fraction board and its sets of cards, readily available in a classroom, serves as a useful 'reference' aid for children who have 'forgotten about fractions'.

## 2 Fractions of measures

The transition from shapes to measures, length in the first instance, is made by using long thin strips of paper which are easily folded into halves and quarters. With help some children may be able to fold into thirds.

Alternatively, unsegmented rods such as Cuisenaire or Colour Factor may be used to make the transition. The rods are used to show relationships which exist between a whole and a fractional part. For example:

It takes 3 red rods to 'measure' a dark green rod.

The red rod is $\frac{1}{3}$ the length of the dark green rod.

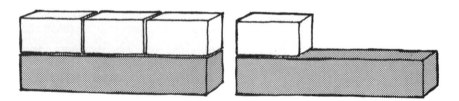

The next step uses strips of centimetre squared paper, one centimetre wide, cut to a whole number of centimetres in length. The measuring can now be done either by counting the centimetre squares or by using a ruler. This provides an opportunity for the two skills of counting and measuring to complement each other.

At this stage it is important that two methods of recording are used with the appropriate units:

$$10 \text{ cm} \div 2 = 5 \text{ cm} \qquad \frac{1}{2} \text{ of } 10 \text{ cm} = 5 \text{ cm}.$$

The narrow strip is then replaced by a straight line. The work on fractions can then be combined with practice in drawing lines to a given length:

'Draw a line 12 cm long. Divide it into quarters en measure and write the length of each quarter.'

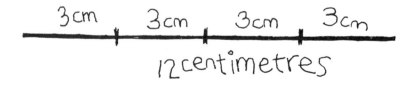

Dividing 60 minutes into halves, quarters and thirds follows as a further link between shapes and measures – in this case the shape is 'swept out' by the minute hand of a clock.

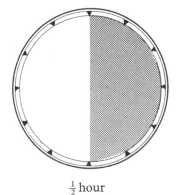 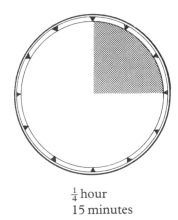 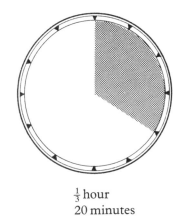

$\frac{1}{2}$ hour
30 minutes

$\frac{1}{4}$ hour
15 minutes

$\frac{1}{3}$ hour
20 minutes

The pupils' book gives further examples on weight and hours in a day but these should be supplemented by the teacher whenever other measures are being discussed.

Discussion about and the recording of units is an important preparation for the next stage. When dealing with shapes the child has been looking at a fractional part as *one piece* of paper or card. Now he is beginning to use 'one half', for example, to mean 30 minutes or 5 centimetres. This leads to the idea of *one part* being made up of a number of separate, countable objects.

10 spoonfuls or 50 ml.

5 spoonfuls or 25 ml.

5 spoonfuls or 25 ml.

### 3 Fractions from sets

The children's previous experience of dividing a set of objects into equal subsets is repeated but this time the newly learned language and notation of fractions is used to describe and record what happens. The first example in the Pupils' Book changes the emphasis from:

'Share out the dominoes equally *between four* children.'
to: 'Give each child a *quarter* of the dominoes.'

The *whole* set (in this case a *whole set* of dominoes) is divided into fractional parts, that is into equal subsets.

Again, the two methods of recording side by side are important:

$28 \div 4 = 7 \qquad \frac{1}{4}$ of $28 = 7$

From now on the number of ways of testing and practising 'tables' has increased still further. For example:

$4 \times 3 = 12 \qquad\qquad 12 \div 3 = 4 \qquad\qquad \frac{1}{3}$ of $12 = 4$
$3 \times 4 = 12 \qquad\qquad 12 \div 4 = 3 \qquad\qquad \frac{1}{4}$ of $12 = 3$

Starting with dividing a whole shape into equal parts by folding or cutting and fitting, then dividing a quantity into equal parts by measuring or counting units, the child has progressed to dividing a whole set of countable objects into equal parts or subsets. Although restricted to simple unit fractions for the time being, the child has been given experience of fractions in shape, quantity and number.

# Pages from the Pupils' Book and Spiritmasters

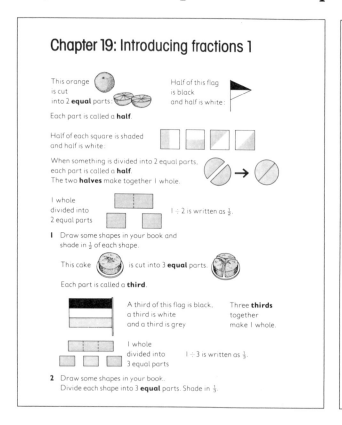

## Chapter 19: Introducing fractions 1

This orange is cut into 2 **equal** parts:

Half of this flag is black and half is white:

Each part is called a **half**.

Half of each square is shaded and half is white:

When something is divided into 2 equal parts, each part is called a **half**. The two **halves** make together 1 whole.

1 whole divided into 2 equal parts

$1 \div 2$ is written as $\frac{1}{2}$.

1 Draw some shapes in your book and shade in $\frac{1}{2}$ of each shape.

This cake is cut into 3 **equal** parts.

Each part is called a **third**.

A third of this flag is black, a third is white and a third is grey

Three **thirds** together make 1 whole.

1 whole divided into 3 equal parts

$1 \div 3$ is written as $\frac{1}{3}$.

2 Draw some shapes in your book. Divide each shape into 3 **equal** parts. Shade in $\frac{1}{3}$.

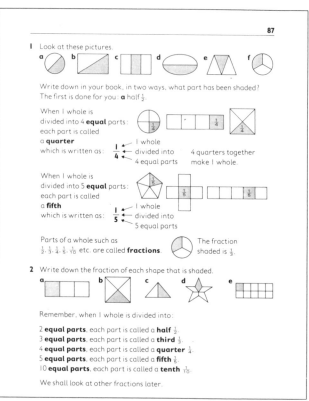

1 Look at these pictures.

a  b  c  d  e  f

Write down in your book, in two ways, what part has been shaded? The first is done for you: **a** half $\frac{1}{2}$.

When 1 whole is divided into 4 **equal** parts: each part is called a **quarter** which is written as: $\frac{1}{4}$

$\frac{1}{4}$ ← 1 whole ← divided into 4 equal parts

4 quarters together make 1 whole.

When 1 whole is divided into 5 **equal** parts: each part is called a **fifth** which is written as: $\frac{1}{5}$

$\frac{1}{5}$ ← 1 whole ← divided into 5 equal parts

Parts of a whole such as $\frac{1}{2}, \frac{1}{3}, \frac{1}{4}, \frac{1}{5}, \frac{1}{10}$ etc. are called **fractions**.

The fraction shaded is $\frac{1}{3}$.

2 Write down the fraction of each shape that is shaded.

a  b  c  d  e

Remember, when 1 whole is divided into:

2 **equal parts**, each part is called a **half** $\frac{1}{2}$.
3 **equal parts**, each part is called a **third** $\frac{1}{3}$.
4 **equal parts**, each part is called a **quarter** $\frac{1}{4}$.
5 **equal parts**, each part is called a **fifth** $\frac{1}{5}$.
10 **equal parts**, each part is called a **tenth** $\frac{1}{10}$.

We shall look at other fractions later.

---

This kite shape has been divided into 2 parts but the shaded part is **not** a half because the parts are not **equal**.

Draw another kite in your book and divide it into 2 **equal parts**, that is 2 halves.

1 **a** Use a strip of paper.

Fold it into 2 equal parts.

Open it out and colour one half.

Write half on each part. Paste it into your book.

$\frac{1}{2}$ $\frac{1}{2}$

**b** Use a strip of paper to show quarters. Colour the quarters and paste the strip in your book.

2 Here is a strip of centimetre squared paper 10 cm long.

10 cm
5 cm  5 cm

The strip has been divided into 2 equal parts. This can be written as: 10 cm $\div$ 2 = 5 cm or $\frac{1}{2}$ of 10 cm = 5 cm.

Copy and complete two number sentences for each of these pictures:

a
12 cm
4 cm

12 cm $\div$ ☐ = ☐ cm  or  ☐ of 12 cm = ☐ cm

b
12 cm
3 cm

12 cm $\div$ ☐ = ☐ cm  or  ☐ of 12 cm = ☐ cm

---

1 The length of this line is 15 cm. It is divided into 3 equal parts.

To find the length of one part we say: 15 cm $\div$ 3 = 5 cm or $\frac{1}{3}$ of 15 cm = 5 cm

Write down the two ways of finding the length of a part for:

**a** 20 cm divided into 2 equal parts

**b** 8 cm divided into 4 equal parts

**c** 24 cm divided into 2 equal parts

**d** 20 cm divided into 10 equal parts

**e** 16 cm divided into 2 equal parts

**f** 18 cm divided into 3 equal parts

**g** 35 cm divided into 5 equal parts

2 There are 60 minutes in 1 hour. Copy and complete.

**a** 60 $\div$ 2 = ☐  There are ☐ minutes in $\frac{1}{2}$ hour.

**b** 60 $\div$ 4 = ☐  There are ☐ minutes in $\frac{1}{4}$ hour.

**c** 60 $\div$ 3 = ☐  There are ☐ minutes in $\frac{1}{3}$ hour.

3 This bar of chocolate weighs 100 grams. Copy and complete.

Chocbar

**a** 100 $\div$ 2 = ☐  $\frac{1}{2}$ a bar weighs ☐ grams.

**b** 100 $\div$ 5 = ☐  $\frac{1}{5}$ a bar weighs ☐ grams.

**c** 100 $\div$ 10 = ☐  $\frac{1}{10}$ a bar weighs ☐ grams.

4 There are 24 hours in a day. Copy and complete.

**a** 24 $\div$ 2 = ☐  $\frac{1}{2}$ of a day is ☐ hours.

**b** 24 $\div$ 4 = ☐  $\frac{1}{4}$ of a day is ☐ hours.

**c** 24 $\div$ 3 = ☐  $\frac{1}{3}$ of a day is ☐ hours.

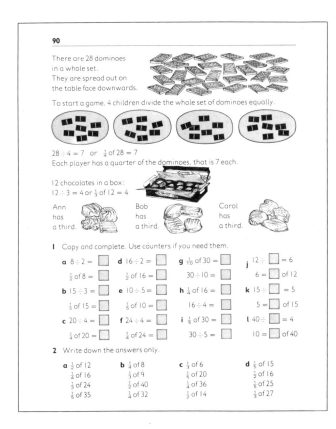

**90**

There are 28 dominoes
in a whole set.
They are spread out on
the table face downwards.

To start a game, 4 children divide the whole set of dominoes equally.

$28 \div 4 = 7$ or $\frac{1}{4}$ of $28 = 7$
Each player has a quarter of the dominoes, that is 7 each.

12 chocolates in a box :
$12 \div 3 = 4$ or $\frac{1}{3}$ of $12 = 4$

Ann has a third.  Bob has a third.  Carol has a third.

1  Copy and complete. Use counters if you need them.

**a** $8 \div 2 = \square$   **d** $16 \div 2 = \square$   **g** $\frac{1}{10}$ of $30 = \square$   **j** $12 \div \square = 6$
  $\frac{1}{2}$ of $8 = \square$    $\frac{1}{2}$ of $16 = \square$    $30 \div 10 = \square$    $6 = \square$ of $12$

**b** $15 \div 3 = \square$   **e** $10 \div 5 = \square$   **h** $\frac{1}{4}$ of $16 = \square$   **k** $15 \div \square = 5$
  $\frac{1}{3}$ of $15 = \square$    $\frac{1}{5}$ of $10 = \square$    $16 \div 4 = \square$    $5 = \square$ of $15$

**c** $20 \div 4 = \square$   **f** $24 \div 4 = \square$   **i** $\frac{1}{5}$ of $30 = \square$   **l** $40 \div \square = 4$
  $\frac{1}{4}$ of $20 = \square$    $\frac{1}{4}$ of $24 = \square$    $30 \div 5 = \square$    $10 = \square$ of $40$

2  Write down the answers only.

**a** $\frac{1}{2}$ of $12$   **b** $\frac{1}{4}$ of $8$   **c** $\frac{1}{3}$ of $6$   **d** $\frac{1}{5}$ of $15$
  $\frac{1}{4}$ of $16$    $\frac{1}{3}$ of $9$    $\frac{1}{5}$ of $20$    $\frac{1}{2}$ of $16$
  $\frac{1}{3}$ of $24$    $\frac{1}{2}$ of $40$    $\frac{1}{4}$ of $36$    $\frac{1}{5}$ of $25$
  $\frac{1}{5}$ of $35$    $\frac{1}{4}$ of $32$    $\frac{1}{2}$ of $14$    $\frac{1}{3}$ of $27$

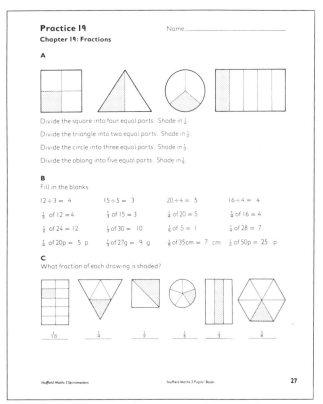

**Practice 19**                    Name

**Chapter 19: Fractions**

**A**

Divide the square into four equal parts.  Shade in $\frac{1}{4}$.
Divide the triangle into two equal parts.  Shade in $\frac{1}{2}$.
Divide the circle into three equal parts.  Shade in $\frac{1}{3}$.
Divide the oblong into five equal parts.  Shade in $\frac{1}{5}$.

**B**
Fill in the blanks.

$12 \div 3 = 4$   $15 \div 5 = 3$   $20 \div 4 = 5$   $16 \div 4 = 4$

$\frac{1}{3}$ of $12 = 4$   $\frac{1}{3}$ of $15 = 3$   $\frac{1}{4}$ of $20 = 5$   $\frac{1}{4}$ of $16 = 4$

$\frac{1}{2}$ of $24 = 12$   $\frac{1}{3}$ of $30 = 10$   $\frac{1}{5}$ of $5 = 1$   $\frac{1}{4}$ of $28 = 7$

$\frac{1}{4}$ of $20p = 5$ p   $\frac{1}{3}$ of $27g = 9$ g   $\frac{1}{5}$ of $35cm = 7$ cm   $\frac{1}{2}$ of $50p = 25$ p

**C**
What fraction of each drawing is shaded?

$\frac{1}{10}$      $\frac{1}{4}$      $\frac{1}{2}$      $\frac{1}{6}$      $\frac{1}{3}$      $\frac{1}{6}$

# References and resources

Nuffield Mathematics Teaching Project, *Computation and Structure* ⑤, Nuffield Guide, Chambers/Murray 1967. (See Introduction, page xii.)

Shuard, H. and Williams, E., *Primary Mathematics Today* (Chapters 20, 25), Longman Group Ltd 1970

*Fraction and Geometric Pieces, Pinboards*, Taskmaster

*Aspex Fractions Set 1, Comparative Fractions Strips, Magna-cel Multipurpose Display Board, Practi-metric Gummed Paper Shapes, Visi-clear Fractions Rubber Stamps, Visual Fractions Apparatus*, Philip & Tacey

# Chapter 20

# Time 2

## For the teacher

The work described in *Nuffield Maths 1 and 2 Worksheets* and *Teachers' Handbooks* has already dealt informally with the passage of time as a real, observable phenomenon. The first chapter on Time in this book concentrated on the technique of measuring time – but only in the way that, for example, length or weight can be measured. While time is a measurable dimension, it is not like the other dimensions of length, weight or capacity.

Time is seen as a continuous process which goes on in one direction and cannot be stopped or reversed. To measure it, the measuring instrument must itself move, unlike a ruler or a measuring jug, and it must move forwards. It is as if you could only measure distances upwards, and not downwards. The children can hardly be expected to understand how time differs from other dimensions. Nevertheless, they probably feel intuitively that measuring time is not the same as measuring length, even if they can't explain why. All that can reasonably be advised at this crucial stage is to introduce new ideas gradually and carefully, and to ensure that the children do not get any incorrect notions.

When they have completed this chapter children should be able to read off any time from a clock face, and to state it both in numeral form, for example '9.46', and in the traditional manner, for example, '14 minutes to 10'. Digital watch displays (12-hour) are briefly mentioned. Simple calculations of elapsed time have been extended to pods of a little more than an hour. The final section, though superficially an amusing diversion, prepares the children to cope with the often illegible and misleading faces of real clocks. (Incidentally, the comparative illegibility of digital displays using the '7-bar' array of liquid crystals and light-emitting diode devices is generally found to be much more of a problem for adults than for children, who have grown up with them.)

The problem of the hour hand's continuous movement, so that it does not point exactly at the hour numeral, is approached gradually. Many ordinary teaching clocks do not include gearing to keep the hour hand in the right position, and so they are awkward to use for demonstrations dealing with work after the first section.

A simple solution is to use the largest possible cheap alarm clock, provided that it has suitable face markings. An old wall clock could be used, if available. A smaller, perhaps broken alarm clock should be provided for the children to handle. Ideally it should have an intact glass so that they have to use the adjustment knob to turn the hands. Seeing the hour hand actually moving at one-twelfth the speed of the minute hand, and passing the hour number at every 'o'clock', will give them an intuitive understanding of the process which no verbal tuition or still picture can impart.

## Summary of the stages

1 Counting hours. Telling the time in whole numbers of hours ('o'clock')

2 Between the hours – all number notation – relation of digital displays to clock hand position – continuous movement of the hour hand

3 Time past and to the hour

4 Calculation of intervals of time, including some greater than 1 hour

5 Strange faces – a diversion introducing non-standard clock faces.

## Vocabulary

Hour hand, minute hand, o'clock, digital, past and to, half-past, quarter-past and quarter-to, slow, fast, lose, gain, Roman numerals.

## Equipment and apparatus

All clocks and watches shown to the children, except digital ones and in work connected with the last section, should have Arabic numerals and minute divisions, but preferably not second hands. Teaching clock face – wood or cardboard, no mechanism. Clock face rubber stamp (with numerals 1 to 12). Large, cheap or old clock (see For the teacher), for demonstration. Broken alarm clock (see For the teacher) for children to handle.

## Working with the children

### 1 Counting hours

The hour has already been introduced, but only as an abstract unit of measurement, and only briefly. Here it is linked to the actual time of day, and a clock with an hour hand is demonstrated.

The expression 'o'clock' is so familiar that children may not query its odd form. It is, of course, a contraction of 'of the clock'. But a clock tells any time, not just exact hours. Why reserve 'o'clock' for the hour?

The word 'clock' originally meant 'bell' (cf. French *cloche*, German *Glocke*). In a monastery, a bell would be sounded every hour. This was the task of a watchman (i.e. the watch – the origin of the use of the word for a timing device), who kept an eye on a sand hourglass. Every hour he rang the bell and turned over the glass. At some time around the beginning of the 14th century, a mechanism was invented for sounding the bell repeatedly. This 'clockwork' was driven by a falling weight on a chain. Soon some ingenious monk conceived the idea of building a smaller version of the original clockwork to measure time, and to set off the main clockwork automatically. The watch was deprived of his job – probably the first victim of automation. The earliest clocks had no dials; they were just devices which rang bells every hour.

The exercises begin by testing that the children have grasped the concept of 'o'clock'. The hour hand will, of course, be pointing directly at an hour numeral in each case. The problem of its continuous movement does not turn up until the next section. Therefore 'o'clock' times can easily be demonstrated with the mechanism-less teaching clock – but it would be a good idea if, when advancing it from, for example, 6 o'clock to 7 o'clock, you turned the minute hand right round the face as well as pushing the hour hand along to the next numeral. The children must not lose sight of the fact that both hands move even though the minute hand is always pointing straight up in the examples.

The remaining exercises explore the children's understanding of the 12-hour cycle. Make sure that they realise first that there are two lots of 12 hours in a day; and second that the hours go straight from 12 to 1 with no intervening 0. (They have already faced a similar problem with minutes.)

## 2 Between the hours

This section brings in more difficult concepts. It might seem an extra complication to introduce digital watch displays at the same time; but since the children will be familiar with, or even have, digital watches, it is important that they should link the once-a-minute jumps of the display to the continuous movement of the clock hands. The time notation used initially is all figure, i.e. '6.10', not '10 past 6', as shown by a digital watch. This links with the work on reading minutes in Time 1, Chapter 10.

The problem of the hour hand's movement has to be faced. At first four times during an hour are shown, and the hour hand is drawn in its correct position; but the fact is not mentioned till afterwards. In any case the main subject here is reading minutes. (It may be found necessary to revise earlier work on this.)

Then the children are asked to look back at the pictures and note the displacement of the hour hand. Still pictures can only show successive positions; now is the time to demonstrate continuous movement by turning on the hands of a real clock. If possible, the children should have an old broken clock to experiment with themselves.

A good idea is to show a teaching clock with the minute hand removed and the hour hand set to various positions, and to ask the children to estimate the time indicated. Real one-handed clocks are rather rare, but Londoners will be familiar with the one on Westminster Abbey. In fact, a clock of the design shown in the picture would certainly have Roman figures; but it is a harmless falsification at this stage to show Arabic ones.

It is important that the children should learn to write the '0' in, for example, 6.01, to indicate that there are no 'tens' of minutes. The subsequent exercises include examples.

## 3 Time past and to the hour

Besides being able to count minutes clockwise round the dial, it is necessary to use and understand the 'minutes to' system of indicating the time. No other dial instrument suffers from this complication. Nevertheless people do talk about minutes to the hour, and the matter cannot be avoided.

The subject is approached by way of halves and quarters of an hour, which should already be familiar. There is no logical reason why we should not say 'three-quarters past four'; it is just that people don't say it.

One of the reasons why people use the 'minutes to' system is that at a quarter to five, for example, the hour hand is nearer the 5 than the 4. This would have been much more evident on an early one-handed clock. For the same reason people say 'twenty-five to' rather than 'thirty-five past'. The half-hour mark is the dividing line between 'past' and 'to'.

Another habit which is prevalent when talking about the time is the inclusion of the word minutes for non-multiples of 5. For example, we tend to say 'ten to' but 'twelve minutes to' and 'twenty past' but 'eighteen minutes past'.

## 4 Calculation of intervals of time

In order to work out the time which has elapsed, for example, from 10 to 6 to quarter past 6, some children may need to adjust the hands of a clock face whilst counting the minutes. Others may be able to use a printed clock face and count round.

From 10 minutes to 6          to quarter past 6          is 25 minutes

## 5 Strange faces

After some quite tough work in the early sections, a little relaxation is in order. Children may be able to find examples of even odder faces than the ones illustrated.

The traditional mistake of IIII for IV on a Roman-numeral clock face is very long established. Nobody knows how it arose. The children might be interested in learning the Roman numerals from I to XX or thereabouts.

It is often difficult to distinguish between the hour and minute hands when they are the arms of a cartoon character as in the 'frog' example illustrated.

# Pages from the Pupils' Book and Spiritmasters

## Chapter 20: Time 2

### Counting hours

An ordinary clock has two hands.
The long hand measures minutes:
The short hand measures hours:

The numbers 1 to 12
on the clock face are in hours.
The hour hand goes right round
in 12 hours. There are 24 hours
in a day, so the hour hand
goes round twice a day.

When the minute hand starts at
the top of the clock face, it takes
1 hour (60 minutes) to go round
and get back to the top.
During this hour the hour hand
moves from 1 hour to the next.

When the minute hand is at the top, the hour hand points exactly
to one of the hour numbers. In the picture it points at 4.
This means that the time is 4 o'clock.

1 Look at these clock faces. Write in your book the times they show:

a   b   c   d   e   f

2 Use the clock face rubber stamp to print 4 clock faces
in your book. Draw hands to show these times:

a 7 o'clock   b 1 o'clock   c 5 o'clock   d 9 o'clock

---

Write the answers to these questions in your book.

1 How many times round the clock does the minute hand go:
 a While the hour hand moves from 12 to 5?
 b While the hour hand goes round once?
 c In one day?

2 How many days does it take the hour hand to go round four times?

3 Which times are 3 hours later than each of these:
 a 1 o'clock   b 8 o'clock   c 12 o'clock   d 10 o'clock

4 Which times are 4 hours earlier than each of these times:
 a 6 o'clock   b 4 o'clock   c 12 o'clock   d 1 o'clock

### Between the hours

The minute hand shows
how many minutes
have gone by
since the exact hour.
This clock shows that it is
10 minutes after 6 o'clock.

One way of writing
this time is 6.10.
If you have a digital
watch, it will show
the time
like this: 6:10

Here are some times later in the hour:

 6:30      6:12      6:57

Look at the hour hand in each of these pictures.
On a real clock, it moves slowly all the time,
so at 6.30 it is exactly halfway between the 6 and the 7.
At 6.57 it has almost reached the 7.
You have to be careful about this when you tell the time.

---

If the minute hand fell off
a clock, you could
still tell roughly
what time it was
by looking at the hour hand.
Clocks in the 14th century
had an hour hand only
and no minute hand.

1 Write in your book what time this old clock shows.
2 Write down the times these one-handed clocks show.

 a      b      c

You always write two figures for the minutes.
You write down the time in this way, 6.15, 6.42 and so on.
If the minutes are less than 10, you put a 0 in like this:
6.01, 6.02, 6 o'clock is written 6.00.

3 Look at these clock faces. Write in your book what times they show.

a   b   c   d   e   f

4 Print clock faces in your book with the rubber stamp.
Draw hands on them in the places where they will be
when a digital watch reads like this:

a 10:15    c 11:05    e 11:06    g 3:33
b 2:52    d 7:38    f 6:30    h 9:57

---

### Past and to

At 4.30 the time
is exactly
halfway between
4 o'clock and
5 o'clock
People say:
"It is half past 4."

At 4.15, a quarter
($\frac{1}{4}$) of the time
between 4 o'clock
and 5 o'clock
has passed.
People say:
"It is quarter past 4."

At 4.45 three quarters
($\frac{3}{4}$) of the time between
4 o'clock and 5 o'clock
has passed. There is a
quarter of an hour to go
until 5 o'clock so people
say "It is quarter to five."

Often this way of speaking about
the time is used for other times:
10 past 5, 5 past 8, 5 to 7, and so on.
All times after the o'clock and before
half past are called past. All times
after half past and before the next
o'clock are called to. You don't say,
"35 past 1". You say, "25 to 2."

1 Look at these clock faces.
Write in your book the times they show.
Write the time both ways for each, for example.
"17 minutes past 4" and "4.17" or "23 minutes to 3" and "2.37".

a   b   c   d   e   f

---

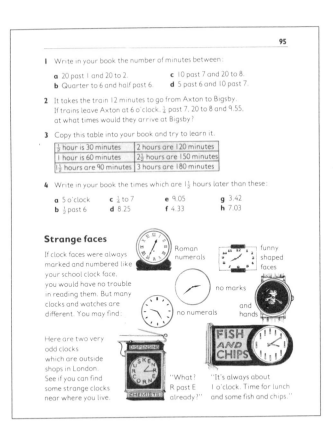

95

1  Write in your book the number of minutes between:

   **a** 20 past 1 and 20 to 2.    **c** 10 past 7 and 20 to 8.
   **b** Quarter to 6 and half past 6.    **d** 5 past 6 and 10 past 7.

2  It takes the train 12 minutes to go from Axton to Bigsby.
If trains leave Axton at 6 o'clock, $\frac{1}{2}$ past 7, 20 to 8 and 9.55,
at what times would they arrive at Bigsby?

3  Copy this table into your book and try to learn it.

| | |
|---|---|
| $\frac{1}{2}$ hour is 30 minutes | 2 hours are 120 minutes |
| 1 hour is 60 minutes | $2\frac{1}{2}$ hours are 150 minutes |
| $1\frac{1}{2}$ hours are 90 minutes | 3 hours are 180 minutes |

4  Write in your book the times which are $1\frac{1}{2}$ hours later than these:

   **a** 5 o'clock    **c** $\frac{1}{4}$ to 7    **e** 9.05    **g** 3.42
   **b** $\frac{1}{2}$ past 6    **d** 8.25    **f** 4.33    **h** 7.03

**Strange faces**

If clock faces were always
marked and numbered like
your school clock face,
you would have no trouble
in reading them. But many
clocks and watches are
different. You may find:

Roman numerals

funny shaped faces

no marks

no numerals

and hands

Here are two very
odd clocks
which are outside
shops in London.
See if you can find
some strange clocks
near where you live.

"What?
R past E
already?"

"It's always about
1 o'clock. Time for lunch
and some fish and chips."

---

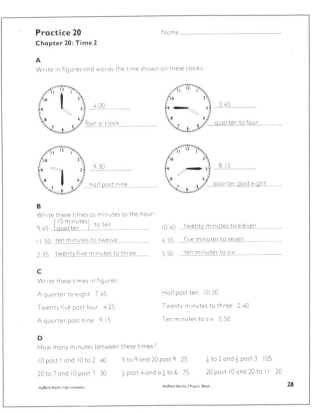

**Practice 20**        Name _____
**Chapter 20: Time 2**

**A**
Write in figures and words the time shown on these clocks.

   4.00            3.45
   four o'clock      quarter to four

   9.30            8.15
   half past nine      quarter past eight

**B**
Write these times as minutes to the hour:
     {15 minutes}
9.45 {quarter} to ten      10.40 twenty minutes to eleven

11.50 ten minutes to twelve      6.55 five minutes to seven

2.35 twenty five minutes to three      5.50 ten minutes to six

**C**
Write these times in figures:
A quarter to eight 7.45      Half past ten 10.30

Twenty five past four 4.25      Twenty minutes to three 2.40

A quarter past nine 9.15      Ten minutes to six 5.50

**D**
How many minutes between these times?
10 past 1 and 10 to 2 40   5 to 9 and 20 past 9 25   $\frac{1}{4}$ to 2 and $\frac{1}{2}$ past 3 105

20 to 7 and 10 past 7 30   $\frac{1}{2}$ past 4 and a $\frac{1}{4}$ to 6 75   20 past 10 and 20 to 11 20

    28

---

# References and resources

*Clocks*, Starters Series, Macdonald 1972

*How Much Time?*, *Times Through the Day* (stripbooks), Philip & Tacey 1970

Williams, M. E., *Come and Measure – Time*, Macmillan 1975

*Clock Face Rubber Stamp*, *Working Clock*, E. J. Arnold

*Clock Face Tracers*, Invicta Plastics

*Wooden Clock Face* (diam. 35 cm), Metric-Aids

*Rotascan Clock*, Osmiroid

*Teach-a-time Clock*, Playcraft Toys

# Division 2

## For the teacher

This chapter extends previous work done on division by emphasising the strong connection with multiplication and by introducing remainders.

## Summary of the stages

1   Division and multiplication
2   Division with remainders

## Vocabulary

Divide, division, divided by, multiplication, multiply, multiplied by, row, subsets, remainder, left over, equal hops, forward, backwards.

## Equipment and apparatus

Collections of objects such as shells, beads, marbles, buttons, counters, etc., pieces of apparatus for use with sets – hoops, cake tins, trays. Structural apparatus – rods, interlocking cubes, number lines number tracks, squared paper.

## Working with the children

### 1   Division and multiplication

The idea of division as the *inverse* of multiplication is presented to the child in the form, 'Division undoes what is done by multiplication.' It is important that activities similar to those illustrated in the Pupils' Book should be carried out using concrete objects such as counters, cubes, pegs, bottle tops, etc. These practical experiences should help children to appreciate that whereas multiplication involves the *putting together* of equal subsets, division means the splitting or *dividing up* into equal subsets.

Although the two aspects of division (sharing and repeated subtraction) present different types of practical problem, in both cases division is the inverse of multiplication.

*Sharing*

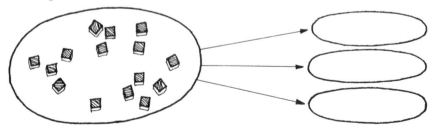

15 divided equally between 3 subsets. How many in each subset?

$15 \div 3 = \square$

3 subsets of how many make 15?

$3(\square) = 15$

*Repeated subtraction*

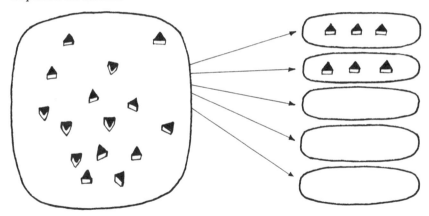

If 15 is divided into subsets
with 3 in each, how many subsets?

$15 \div 3 = \square$

How many 3's make 15?

$\square (3) = 15$

The close connection between these four number sentences is emphasised by the block of pupils' exercises which involve arranging counters in columns and rows.

$4 \times \square = 12$
$12 \div 4 = \square$
$\square \times 3 = 12$
$12 \div 3 = \square$

Further examples of division 'unpicking' what multiplication has 'knitted together' are given on the number line and by using the multiplication square. (*Nuffield Maths 3 Spiritmasters*, Grids 4 and 5.)

*Multiplication*
Starting at zero, take 3 'hops' of 6 *forward*. Where do you finish?

$6 \times 3 = \square$

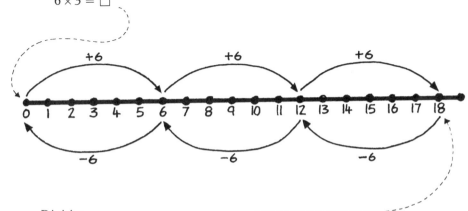

*Division*
Starting at 18,
take 'hops' of 6 *backwards*. How many hops to reach zero?

$18 \div 6 = \square$

Quotients (the answers to division problems) may also be found from the multiplication square. For multiplication, two factors are given and the square is used to find the product; for division, the product and one factor are given and the missing factor is found from the square. Division is seen as finding the missing factor in a multiplication sentence. $18 \div 3 = \square$ is interpreted as 'Three multiplied by what number equals 18?' or $3 \times \square = 18$.

| **6** | 6 | 12 | 18 | 24 | 30 | 36 |
|---|---|---|---|---|---|---|
| **5** | 5 | 10 | 15 | 20 | 25 | 30 |
| **4** | 4 | 8 | 12 | 16 | 20 | 24 |
| **③** | 3 | 6 | 9 | 12 | 15 | 18 |
| **2** | 2 | 4 | 6 | 8 | 10 | 12 |
| **1** | 1 | 2 | 3 | 4 | 5 | 6 |
| **X** | 1 | 2 | 3 | 4 | 5 | ⑥ |

Some time should be spent on the idea that in multiplication you find the product of two factors and in division you find one of the factors. Numbers may be taken from the body of the square and the related multiplication and division facts shown, perhaps by using small cards.

The solution of division problems depends so much on multiplication facts that 'knowing your tables' becomes even more important. In fact the emphasis should be on knowing tables *'inside out'* so that rather than just '5 times 4 is what?' related questions should be asked. For example:

'5 multiplied by what number equals 20?'
'How many subsets of 4 are there in 20?'
'What number of 5's equal 20?'

$6 \times 3 = 18$
$3 \times 6 = 18$
$18 \div 3 = \phantom{0}6$
$18 \div 6 = \phantom{0}3$

## 2 Division with remainders

It is essential that children's first meeting with remainders arises out of practical activities. In the case of sharing it is important to stress that there are not enough objects in the 'remainder' to go round again putting one more in each 'share'. For example:

'Can you share 14 marbles equally between 3 children?'

Each child has 4 marbles and there are 2 marbles remaining.
There are not enough marbles left to give one more to each child.
$14 \div 3 = 4$, remainder 2

For repeated subtraction or grouping the remainder must be too small to make another full group. For example:

'How many children can be given 4 sweets each from 23 sweets?'

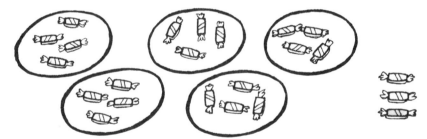

5 children receive 4 sweets each and there are 3 remaining, not enough to give 4 to another child.

$23 \div 5 = 4$, remainder 3

It is a good idea to pause in the middle of a practical activity to ask, 'Is that the remainder?' For example, when sharing 17 counters equally between 5 people, stop at this stage:

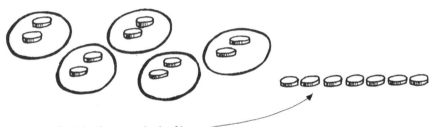

and ask, 'Is this the remainder?'

From answers such as, 'There's enough to give out one more each', the children will gradually be led to see that the remainder must always be smaller than the number they are dividing by.

When arranging counters into arrays, the counters not included in the rectangular shape show the remainder.

Arrange 23 counters in rows of 5. How many rows are there? Are there any counters left over?

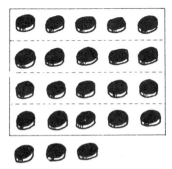

There are 4 rows of 5 and 3 counters left over.

Some children may be able to use a 'counting on in fives' technique to get as close as possible to 23 without 'going over'.

5, 10, 15, 20, . . . (25 is too big)

Four lots of 5 and 3 left over

$23 \div 5 = 4$, remainder 3

Remainders may also be illustrated by 'hopping back' on a number line. For example:

17 ÷ 5

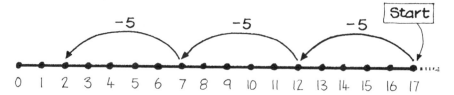

Not enough left over for another hop,
so 2 is the remainder.
17 ÷ 5 = 3, remainder 2

Exercises in the Pupil's Book show the patterns made by remainders.

◯ no remainder,  ▢ remainder 1,  △ remainder 2

Alternatively, listing the remainders not only shows the pattern but emphasises again that remainders are always less than the divisor (the number you are dividing by). For example:

Divide these numbers by 3 and underneath each write the remainder.

| 9 | 10 | 11 | 12 | 13 | 14 | 15 | 16 | 17 | 18 | 19 |
|---|----|----|----|----|----|----|----|----|----|----|
| 0 | 1  | 2  | 0  | 1  | 2  | 0  | 1  | 2  | 0  | 1  |

Divide these numbers by 5 and underneath each write the remainder.

| 10 | 11 | 12 | 13 | 14 | 15 | 16 | 17 | 18 | 19 | 20 |
|----|----|----|----|----|----|----|----|----|----|----|
| 0  | 1  | 2  | 3  | 4  | 0  | 1  | 2  | 3  | 4  | 0  |

# Pages from the Pupils' Book and Spiritmasters

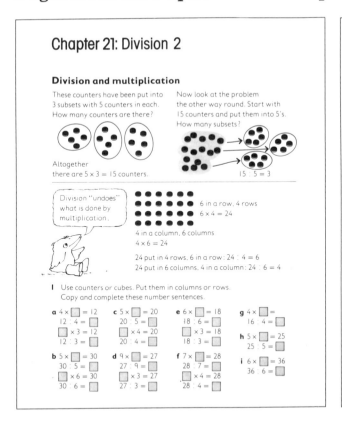

## Chapter 21: Division 2

### Division and multiplication

These counters have been put into 3 subsets with 5 counters in each. How many counters are there?

Now look at the problem the other way round. Start with 15 counters and put them into 5's. How many subsets?

Altogether there are 5 × 3 = 15 counters.

15 ÷ 5 = 3

Division "undoes" what is done by multiplication.

6 in a row, 4 rows
6 × 4 = 24

4 in a column, 6 columns
4 × 6 = 24

24 put in 4 rows, 6 in a row: 24 ÷ 4 = 6
24 put in 6 columns, 4 in a column: 24 ÷ 6 = 4

I  Use counters or cubes. Put them in columns or rows. Copy and complete these number sentences.

a  4 × ☐ = 12
12 ÷ 4 = ☐
☐ × 3 = 12
12 ÷ 3 = ☐

b  5 × ☐ = 30
30 ÷ 5 = ☐
☐ × 6 = 30
30 ÷ 6 = ☐

c  5 × ☐ = 20
20 ÷ 5 = ☐
☐ × 4 = 20
20 ÷ 4 = ☐

d  9 × ☐ = 27
27 ÷ 9 = ☐
☐ × 3 = 27
27 ÷ 3 = ☐

e  6 × ☐ = 18
18 ÷ 6 = ☐
☐ × 3 = 18
18 ÷ 3 = ☐

f  7 × ☐ = 28
28 ÷ 7 = ☐
☐ × 4 = 28
28 ÷ 4 = ☐

g  4 × ☐ =
16 ÷ 4 = ☐

h  5 × ☐ = 25
25 ÷ 5 = ☐

i  6 × ☐ = 36
36 ÷ 6 = ☐

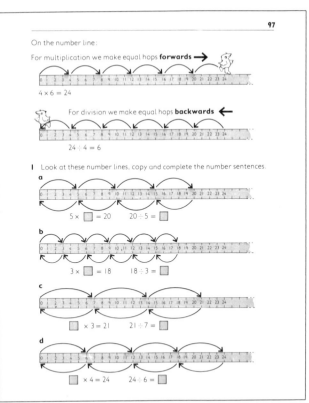

On the number line:

For multiplication we make equal hops **forwards** →

4 × 6 = 24

For division we make equal hops **backwards** ←

24 ÷ 4 = 6

I  Look at these number lines, copy and complete the number sentences.

a
5 × ☐ = 20      20 ÷ 5 = ☐

b
3 × ☐ = 18      18 ÷ 3 = ☐

c
☐ × 3 = 21      21 ÷ 7 = ☐

d
☐ × 4 = 24      24 ÷ 6 = ☐

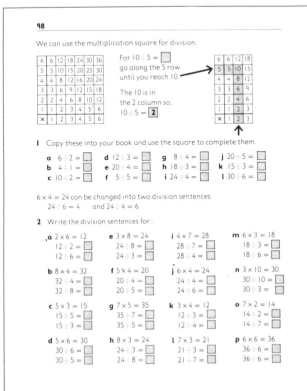

We can use the multiplication square for division.

| 6 | 6 | 12 | 18 | 24 | 30 | 36 |
| 5 | 5 | 10 | 15 | 20 | 25 | 30 |
| 4 | 4 | 8 | 12 | 16 | 20 | 24 |
| 3 | 3 | 6 | 9 | 12 | 15 | 18 |
| 2 | 2 | 4 | 6 | 8 | 10 | 12 |
| 1 | 1 | 2 | 3 | 4 | 5 | 6 |
| × | 1 | 2 | 3 | 4 | 5 | 6 |

For 10 ÷ 5 = ☐
go along the 5 row until you reach 10.

The 10 is in the 2 column so, 10 ÷ 5 = **2**.

I  Copy these into your book and use the square to complete them.

a  6 ÷ 2 = ☐
b  4 ÷ 1 = ☐
c  10 ÷ 2 = ☐

d  12 ÷ 3 = ☐
e  20 ÷ 4 = ☐
f  5 ÷ 5 = ☐

g  8 ÷ 4 = ☐
h  18 ÷ 3 = ☐
i  24 ÷ 4 = ☐

j  20 ÷ 5 = ☐
k  15 ÷ 3 = ☐
l  30 ÷ 6 = ☐

6 × 4 = 24 can be changed into two division sentences.
24 ÷ 6 = 4    and   24 ÷ 4 = 6

2  Write the division sentences for:

a  2 × 6 = 12
12 ÷ 2 = ☐
12 ÷ 6 = ☐

b  8 × 4 = 32
32 ÷ 4 = ☐
32 ÷ 8 = ☐

c  5 × 3 = 15
15 ÷ 5 = ☐
15 ÷ 3 = ☐

d  5 × 6 = 30
30 ÷ 6 = ☐
30 ÷ 5 = ☐

e  3 × 8 = 24
24 ÷ 8 = ☐
24 ÷ 3 = ☐

f  5 × 4 = 20
20 ÷ 4 = ☐
20 ÷ 5 = ☐

g  7 × 5 = 35
35 ÷ 7 = ☐
35 ÷ 5 = ☐

h  8 × 3 = 24
24 ÷ 3 = ☐
24 ÷ 8 = ☐

i  4 × 7 = 28
28 ÷ 7 = ☐
28 ÷ 4 = ☐

j  6 × 4 = 24
24 ÷ 4 = ☐
24 ÷ 6 = ☐

k  3 × 4 = 12
12 ÷ 3 = ☐
12 ÷ 4 = ☐

l  7 × 3 = 21
21 ÷ 3 = ☐
21 ÷ 7 = ☐

m  6 × 3 = 18
18 ÷ 3 = ☐
18 ÷ 6 = ☐

n  3 × 10 = 30
30 ÷ 10 = ☐
30 ÷ 3 = ☐

o  7 × 2 = 14
14 ÷ 2 = ☐
14 ÷ 7 = ☐

p  6 × 6 = 36
36 ÷ 6 = ☐
36 ÷ 6 = ☐

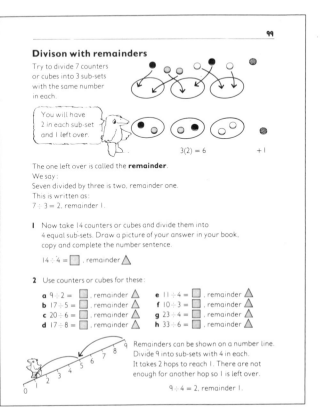

### Divison with remainders

Try to divide 7 counters or cubes into 3 sub-sets with the same number in each.

You will have 2 in each sub-set and 1 left over.

3(2) = 6         + 1

The one left over is called the **remainder**.
We say:
Seven divided by three is two, remainder one.
This is written as:
7 ÷ 3 = 2, remainder 1.

I  Now take 14 counters or cubes and divide them into 4 equal sub-sets. Draw a picture of your answer in your book, copy and complete the number sentence.

14 ÷ 4 = ☐ , remainder △

2  Use counters or cubes for these:

a  9 ÷ 2 = ☐ , remainder △
b  17 ÷ 5 = ☐ , remainder △
c  20 ÷ 6 = ☐ , remainder △
d  17 ÷ 8 = ☐ , remainder △

e  11 ÷ 4 = ☐ , remainder △
f  10 ÷ 3 = ☐ , remainder △
g  23 ÷ 4 = ☐ , remainder △
h  33 ÷ 6 = ☐ , remainder △

Remainders can be shown on a number line.
Divide 9 into sub-sets with 4 in each.
It takes 2 hops to reach 1. There are not enough for another hop so 1 is left over.

9 ÷ 4 = 2, remainder 1.

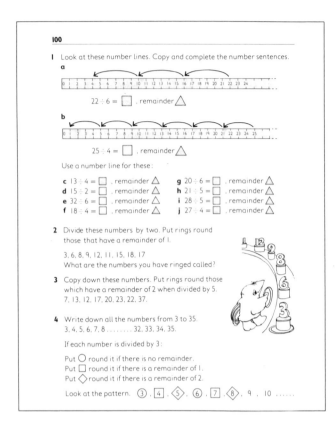

**100**

I Look at these number lines. Copy and complete the number sentences.

a

$22 \div 6 = \square$ , remainder $\triangle$

b

$25 \div 4 = \square$ , remainder $\triangle$

Use a number line for these:

c $13 \div 4 = \square$ , remainder $\triangle$   g $20 \div 6 = \square$ , remainder $\triangle$
d $15 \div 2 = \square$ , remainder $\triangle$   h $21 \div 5 = \square$ , remainder $\triangle$
e $32 \div 6 = \square$ , remainder $\triangle$   i $28 \div 5 = \square$ , remainder $\triangle$
f $18 \div 4 = \square$ , remainder $\triangle$   j $27 \div 4 = \square$ , remainder $\triangle$

2 Divide these numbers by two. Put rings round those that have a remainder of 1.

3, 6, 8, 9, 12, 11, 15, 18, 17
What are the numbers you have ringed called?

3 Copy down these numbers. Put rings round those which have a remainder of 2 when divided by 5.
7, 13, 12, 17, 20, 23, 22, 37.

4 Write down all the numbers from 3 to 35.
3, 4, 5, 6, 7, 8 . . . . . . . 32, 33, 34, 35.

If each number is divided by 3:

Put ◯ round it if there is no remainder.
Put ▢ round it if there is a remainder of 1.
Put ◇ round it if there is a remainder of 2.

Look at the pattern. ③ , ④ , ◇5 , ⑥ , ⑦ , ◇8 , 9 , 10 . . . . . .

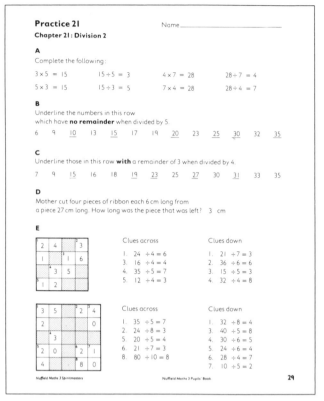

**Practice 21**                           Name_____

**Chapter 21 : Division 2**

**A**
Complete the following :

$3 \times 5 = 15$      $15 \div 5 = 3$      $4 \times 7 = 28$      $28 \div 7 = 4$
$5 \times 3 = 15$      $15 \div 3 = 5$      $7 \times 4 = 28$      $28 \div 4 = 7$

**B**
Underline the numbers in this row
which have **no remainder** when divided by 5.

6    9    <u>10</u>    13    <u>15</u>    17    19    <u>20</u>    23    <u>25</u>    <u>30</u>    32    <u>35</u>

**C**
Underline those in this row **with** a remainder of 3 when divided by 4.

7    9    <u>15</u>    16    18    <u>19</u>    <u>23</u>    25    <u>27</u>    30    <u>31</u>    33    35

**D**
Mother cut four pieces of ribbon each 6 cm long from
a piece 27 cm long. How long was the piece that was left?    3 cm

**E**

| Clues across | Clues down |
|---|---|
| 1.  24 ÷ 4 = 6 | 1.  21 ÷ 7 = 3 |
| 3.  16 ÷ 4 = 4 | 2.  36 ÷ 6 = 6 |
| 4.  35 ÷ 5 = 7 | 3.  15 ÷ 5 = 3 |
| 5.  12 ÷ 4 = 3 | 4.  32 ÷ 4 = 8 |

| Clues across | Clues down |
|---|---|
| 1.  35 ÷ 5 = 7 | 1.  32 ÷ 8 = 4 |
| 2.  24 ÷ 8 = 3 | 3.  40 ÷ 5 = 8 |
| 5.  20 ÷ 5 = 4 | 4.  30 ÷ 6 = 5 |
| 6.  21 ÷ 7 = 3 | 5.  24 ÷ 6 = 4 |
| 8.  80 ÷ 10 = 8 | 6.  28 ÷ 4 = 7 |
| | 7.  10 ÷ 5 = 2 |

*Nuffield Maths 3 Spiritmasters*                           *Nuffield Maths 3 Pupils' Book*                           **29**

# References and resources

Shuard, H. and Williams, E., *Primary Mathematics Today* (Chapter 17), Longman Group Ltd 1970

*Multilink Number Track, Stern Number Track*, E.S.A.

*Number Strips and Rods*, Invicta Plastics

*Centicube Number Track (Metline)*, Osmiroid

*Unifix Multiplication/Division Markers*, Philip & Tacey

# Chapter 22

# Weight 2

## For the teacher

The aim of this chapter is to widen the child's experience of weight as much as possible. This might be a good point at which to remind children of the need for a standard unit of weight by looking briefly at the history of weighing.

Because it changes very little, a grain of wheat was chosen as a standard by early man. The Egyptians used clay weights which balanced 1000 grains of wheat.

The Romans brought their standard weights to Britain 2000 years ago. They used a weight called the 'Libra' – a word linked with the balance as in the Zodiac sign. Libra also meant 'pound' and was used for both weight and money. The abbreviation 'lb' '£' for the pound in weight and the £ sign in money are both derived from the word 'Libra'.

After the Romans left Britain people no longer bothered about standard weights and arguments arose about the different weights used. Many people were cheated. In the reign of Elizabeth I a law was passed fixing the standard pound as the weight of 7000 grains of wheat. Inspectors travelled around Britain, as they do today, to inspect the weights being used.

Further details about the history of weighing can be found in a series of booklets called *The Story of Measurement* by Thyra Smith (Basil Blackwell 1954) or in *Romance in Arithmetic* by M. E. Bowman (University of London Press 1950).

Also included in the chapter is experience in dealing with a variety of weights, with particular sections on the hecto (hectogram, or 100 gram unit) and on smaller units.

## Summary of the stages

1  The hecto (100 g) weight

2  The hecto as part of the kilogram

3  Using hecto weights

4  Using kilogram weights – weighing people

5  Using smaller weights – less than 100 g

## Vocabulary

Weight, heavy, heavier, light, lighter, comparing, estimate, materials, more, less, than, standard measure, kilogram, hecto.

## Equipment and apparatus

Balances and scales – various types, including bathroom scales. Materials for weighing: marbles, pencils, crayons, sweets, shells, rulers, pebbles, potatoes, counters, modelling clay, rice, dried peas, sand, sawdust, bottle tops, sheets of paper and miscellaneous classroom objects.
Weights: 1 kg, 500 g, 200 g, 100 g (plenty of these), 50 g, 20 g, 10 g.

# Working with the children

### 1 The hecto (100 g) weight

By this stage the child should have had a fair amount of experience in handling the 1 kg and 500 g weights. Since the kilogram is one of the official standard measuring weights laid down by the Metrication Board, it would now seem logical to deal with another standard measure, the gram; but unfortunately it is far too small for young children to handle in practice. Another problem, as already mentioned in Weight 1, is that 1000 grams make up the kilogram; and for many children at this stage of their development full understanding of what a thousand is made up of is still difficult.

If the 100 g weight had originally been recognised as a unit of measure within the Metric System, this problem would not have occurred. A compromise is clearly needed here; and in fact the problem has already been solved by Italian shopkeepers who weigh out goods by the 'etto' (hectogram). A suitable English name for this 100 g 'unit' would be 'hecto' as suggested by E. Williams and H. Shuard in *Primary Mathematics Today* (Longman Group Ltd), 100 g weights are readily available, have a good 'feelable' heaviness, and, since there are only ten to the kilogram, do not make large demands on either the child's counting ability or the school's equipment budget.

Since the child will think of, say, 700 g as 7 hectos, there will not be too much difficulty later on in making the verbal transition from 'seven hectos' to 'seven hundred grammes'. (In fact, in a few years the hecto under some name or other may well be a reality in British shops.)

The use of parts of a hundred, for example, 750 g, is avoided completely to begin with.

Some children will simply use the hecto weight as a unit in itself, while others will be able to realise that the weight represents $100 \times 1$ g. Work on the parts of 100 g will be dealt with later in the chapter. In the meantime the exercises are mainly concerned with developing the experience of handling the hecto weight in comparison with everyday articles, which should be made available for the children to use. The terms hecto and 100 g are freely interchanged in the text to assist children to grasp the concept of the gram – and the weights they will be handling are marked '100 g' anyway.

### 2 The hecto as part of the kilogram

The hecto weight should by now be established as a temporary unit. It is important that the child sees the relationship between 100 g and 1 kg.

Before starting this section children should be familiar with simple fractions and know what a half or a tenth is. (A quarter is avoided here because it splits the hecto.) In some cases it may be necessary to remind the children that when a whole is divided into ten equal parts, for example, each part is called a tenth.

Most children enjoy counting in hundreds, as they enjoy counting in tens. It is an important part of weighing ability to know that, for example, eight lots of 100 g can be called 800 g – although there may be some children who still cannot count in 'ones' up to 800.

### 3 Using hecto weights

The balance should now be used to give the child experience in using 100 g weights. Many recipe books give weights in grams, and a recipe has been included to add reality to weighing.

The table on page 5 of the Pupils' Book is intended to encourage the child to identify objects which may fall within a certain range, for example, 100 g–200 g, or 600 g–700 g. This activity will force the child into estimating – simply to save the time and effort of weighing objects that he knows will not fall within the range that he is working on. The idea is for the child to find up to three or four objects for each range, and to work numerically through the ranges, starting with 'under 100 g'. Where there are a lot of children working on this activity some of them could work the other way, starting at 900–1 kg and work down to 'under 100 g'. This will prevent them from all trying to use the same objects. *Nuffield Maths 3 Spiritmasters*, Grid 15.

An obvious point of class organisation is for the teacher to make available a good selection of objects: at least 30–40 equally distributed throughout the ranges.

In order to check if children are able to match, discriminate between and order weights, the following 'mystery parcel' activities are useful:
1  Make a set of five parcels which look identical but which weigh 1 kilogram, 700 g, 500 g, 200 g and 100 g respectively. On each parcel mark its weight in both grams and hectos. Make a similar unmarked set. Ask the child to pair the parcels according to their weight.
2  Take away the marked set. Mix up the unmarked set. Ask the child to put them in order of weight, starting with the heaviest.
3   Mix them up again. Add two more parcels which look the same as the others, one of which weighs more than 1 kilogram and one which weighs less than 100 g. Ask the child to pick out the parcel which weighs 1 kilogram, the one which weighs 500 g and the one which weighs 100 g.

### 4   Using kilograms – weighing people
It is well to intermix the experiences associated with the use of grams with those associated with the use of kilograms. It is important for children to realise that grams are normally used for weighing lighter objects and kilograms for heavier objects. This simple fact only becomes concrete in the child's mind through experiencing both units side by side, and gradually developing a link between them.

It should be noted that reading the weight on a pair of bathroom scales is not an easy thing to do. The skill is dealt with later in the series in more detail. For the purposes of this activity some children may need a considerable amount of help from the teacher. *Nuffield Maths 3 Spiritmasters*, Grid 14.

### 5   Using smaller weights – less than 100 g
We now return to handling smaller weights: those making up 100 g. A link can be made here with the development of number work – counting in tens. When dealing with money we often ask children to tell us ways of making up 80p – in other words how to make full use of coins that are available. A similar skill is necessary for handling weights, and an exercise has been included for this purpose.

The second exercise is intended to give experience in handling smaller weights at the same time as an appreciation of their size. The weights are used to weigh commonplace materials, which should be available for the children to use.

# Pages from the Pupils' Book and Spiritmasters

---

## Chapter 22: Weight 2

101

### The handy "hecto"

Suppose you wanted to buy
four apples. They would weigh much
less than 1 kg and much more than 1 g.
These weights are just not a handy size.
People in Italy know what to do.
They use an inbetween weight of 100 g.
That is about the weight of one apple.
The weight's real name is "hectogram" –
that only means "100 g". The Italians
call it "etto" for short, they can't
say "h". We will call it "hecto".

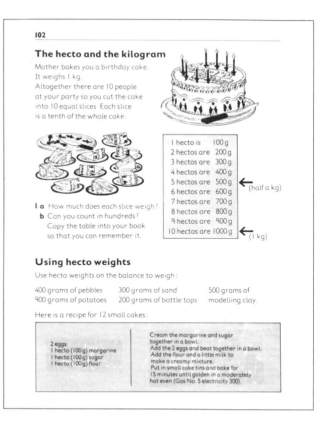

1  Pick up a "hecto" weight. Get the feel of it.
  **a** Estimate how many marbles weigh 1 hecto (100 g). Then estimate
    how many pencils, crayons, sweets, rulers, pebbles weigh 100 g.

  **b** Use a balance and a hecto weight to see how close your estimates are.
    Record in your book:
    ☐ marbles balance 1 hecto (100 g), and so on.
    ☐ marbles ☐ pencils ☐ crayons ☐ sweets ☐ rulers ☐ pebbles

2  Take a piece of modelling clay and roll it into a ball
  that you think will weigh 100 g. Check with your hecto weight on
  the balance. If the ball is less than 100 g add some clay
  till it balances. If it is more, take some away.

3  Use an eggcup as a measure for
  rice, dried peas, sand and sawdust.
  Find how many eggcupfuls of each
  weigh a hecto. Record like this:
  ☐ eggcupfuls of rice balance 1 hecto.

  **a** eggcupfuls of rice   **b** eggcupfuls of sand   **c** eggcupfuls of sawdust

---

102

### The hecto and the kilogram

Mother bakes you a birthday cake.
It weighs 1 kg.
Altogether there are 10 people
at your party so you cut the cake
into 10 equal slices. Each slice
is a tenth of the whole cake.

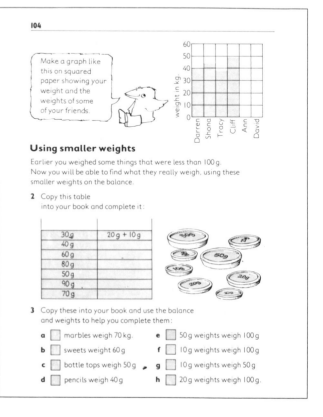

1 **a** How much does each slice weigh?
  **b** Can you count in hundreds?
    Copy the table into your book
    so that you can remember it.

| | |
|---|---|
| 1 hecto is | 100 g |
| 2 hectos are | 200 g |
| 3 hectos are | 300 g |
| 4 hectos are | 400 g |
| 5 hectos are | 500 g ← (half a kg) |
| 6 hectos are | 600 g |
| 7 hectos are | 700 g |
| 8 hectos are | 800 g |
| 9 hectos are | 900 g |
| 10 hectos are | 1000 g ← (1 kg) |

### Using hecto weights

Use hecto weights on the balance to weigh:

400 grams of pebbles   300 grams of sand   500 grams of
900 grams of potatoes   200 grams of bottle tops   modelling clay.

Here is a recipe for 12 small cakes:

| | |
|---|---|
| 2 eggs<br>1 hecto (100 g) margarine<br>1 hecto (100 g) sugar<br>1 hecto (100 g) flour | Cream the margarine and sugar<br>together in a bowl.<br>Add the 2 eggs and beat together in a bowl.<br>Add the flour and a little milk to<br>make a creamy mixture.<br>Put in small cake tins and bake for<br>15 minutes until golden in a moderately<br>hot even (Gas No. 5 electricity 300). |

---

103

1  Find at least 20 different objects.
  Pick each one up and estimate what it weighs.
  Now use the balance and hecto weights to find
  if your estimate was right.
  Make a chart in your book like this to record your findings.
  Remember – always estimate before weighing.

| | object | |
|---|---|---|
| weight | estimate | using balance |
| less than 100 g | rubber, pencil | rubber, pencil |
| 100 to 200 g | | |
| 200 to 300 g | maths book | |
| 300 to 400 g | | maths book |
| 400 to 500 g | | |
| 500 to 600 g | | |
| 700 to 800 g | | |
| 800 to 900 g | | |
| 900 to 1 kg | | |
| over 1 kg | | |

In this example, the weight of the maths book was
estimated as more than 1 hecto but less than 2 hectos,
that is, between 200 g and 300 g.
On the balance, it weighed between 300 g and 400 g.

### Weighing people

We use kilograms
to weigh people.
A pair of bathroom scales
shows the weight in
kilograms on the dial like this:

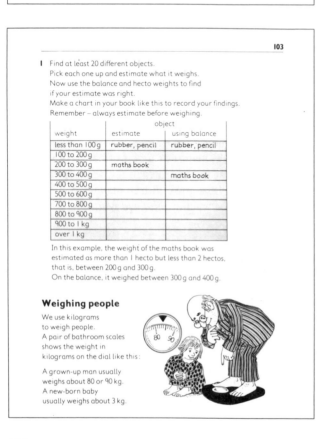

A grown-up man usually
weighs about 80 or 90 kg.
A new-born baby
usually weighs about 3 kg.

---

104

Make a graph like
this on squared
paper showing your
weight and the
weights of some
of your friends.

(graph: weight in kg, axis 0 to 60; Darren, Shona, Tracy, Cliff, Ann, David)

### Using smaller weights

Earlier you weighed some things that were less than 100 g.
Now you will be able to find what they really weigh, using these
smaller weights on the balance.

2  Copy this table
  into your book and complete it:

| | |
|---|---|
| 30 g | 20 g + 10 g |
| 40 g | |
| 60 g | |
| 80 g | |
| 50 g | |
| 90 g | |
| 70 g | |

3  Copy these into your book and use the balance
  and weights to help you complete them:

  **a** ☐ marbles weigh 70 kg.    **e** ☐ 50 g weights weigh 100 g
  **b** ☐ sweets weight 60 g    **f** ☐ 10 g weights weigh 100 g
  **c** ☐ bottle tops weigh 50 g    **g** ☐ 10 g weights weigh 50 g
  **d** ☐ pencils weigh 40 g    **h** ☐ 20 g weights weigh 100 g

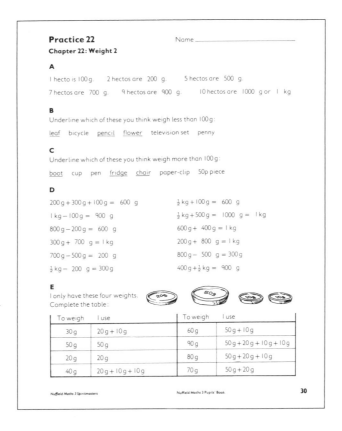

**Practice 22**                          Name _____

**Chapter 22: Weight 2**

**A**

1 hecto is 100 g.    2 hectos are 200 g.    5 hectos are 500 g.

7 hectos are 700 g.    9 hectos are 900 g.    10 hectos are 1000 g or 1 kg

**B**

Underline which of these you think weigh less than 100 g:

<u>leaf</u>   bicycle   <u>pencil</u>   <u>flower</u>   television set   penny

**C**

Underline which of these you think weigh more than 100 g:

<u>boot</u>   cup   pen   <u>fridge</u>   <u>chair</u>   paper-clip   50p piece

**D**

| | |
|---|---|
| 200 g + 300 g + 100 g = 600 g | ½ kg + 100 g = 600 g |
| 1 kg − 100 g = 900 g | ½ kg + 500 g = 1000 g = 1 kg |
| 800 g − 200 g = 600 g | 600 g + 400 g = 1 kg |
| 300 g + 700 g = 1 kg | 200 g + 800 g = 1 kg |
| 700 g − 500 g = 200 g | 800 g − 500 g = 300 g |
| ½ kg − 200 g = 300 g | 400 g + ½ kg = 900 g |

**E**

I only have these four weights.
Complete the table:

| To weigh | I use | To weigh | I use |
|---|---|---|---|
| 30 g | 20 g + 10 g | 60 g | 50 g + 10 g |
| 50 g | 50 g | 90 g | 50 g + 20 g + 10 g + 10 g |
| 20 g | 20 g | 80 g | 50 g + 20 g + 10 g |
| 40 g | 20 g + 10 g + 10 g | 70 g | 50 g + 20 g |

*Nuffield Maths 3 Spiritmasters*          *Nuffield Maths 3 Pupils' Book*          **30**

# References and resources

Chaplin, S., *Bakery* (Teaching 5 to 13 Projects), Macdonald 1974

Nuffield Mathematics Teaching Project, *Beginnings* ▽, Nuffield Guide, Chambers/Murray 1967. (See Introduction, page xii.)

Shuard, H. and Williams, E., *Primary Mathematics Today* (Chapter 5), Longman Group Ltd 1970

*Adjusted Metric Weights, Bucket Balance, Compression Scale* (10 kg), *Cylindrical Weights, Flat Pan Scale* (5 kg), *Plastic Simple Balance, Simple Balance,* E. J. Arnold

*Primary Balance* (with buckets or pans), E.S.A.

*Rocker Scales, Simple Scales, Weights Board* (age 6–12), Invicta Plastics

*Compression Scales* (5 kg), *Metric Weights Set, Simple Scales,* Metric-Aids

*100 g Board, Analysis of a Kilogram, Bucket Balance, Compression Scales* (10 kg), *Equal Pan Balance, Personal Scales, Weighing Set,* Nicolas Burdett

*Super Beamer Balance,* Osmiroid

*Set of Iron Masses: Lead Adjusted,* Philip & Tacey

*Circular Steel Weights, Hexagonal Iron Weights, Personal Scales, Stowaway Scales,* Taskmaster

# Chapter 23

# Area

## For the teacher

In *Vision in Elementary Mathematics*, W. W. Sawyer has this to say on the subject of area:

> '. . . It seems to take children a long time to distinguish between *area* and the *distance round* some region. . . . It seems necessary to emphasise this distinction, perhaps by having children actually pasting square pieces of paper over the region for which the area has been asked. Every time the word or idea of area is involved, it is well to make some reference to pasting paper squares or to covering the floor, or to some similar illustration that will make it clear which concept we have in mind. Anyone without classroom experience may be suprised how long it takes some children (even the clever ones) to fix this distinction.'

The confusion between area (the amount of surface) and perimeter (distance round a region) is nearly always due to inadequate preparation in the early stages. In the past, most children responded to the word 'area' by saying 'length times breadth' irrespective of the shape being considered. The slick formula $A = L \times B$ is completely divorced from the idea of covering a surface.

This chapter concentrates on the idea of covering a surface with suitable shapes or 'tiles' which fit together without gaps between them. The 'tiles' can then be counted to give a simple measure of area.

## Summary of the stages

1  Comparing surfaces

2  Which shapes cover best?

3  Area by counting squares

## Vocabulary

Surface, area, compare, cover, triangle, square, hexagon, circle, pentagon, overlap, fit together, gaps, spaces, tiles.

## Working with the children

### 1  Comparing surfaces
Surfaces which are of the same shape can be compared simply by placing one on top of the other.

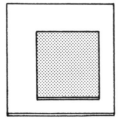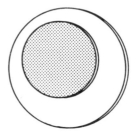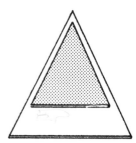

When comparing the *amount of surface* or *area* of dissimilar shapes, however, this does not always work:

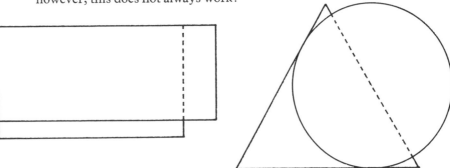

To reduce the possibility of overlapping, the first 'covering units' used are matchboxes all the same size. The next step involves using slightly thinner units such as exercise books, again all the same size, and the children are asked to estimate first. If plastic tiles are available these could be used as 'covering units'.

It takes 9 triangles to cover the flag.

Post cards, picture cards or playing cards also make good 'tiles'. The rounded corners of the latter did not appear to bother the little girl who said, 'Well, if they had pointed corners, they'd still fit.'

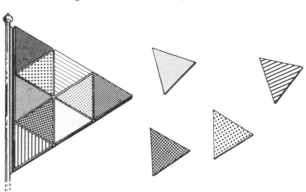

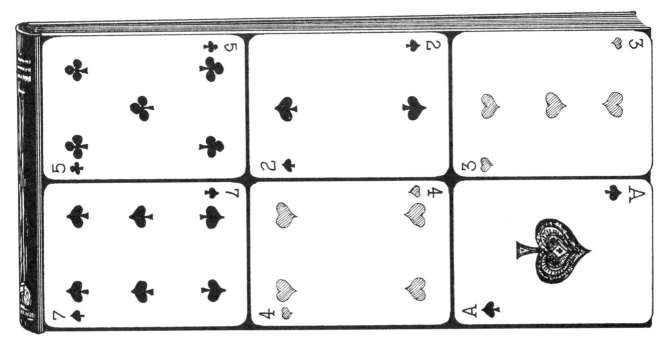

## 2 Which shapes cover best?

Some children may be meeting the idea of fitting two-dimensional shapes without gaps between them for the first time; others will have had some previous experience (*Nuffield Maths 2 Teachers' Handbook*, page 91). In either case, sets of 'tiles' all the same shape and size – for example, a set of squares, a set of triangles, a set of hexagons, etc. – should be provided so that children can experiment for themselves.

Children should also be encouraged to look for examples of shapes in the environment which fit together without gaps, that is shapes which *tessellate* (from the Latin word *tessella*, a tile).

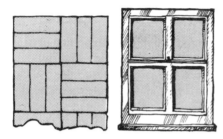 

The exercises provide opportunities for comparing the areas of pairs of shapes by counting 'unit tiles' – triangles or rectangles or hexagons, etc.

## 3 Area by counting squares

The experience gained from tiling or tessellation is an important stage leading to measurement of area. In the same way that the measurement of length is dependent upon the fact that units of length placed end to end on a line make an aggregate or total length, so the measurement of area is dependent upon the fact that units of area, when tessellated, make an aggregate or total area.

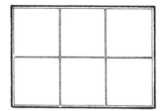

6 units of area

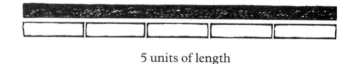

5 units of length

The exercises involve counting squares to find the area of shapes, drawing shapes of a given area on squared paper and comparing the areas of pairs of shapes. The unit of area is called a 'square'. Standard units such as square centimetres ($cm^2$) and square metres ($m^2$) are not introduced at this stage.

These activities are structured to emphasise the idea of covering or 'tiling' a surface, so the examples are designed to make use of whole units only. Some children, however, may be able to progress to using paper 'tiles' which can be cut in order to complete the covering of slightly more complicated shapes:

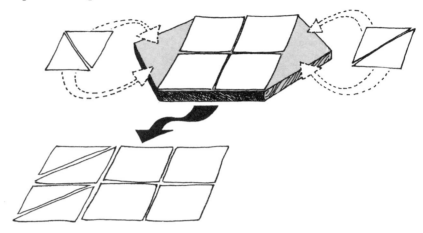

# Pages from the Pupils' Book

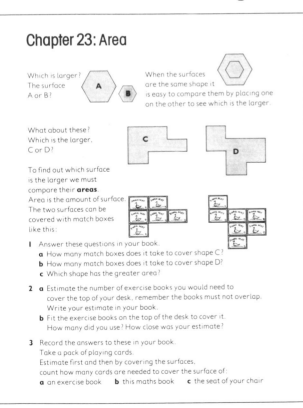

## Chapter 23: Area

Which is larger?
The surface
A or B?

When the surfaces
are the same shape it
is easy to compare them by placing one
on the other to see which is the larger.

What about these?
Which is the larger,
C or D?

To find out which surface
is the larger we must
compare their **areas**.
Area is the amount of surface.
The two surfaces can be
covered with match boxes
like this:

1 Answer these questions in your book.
   **a** How many match boxes does it take to cover shape C?
   **b** How many match boxes does it take to cover shape D?
   **c** Which shape has the greater area?

2 **a** Estimate the number of exercise books you would need to
      cover the top of your desk, remember the books must not overlap.
      Write your estimate in your book.
   **b** Fit the exercise books on the top of the desk to cover it.
      How many did you use? How close was your estimate?

3 Record the answers to these in your book.
   Take a pack of playing cards.
   Estimate first and then by covering the surfaces,
   count how many cards are needed to cover the surface of:
   **a** an exercise book   **b** this maths book   **c** the seat of your chair

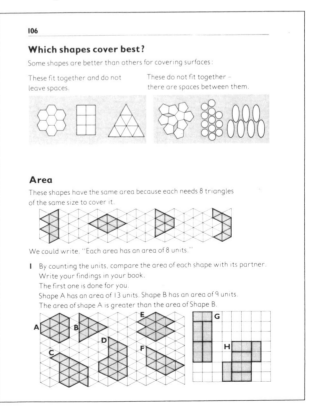

106

## Which shapes cover best?

Some shapes are better than others for covering surfaces:

These fit together and do not
leave spaces.

These do not fit together –
there are spaces between them.

## Area

These shapes have the same area because each needs 8 triangles
of the same size to cover it.

We could write, "Each area has an area of 8 units."

1 By counting the units, compare the area of each shape with its partner.
   Write your findings in your book.
   The first one is done for you.
   Shape A has an area of 13 units. Shape B has an area of 9 units.
   The area of shape A is greater than the area of Shape B.

## Area by counting squares

The tiles on bathroom walls or lino tiles on the floor are usually square. It is easier to cover most surfaces with squares than with any other shape.

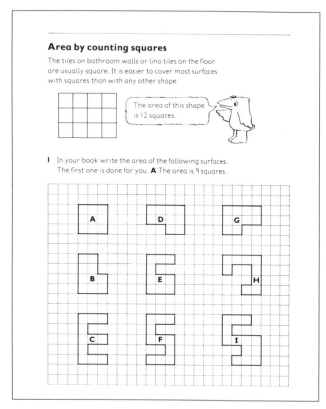

The area of this shape is 12 squares.

I In your book write the area of the following surfaces. The first one is done for you. **A** The area is 9 squares.

---

**108**

I On squared paper draw:

a 3 different shapes, each with an area of 10 squares.
b 3 different shapes, each with an area of 18 squares.

2 In your book write down the area of each shape by counting the squares and then compare it with its partner. The first is done for you.

Shape **A** has an area of 9 squares.
Shape **B** has an area of 8 squares.
Shape **A** has a greater area than shape **B**.

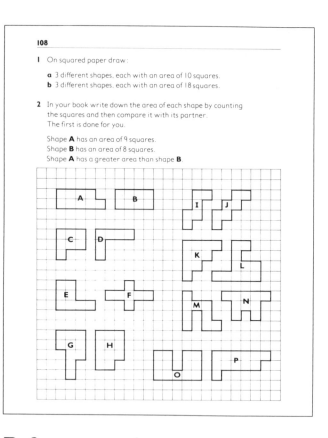

---

**Practice 23**
**Chapter 23: Area**

Name_____

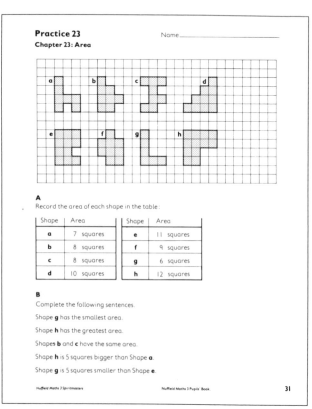

**A**
Record the area of each shape in the table:

| Shape | Area | Shape | Area |
|-------|------|-------|------|
| a | 7 squares | e | 11 squares |
| b | 8 squares | f | 9 squares |
| c | 8 squares | g | 6 squares |
| d | 10 squares | h | 12 squares |

**B**
Complete the following sentences.

Shape **g** has the smallest area.

Shape **h** has the greatest area.

Shapes **b** and **c** have the same area.

Shape **h** is 5 squares bigger than Shape **a**.

Shape **g** is 5 squares smaller than Shape **e**.

---

# References and resources

Nuffield Mathematics Teaching Project, *Beginnings* ▽, *Shape and Size* ▽, *Shape and Size* ▽, *Environmental Geometry*, Nuffield Guides, Chambers/Murray 1967. (See Introduction, page xii.)

Shuard, H. and Williams, E., *Primary Mathematics Today* (Chapters 6 and 24), Longman Group Ltd 1970

*Altair Designs*, Longman Group Ltd

*Tracing Shapes*, E. J. Arnold

*Shape Silhouettes*, Metric-Aids

*Geometric Shapes*, E.S.A.

*Gridsheets*, Excitement in Learning

*Basic Shapes Metrirule, Early Cognitive Shapes, Mosaic Shapes, Shape Tracer*, Invicta Plastics

*Geoshape Stencils*, Osmiroid

# Chapter 24

# Capacity 2 and volume

Wax seal (corks had not been invented).

Didn't stand up!

Old

New

## For the teacher

The previous chapter on Capacity referred to one of the main difficulties children face when learning about capacity – the problem of tangibility.

The second main problem arises with measurement in standard units. With other forms of quantity measurement, materials to be measured are usually compared with the standard measure, and are quite separate from it. When dealing with capacity the liquid has to be poured into the measure. Obviously, there is the risk of a flooded classroom. In any case the whole operation becomes more time consuming and requires more self discipline on the part of the child.

A few historical facts may whet the children's appetite for more. It will certainly enrich the experiences gained by the children if the topic of capacity is extended in this way.

When people first started to sell crops they had grown and wine or ale they had made, they used special containers for each kind of crop or drink. These containers were always standard – the same size, so that people could measure how much they were selling or buying.

The ancient Greeks and Romans measured their wine in a large jar called an amphora. It held about 48 glassfuls of wine.

Barrels have been used for many years to store and measure ale and beer. For about a thousand years in Britain a barrel has always held 36 gallons – about 600 glassfuls.

In the Middle Ages people drank their beer from a tankard. This usually held a pint or a quart (two pints). Some were silver or pewter and some had lids. People still use them today.

Milk is sold in pints and petrol in gallons but this will gradually change. For a long time people used capacity measures for corn. This shallow tub was called a corn bushel.

Another measure, for fruit, was a punnet. We can still buy strawberries in this way but today grain and fruit are usually weighed, this is more accurate.

A corn bushel

A punnet

Volume is introduced as 'the amount of space taken up'. After reminding the children that some shapes pack together better than others, cubes are used as units which can be counted as a simple measure of volume.

145

## Summary of the stages

1    Standard measures of capacity – the litre and half litre (500 ml)

2    Cuboids, cubes and volume

## Vocabulary

Standard, accurate, litre, millilitre, volume, cuboid, cube, layer.

## Equipment and apparatus

Proprietary bottles, jars and cans in which various liquids are sold. Standard transparent litre and 500 ml measures, small cubes – wood or plastic. Cardboard boxes in the shape of cubes or cuboids.

## Working with the children

### 1   Standard measures of capacity – the litre and half litre (500 ml)

By now the child should be at the stage of appreciating the need for a standard measure.

The litre is the first to be introduced. The important point to establish is that 1 litre is a fair amount of water to handle – hence the question, 'Could you drink a litre of water in one go?'

The litre of water is then related to containers smaller than a litre (drinking glass) and larger (bucket).

A display of several different shaped containers which all hold 1 litre – bottles, measuring cans, hollow boxes, plastic containers cut to size so that they just hold a litre – will help the children to appreciate that a litre does not always have to be of a certain shape.

If the children are already familiar with the kilogram they may be intrigued to discover that 1 litre of water weighs 1 kilogram. This can be shown either by balancing a litre jug of water against an empty litre jug and a kilogram weight, or by first standing an empty litre container on the kitchen scales, setting the dial to 'zero' and then pouring in 1 litre of water. Some may wish to experiment with a litre of sand or of rice to see if they are heavier or lighter than 1 kilogram.

*The half litre (500 ml)*

When introducing the half litre it is important at the same time to introduce its other name – 500 millilitres. It is not important at this stage for the child to understand why half a litre is called 500 ml. In any case it is unlikely that he will have had experience in dealing with three or four-digit numbers. It should be enough to use the two names as freely interchangeable synonyms.

Allow the child to discover for himself that two 500 ml measures are equivalent to 1 litre.

A collection of 10 containers, clearly labelled A–J, is required. The child is asked to draw a table and tick boxes to record the approximate capacity of each container. *Nuffield Maths 3 Spiritmasters*, Grid 16.

Half a litre is not a very common size for bottles, though it is a standard size for non-returnable bottles of soda water and other 'minerals'. This is why the collecting activity suggested is to find larger bottles and mark the 500 ml level on the side.

See Appendix of this chapter for diagrams showing how to make 1 litre and half litre containers suitable for dry materials.

## 2   Cuboids, cubes and volume

Most children will have already met the idea that some shapes fit together without spaces between them (Chapter 14, Shape 2). Any who seem unconvinced by the illustrations should be given further practical experience of packing bricks together.

The exercises on fitting cubes together to make 'walls' are designed to develop the idea of invariance of volume. The children are given a certain number of cubes all the same size and asked to arrange them in different ways. It is important to ensure that they understand that the amount of space occupied remains constant. The more practical the approach to this idea the better, since many children find it difficult to interpret three-dimensional arrangements of cubes from flat pictures.

Using a suitable number of cubes to build different solid cuboids – that is shapes with no gaps inside or pieces jutting out – has obvious links with multiplication. The examples chosen involve first 12 and then 24 cubes, but other numbers such as 18, 20, 36, 40 which have several factors, could be used for further practice.

Children have already used multiplication when dealing with rows and columns (Chapters 9 and 17). They are encouraged to use this experience to find the number of cubes in a layer. The number of cubes in each layer is then multiplied by the number of layers to find the total number of cubes in the cuboid.

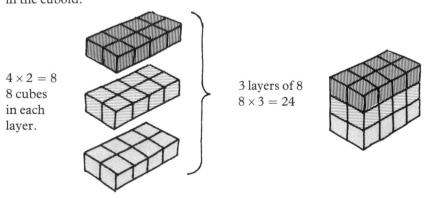

$4 \times 2 = 8$
8 cubes
in each
layer.

3 layers of 8
$8 \times 3 = 24$

Using cubes as units for measuring volume is taken a stage further in comparing the amount of space inside two boxes. The cubes which will just fit inside are stacked in front of each box so that by counting the cubes it is possible to compare the amount of space inside or the *internal volume* of the boxes.

With help, the children can cut down and adapt cornflake cartons to make boxes into which other stacks of cubes will just fit.

Standard units such as cubic centimetres are not introduced at this stage but the experience gained from stacking or packing cubes of the same size to fill space, is an important preparation for the measurement of volume.

The measurement of length depends upon units of length placed end to end on a line to make an aggregate or total length.

The measurement of area depends upon units of area (tiles) tessellated to make an aggregate or total area.

Similarly, the measurement of volume depends upon units of volume (cubes) packed together without intervening spaces to make an aggregate or total volume.

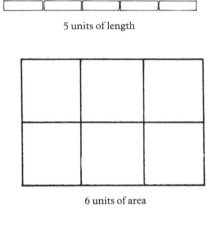

5 units of length

6 units of area

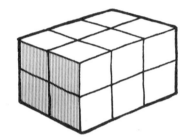

12 units of volume

# Pages from the Pupils' Book and Spiritmasters

---

## Chapter 24: Capacity 2 and volume

### Standard measures of capacity

1 Make a list of as many liquids as you can. Ask your teacher if you can start a class collection of liquids. Make a collection of empty containers in which different liquids have been sold.

2 Look carefully at the labels to see if the amount is recorded in litres or millilitres – ml may be used for millilitres. Make a list of these amounts in your book like this:

| container for | capacity |
|---|---|
| paint | |
| vinegar | |
| wine | |
| orange squash | |
| bitter lemon | |

List any more you have in your classroom.

When liquids are sold in shops they have to be sold in standard amounts so that people know how much they are buying. Liquids are usually sold in litres or parts of a litre.

3 Look at a 1 litre measure. Could you drink a litre of water in one go?

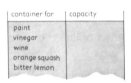

4 Take a drinking glass and find how many times you can fill it from 1 litre.

Some containers are larger than 1 litre

5 How many litres fill a bucket?

---

### The half litre (500 ml)

The small measure here holds 500 millilitres (500 ml for short).

1 How many times can you fill the 500 ml measure from 1 litre of water?

2 Take 10 containers and label them with the letters of the alphabet A, B, C, and so on up to J.

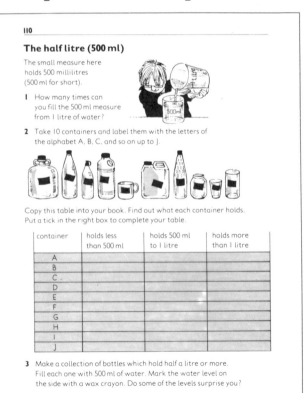

Copy this table into your book. Find out what each container holds. Put a tick in the right box to complete your table.

| container | holds less than 500 ml | holds 500 ml to 1 litre | holds more than 1 litre |
|---|---|---|---|
| A | | | |
| B | | | |
| C | | | |
| D | | | |
| E | | | |
| F | | | |
| G | | | |
| H | | | |
| I | | | |
| J | | | |

3 Make a collection of bottles which hold half a litre or more. Fill each one with 500 ml of water. Mark the water level on the side with a wax crayon. Do some of the levels surprise you?

## 111

### Cuboids, volume and cubes

These containers are taking up space on a shelf.

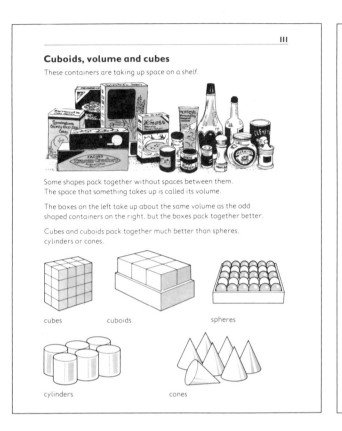

Some shapes pack together without spaces between them.
The space that something takes up is called its volume.

The boxes on the left take up about the same volume as the odd shaped containers on the right, but the boxes pack together better.

Cubes and cuboids pack together much better than spheres, cylinders or cones.

cubes          cuboids          spheres

cylinders          cones

## 112

### Fitting cubes together

Here are two walls made out of cubes.

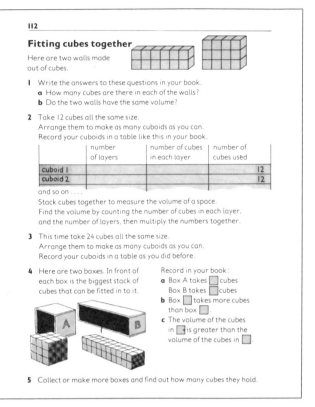

1  Write the answers to these questions in your book.
   a How many cubes are there in each of the walls?
   b Do the two walls have the same volume?

2  Take 12 cubes all the same size.
   Arrange them to make as many cuboids as you can.
   Record your cuboids in a table like this in your book.

|          | number of layers | number of cubes in each layer | number of cubes used |
|----------|------------------|-------------------------------|----------------------|
| cuboid 1 |                  |                               | 12                   |
| cuboid 2 |                  |                               | 12                   |

and so on . . . .
Stack cubes together to measure the volume of a space.
Find the volume by counting the number of cubes in each layer,
and the number of layers, then multiply the numbers together.

3  This time take 24 cubes all the same size.
   Arrange them to make as many cuboids as you can.
   Record your cuboids in a table as you did before.

4  Here are two boxes. In front of
   each box is the biggest stack of
   cubes that can be fitted in to it.

   Record in your book :
   a Box A takes ☐ cubes
     Box B takes ☐ cubes
   b Box ☐ takes more cubes
     than box ☐ .
   c The volume of the cubes
     in ☐ is greater than the
     volume of the cubes in ☐ .

5  Collect or make more boxes and find out how many cubes they hold.

---

### Practice 24          Name_____

**Chapter 24: Capacity 2 and Volume**

**A**
Complete:

Half a litre is the same as  500  ml

500 ml + 500  ml = 1 litre

1 litre − 500 ml =  500  ml.

**B**
Underline the containers that hold *more than* 1 litre:

<u>bucket</u>   cup   <u>bath</u>   milk bottle   <u>barrel</u>

**C**
Underline those that hold *less than* 500 ml.

<u>thimble</u>   fish tank   <u>egg cup</u>   <u>wine glass</u>   watering can

**D**
Complete:

a cuboid has  8  corners. It has  8  edges and  6  surfaces.

**E**

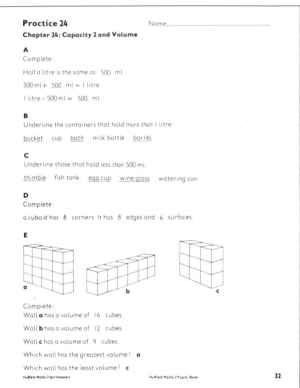

Complete:

Wall **a** has a volume of  16  cubes.

Wall **b** has a volume of  12  cubes.

Wall **c** has a volume of  9  cubes.

Which wall has the greatest volume?  **a**

Which wall has the least volume?  **c**

*Nuffield Maths 3 Spiritmasters*          *Nuffield Maths 3 Pupils' Book*          32

---

# References and resources

Nuffield Mathematics Teaching Project, *Beginnings* ▽,
*Shape and Size* ▽, Nuffield Guides,
Chambers/Murray 1967. (See Introduction, page xii.)

Williams, M. E., *Come and Measure – Capacity*,
Macmillan 1975

*Measuring Volume Kit, Plastic Measuring Cylinders
and Beakers, Plastic Funnels*, E. J. Arnold

*Litre Set*, Invicta Plastics

*Capacity cubes, cubic litre, cubic measures*, Metric-Aids

# Answers to Nuffield Maths 3 Pupil's Book

## Chapter 1: Addition 1

**Page 1**

| Race 1 | Race 2 | Race 3 | Race 4 |
|--------|--------|--------|--------|
| 7+3 | 4+6 | 5+5 | 3+7 |
| 2+8 | 8+2 | 9+1 | 1+9 |
| 5+5 | 1+9 | 4+6 | 9+1 |
| 6+4 | 5+5 | 7+3 | 2+8 |
| 9+1 | 6+4 | 2+8 | 5+5 |
| 4+6 | 7+3 | 3+7 | 7+3 |
| 8+2 | 2+8 | 6+4 | 8+2 |
| 3+7 | 9+1 | 8+2 | 6+4 |
| 1+9 | 3+7 | 1+9 | 4+6 |

**Page 3**

**1a** 4, **d** 0, **g** 18, **j** 14,
**b** 10, **e** 6, **h** 2, **k** 20
**c** 16, **f** 12, **i** 8,

| 2 Block A | Block B | Block C |
|-----------|---------|---------|
| 12 | 14 | 13 |
| 14 | 11 | 16 |
| 11 | 15 | 11 |
| 13 | 13 | 15 |
|    | 12 | 12 |
|    |    | 14 |

| Block D | Block E | Block F |
|---------|---------|---------|
| 13 | 15 | 2 |
| 15 | 14 | 8 |
| 11 | 17 | 4 |
| 17 | 13 | 6 |
| 14 | 12 |   |
| 12 | 16 |   |
| 16 | 15 |   |

| Block G | Block H | Block I |
|---------|---------|---------|
| 9 | 4 | 9 |
| 4 | 8 | 6 |
| 5 | 6 | 7 |
| 6 | 9 | 7 |
|   | 7 | 8 |
|   | 8 | 9 |

**Page 4**

**1a** 6, **d** 9, **g** 16, **j** 9,9;
**b** 8, **e** 2, **h** 5,5; **k** 8,8;
**c** 8, **f** 11, **i** 8,8; **l** 14

**Page 5**

**2a** 30, **b** 50, **c** 13, **d** 40, **e** 29, **f** 56

**3a** 13, **d** 15, **g** 19,
**b** 18, **e** 15, **h** 18,
**c** 16, **f** 20, **i** 20

## Chapter 2: Shape 1

**Page 6**

**1a straight sides only** A, B
 **b curved sides only** C, F, G
 **c straight and curved sides** E, D

**Page 7**

Shape A is a hexagon,
Shape B is a triangle,
Shape C is a pentagon,
Shape D is a quadrilateral,
Shape E is an octagon,
Shape F is a triangle,
Shape G is a hexagon,
Shape H is a pentagon,
Shape I is a quadrilateral

**Page 9**

**1** Shape B has 4 axes of symmetry,
 Shape C has 3 axes of symmetry,
 Shape D has 1 axis of symmetry

## Chapter 3: Place value

**Page 11**

**1a** 3, **b** 5, **c** 8, **d** 10, **e** 14, **f** 22
 **g** Because tallying is done in fives.

‖‖‖ 1

| 2a | 1 | 3→ 8 |
|----|---|------|
| b | 2 | 4→14 |
| c | 1 | 0→ 5 |
| d | 0 | 3→ 3 |
| e | 3 | 4→19 |
| f | 2 | 0→10 |

**Page 12**

| 1 | boxes | units | | boxes | units |
|---|-------|-------|---|-------|-------|
| a | 1 | 4 | d | 3 | 2 |
| b | 2 | 2 | e | 4 | 3 |
| c | 3 | 0 |   |   |   |

**2 number of bars**
**a** 7, **b** 3, **c** 9, **d** 14, **e** 18

| 3 | boxes | units |
|---|-------|-------|
| Tuesday | 1 | 5 |
| Wednesday | 2 | 0 |
| Thursday | 2 | 4 |
| Friday | 3 | 0 |
| Saturday | 0 | 5 |
| Sunday | 2 | 1 |

| 4 | weeks | days |
|----|-------|------|
| 10 | 1 | 3 |
| 6 | 0 | 6 |
| 7 | 1 | 0 |
| 14 | 2 | 0 |
| 23 | 3 | 2 |
| 18 | 2 | 4 |
| 30 | 4 | 2 |

**Page 13**

| 1 | longs | units |
|---|-------|-------|
| 4 units | 1 | 1 |
| 7 units | 2 | 1 |
| 3 units | 1 | 0 |
| 8 units | 2 | 2 |

| 2 | squares | longs | units |
|---|---------|-------|-------|
| 10 units | 1 | 0 | 1 |
| 12 units | 1 | 1 | 0 |
| 14 units | 1 | 1 | 2 |
| 9 units | 1 | 0 | 0 |
| 15 units | 1 | 2 | 0 |
| 17 units | 1 | 2 | 2 |
| 20 units | 2 | 0 | 2 |
| 22 units | 2 | 1 | 1 |

| 1 | longs | units |
|---|---|---|
| 6 units | 1 | 2 |
| 8 units | 2 | 0 |
| 11 units | 2 | 3 |
| 12 units | 3 | 0 |

| 2 | squares | longs | units |
|---|---|---|---|
| 18 units | 1 | 0 | 2 |
| 16 units | 1 | 0 | 0 |
| 19 units | 1 | 0 | 3 |
| 20 units | 1 | 1 | 0 |
| 21 units | 1 | 1 | 1 |
| 24 units | 1 | 2 | 0 |

**Page 15**

**1**
| 1 ten and 3 units | 10 + 3 |
|---|---|
| 13 thirteen | |
| 1 ten and 7 units | 10 + 7 |
| 17 seventeen | |
| 1 ten and 9 units | 10 + 9 |
| 19 nineteen | |
| 1 ten and 6 units | 10 + 6 |
| 16 sixteen | |
| 2 tens and 0 units | 20 + 0 |
| 20 twenty | |
| 2 tens and 5 units | 20 + 5 |
| 25 twenty-five | |
| 2 tens and 8 units | 20 + 8 |
| 28 twenty-eight | |
| 3 tens and 1 unit | 30 + 1 |
| 31 thirty-one | |
| 6 tens and 0 units | 60 + 0 |
| 60 sixty | |
| 9 tens and 3 units | 90 + 3 |
| 93 ninety-three | |
| 4 tens and 4 units | 40 + 4 |
| 44 forty-four | |

# Chapter 4: Length 1

**Page 16**

**1** Other units are too big.
**2a** palm or digit, **b** cubit or handspan, **c** palm or handspan, **d** digit, **e** handspan or cubit, **f** handspan or cubit

**Page 19**

**1** My decimetre rod fits 10 times along my metre stick.

# Chapter 5: Addition 2

**Page 20**

**1a** 15, **e** 22, **i** 33, **m** 42,
**b** 16, **f** 24, **j** 36, **n** 46,
**c** 18, **g** 27, **k** 38, **o** 57,
**d** 20, **h** 29, **l** 40, **p** 64

**2a** 23, **b** 29, **c** 25, **d** 25, **e** 21, **f** 24

**3a** 13, **d** 20, **g** 24,
**b** 13, **e** 20, **h** 22,
**c** 20, **f** 20, **i** 23

**Page 21**

**1a** 9, **e** 12, **i** 16, **m** 34,
**b** 19, **f** 32, **j** 26, **n** 36,
**c** 29, **g** 52, **k** 36, **o** 64,
**d** 59, **h** 72, **l** 46, **p** 66
**2a** 17,22,27; **e** 25,30,35;
**b** 18,25,32; **f** 13,16,19;
**c** 22,24,26; **g** 47,57,67;
**d** 50,60,70; **h** 46,55,64

**Page 22**

**1a** 23, **d** 43, **g** 36, **j** 38,
**b** 33, **e** 16, **h** 46, **k** 58,
**c** 33, **f** 46, **i** 18, **l** 38

**2a** =, **d** =, **g** >,
**b** >, **e** >, **h** <,
**c** <, **f** <,

**Page 23**

**1** yes

**2a**
| 4 | 9 | 2 |
|---|---|---|
| 3 | 5 | 7 |
| 8 | 1 | 6 |

**d**
| 2 | 9 | 4 |
|---|---|---|
| 7 | 5 | 3 |
| 6 | 1 | 8 |

**b**
| 9 | 2 | 7 |
|---|---|---|
| 4 | 6 | 8 |
| 5 | 10 | 3 |

**e**
| 3 | 10 | 5 |
|---|---|---|
| 8 | 6 | 4 |
| 7 | 2 | 9 |

**c**
| 10 | 3 | 8 |
|---|---|---|
| 5 | 7 | 9 |
| 6 | 11 | 4 |

**f**
| 5 | 12 | 7 |
|---|---|---|
| 10 | 8 | 6 |
| 9 | 4 | 11 |

**Page 24**

**1 Input**
9 19 29 39 49  0  6 12 18 24
**Output**
15 25 35 45 55  6 12 18 24 30
**2 Input**
0 10 30 50 60  3 13 53 23 33
**Output**
10 20 40 60 70 13 23 63 33 43
**3 Input**
5  7  8 11 21 31  0  9 18 27
**Output**
14 16 17 20 30 40  9 18 27 36

# Chapter 6: Money 1

**Page 25**

**1a** 50 pence, **d** 20 pence,
**b** 5 pence, **e** 1 penny,
**c** 2 pence, **f** 10 pence

**Page 29**

**1a** 5p + 1p = 6p,
**b** 5p + 2p + 1p = 8p,
**c** 20p + 10p + 1p = 31p,
**d** 50p + 5p + 1p = 56p,
**e** 50p + 10p + 10p + 1p = 71p,
**f** 20p + 20p + 2p + 1p = 43p,
**g** 50p + 20p + 5p + 2p = 77p

**Page 30**

**1a** 5p, **b** 1p, **c** 2p, **d** 2p

**2a** 5p, **b** 2p, **c** 5p, **d** 2p

**Page 31**

**1 Change**
**a** coins to make 6p,
**b** coins to make 2p,
**c** 1p coin,
**d** coins to make 10p,
**e** coins to make 4p,
**f** coins to make 6p,
**g** coins to make 4p,
**h** coins to make 12p

# Chapter 7: Subtraction 1

## Page 32
**1a** 4, **b** 4

**2a** 6, **b** 6, **c** 2, **d** 2

**3a** 5, **b** 7, **c** 5, **d** 7

**4a** 5, **b** 5, **c** 9, **d** 9

**5a** 7, **b** 7, **c** 9, **d** 9

**6a** 6, **b** 19, **c** 13, **d** 6

**7a** 7, **b** 8, **c** 15, **d** 7

**8a** 6, **b** 6, **c** 14, **d** 14

**9a** 9, **b** 8, **c** 5, **d** 8

## Page 33
**1a** $10+6 = 16$   $16-10 = 6$
$10 = 16-6$   $16-6 = 10$
**2a** Open answers, **b** tallying activity, **c** Graph.

## Page 34
**1a** 10, **d** 7, **g** 6,
**b** 2, **e** 9, **h** 8
**c** 9, **f** 8,

**2a** 3, **b** 12, **c** 3, **d** 6,

**3a**
$$\begin{array}{r} 13 \\ -10 \\ \hline 3 \end{array}$$
**b**
$$\begin{array}{r} 20 \\ -18 \\ \hline 2 \end{array}$$
**c**
$$\begin{array}{r} 16 \\ -11 \\ \hline 5 \end{array}$$
**d**
$$\begin{array}{r} 16 \\ -11 \\ \hline 5 \end{array}$$
**e**
$$\begin{array}{r} 19 \\ -7 \\ \hline 12 \end{array}$$

**4a** 30, **b** 20, **c** 0, **d** 50, **e** 0

## Page 35
**1a** 14, **b** 32, **c** 52, **d** 22, **e** 53, **f** 32

**2a**
$$\begin{array}{r} 36 \\ -23 \\ \hline 13 \end{array}$$
**b**
$$\begin{array}{r} 49 \\ -13 \\ \hline 36 \end{array}$$
**c**
$$\begin{array}{r} 64 \\ -52 \\ \hline 12 \end{array}$$
**d**
$$\begin{array}{r} 64 \\ -52 \\ \hline 12 \end{array}$$
**e**
$$\begin{array}{r} 88 \\ -27 \\ \hline 61 \end{array}$$
**f**
$$\begin{array}{r} 88 \\ -27 \\ \hline 61 \end{array}$$

## Page 36
**1a** 7, **d** 2, **g** 11,
**b** 12, **e** 4, **h** 11
**c** 8, **f** 0,

**2a** $8-5 = 3$, **d** $7+4 = 11$,
**b** $3+11 = 14$, **e** 11th floor
**c** $14-7 = 7$

**3** 6

**4** $12-8 = 4$, $4+5 = 9$
6 floors down to floor 3

# Chapter 8: Weight 1

## Page 37
**1** Practical activity.

**2a** P is heavier than Q.
**b** Q is lighter than P.
**c** down, **d** up

## Page 41
**2** half

# Chapter 9: Multiplication 1

## Page 42
**1a** 20
20
**b** 32
32

**c** Packs 1 2 3 4 5 6 7 8 9 10
Bars 4 8 12 16 20 24 28 32 36 40

## Page 43
**1a** $6+6+6 = 18$   **d** $2+2+2 = 6$
$3(6) = 18$       $3(2) = 6$
**b** $7+7+7 = 21$   **e** $3+3+3+3+$
$3(7) = 21$       $3+3 = 18$
$6(3) = 18$

**2a** 8, **e** 16, **i** 30, **m** 4,
**b** 14, **f** 18, **j** 8, **n** 15,
**c** 20, **g** 18, **k** 9, **o** 12
**d** 15, **h** 10, **l** 21,

**3a** 3, **e** 8, **i** 2, **m** 2,
**b** 2, **f** 4, **j** 2, **n** 1,
**c** 3, **g** 3, **k** 2, **o** 6,
**d** 5, **h** 4, **l** 3, **p** 8

## Page 44
**1a** $6(2) = 12$       $2 \times 6 = 12$
**b** $8 \times 3 = 24$       $3(8) = 24$
**c** $3 \times 6 = 18$       $6(3) = 18$
**d** $5(4) = 20$       $4 \times 5 = 20$
**e** $3(8) = 18$       $6 \times 3 = 18$

## Page 45
**1a** 8, **f** 4, **k** 20, **p** 5,
**b** 8, **g** 5, **l** 3, **q** 7,
**c** 8, **h** 2, **m** 24, **r** 21
**d** 12, **i** 15, **n** 3,
**e** 4, **j** 24, **o** 16,

## Page 46
**1** 3 rows of $6 = 18\,(3 \times 6 = 18)$
6 columns of $3 = 18\,(6 \times 3 = 18)$
The product is 18. The factors are 6 and 3.

**2a** $16 = 4 \times 4 = 8 \times 2$
**b** $12 = 4 \times 3 = 6 \times 2$
**c** $20 = 4 \times 5 = 10 \times 2$
**d** $24 = 4 \times 6 = 8 \times 3 = 12 \times 2$

**3**

| F | 5 | 6 | 4 | 8 | 6 | 4 | 4 | 2 | 6 | 12 | 3 |
|---|---|---|---|---|---|---|---|---|---|----|---|
| F | 3 | 3 | 4 | 2 | 2 | 3 | 5 | 10 | 4 | 2 | 8 |
| P | 15 | 18 | 16 | 16 | 12 | 12 | 20 | 20 | 24 | 24 | 24 |

**4b** $16 = 2 \times 8 = 4 \times 4$,
**c** $18 = 2 \times 9 = 3 \times 6$,
**d** $24 = 2 \times 12 = 3 \times 8 = 4 \times 6$,
**e** $36 = 2 \times 18 = 3 \times 12 = 4 \times 9$
$= 6 \times 6$

# Chapter 10: Time 1

## Page 48

**1** Fast horses race at the track.

**4a** 20 mins.
**b** 25 mins.
**c** 35 mins.
**d** 10 mins.
**e** 20 mins.
**f** 40 mins.
**g** 40 mins.
**h** 55 mins.

## Page 49

**1A** 5 mins
**B** 15 mins
**C** 30 mins
**D** 20 mins
**E** 45 mins

**2a** $\frac{1}{4}$,
**b** 15,
**c** $\frac{3}{4}$,
**d** 1,
**e** 1,
**f** 20,
**g** 20 mins.

## Page 50

**1a** 5 mins.
**b** 12 mins.
**c** 7 mins.
**d** 38 mins.

**2a** 12 mins.
**b** 11 mins.
**c** 16 mins.
**d** 10 mins.

# Chapter 11: Capacity

## Page 53

**1b** bath
bucket
ink bottle
flask
bottle
saucepan
jar or jug
spoon
wineglass
wineglass

**2a** activity,
**b** level stays horizontal,
**c** drawing

**3a** 6,
**b** 4,
**c** 5,
**d** 3,
**e** 4,
**f** 5,
**g** 3,
**h** 6,
**i** 2,
**j** 7,
**k** 7,
**l** 4,
**m** 3,
**n** 4,
**o** 8,
**p** 4.

## Page 56

**1a** 5,
**b** 2,
**c** 3,
**d** 6,
**e** 1,
**f** 8,
**g** 9,
**h** 4

## Page 57

**1a** 2,
**b** 3,
**c** 2,
**d** 3,
**e** 4,
**f** 4,
**g** 4,
**h** 3

## Page 58

**1a** 3,
**b** 9,
**c** 4,
**d** 4,
**e** 6,
**f** 6,

**2a** 5,
**b** 5,
**c** 5,
**d** 8,
**e** 3,
**f** 9,
**g** 4,
**h** 6,
**i** 6,
**j** 4,
**k** 7,
**l** 9,
**m** 3

# Chapter 12: Division 1

## Page 54

**1** 3

**2** There are 5 in each row.
$10 \div 2 = 5$

**3** There are 8 in each column.
$24 \div 3 = 8$

## Page 55

**1a** There are 6 in each column.
$18 \div 3 = 6$
**b** There are 8 in each row.
$16 \div 2 = 8$
**c** There are 5 in each row.
$15 \div 3 = 5$
**d** There are 6 in each column.
$30 \div 5 = 6$

**2a** There are 6 columns of 2.
$12 \div 6 = 2$
There are 2 rows of 6.
$12 \div 2 = 6$
**b** There are 3 columns of 5.
$15 \div 3 = 5$
There are 5 rows of 3.
$15 \div 5 = 3$
**c** There are 4 rows of 5.
$20 \div 4 = 5$
There are 5 columns of 4.
$20 \div 5 = 4$
**d** There are 4 rows of 7.
$28 \div 4 = 7$
There are 7 columns of 4.
$28 \div 7 = 4$

# Chapter 13: Addresses

## Page 60

**1a** (3,1),
**b** (2,2),
**c** (5,2),
**d** (1,3),
**e** (6,1),
**f** (6,4),
**g** (5,1),
**h** (5,4)

**2** x 0 x
 0 x
x 0 0

**3a** 0, **b** (1,2)

**4a** John, **b** No one

## Page 61

**1a** Manor House (5,2),
**b** (7,1),
**c** (8,4),
**d** (3,3),
**e** (3,6),
**f** (3,4),
**g** (2,1),
**h** (2,3),
**i** (6,5),
**j** (6,4),
**k** (9,6),
**l** (8,2)

## Page 62

**1a** A happy dog wags its tail,

**2** (3,5) (5,3) (3,3) (5,5)  (4,3) (5,5)
(4,1) (5,2)  (3,1) (5,5) (5,5) (1,3)

# Chapter 14: Shape 2

## Page 63

**1a** curved;
**b** flat, straight;
**c** curved, curved;
**d** curved and flat faces; some edges are curved some are straight.

## Page 64

**1a** A, C and G; **b** B, E; **c** D;
**d** A, C, F, G; **e** B, E.

**2a** cube — 6 12 8
**b** square pyramid — 5 8 5
**c** triangular pyramid — 4 6 4
**d** triangular prism — 5 9 6
**e** cuboid — 6 12 8
**f** cylinder — 3 2 0
**g** cone — 2 1 1

## page 65

**2a** C, **b** 6, **c** hexagon, **d** 4,
**e** 18, **f** 5, **g** rectangle,
**h** rectangle

**3b** cuboids, cubes
**c** sugar cubes, matchboxes, cornflake boxes

# Chapter 15: Subtraction 2

## Page 66
**1a** 8, **b** 8, **c** 9, **d** 11,
12, 8, 13, 9,
8, 14, 11, 1,
18 4 3 17

The answers in **a** and **b** are all even.
The answers in **c** and **d** are all odd.

## Page 67
**1a** 3 13 23 33 43   6 16 26 36 46
**b** 2 12 22 32 42   5 15 25 35 45
**c** 5 15 25   6 16 26   7 17 27 37
**d** 7 17 27 37 47 57 67 77
**e** 8 13 18 23 30 33 38 43

## Page 68
**1a** $9+3 = 12$, **e** $7+8 = 15$,
**b** $5+11 = 16$, **f** $17+3 = 20$,
**c** $11+8 = 19$, **g** $11+6 = 17$,
**d** $8+6 = 14$, **h** $8+12 = 20$

## Page 69
**1a** 28, **e** 38, **i** 17, **m** 38,
**b** 35, **f** 43, **j** 28, **n** 18,
**c** 36, **g** 39, **k** 29, **o** 39,
**d** 23, **h** 23, **l** 38, **p** 59

## Page 70
**1a** $3+6 = 9$, **i** $8+7 = 15$,
**b** $2+8 = 10$, **j** $28+12 = 40$,
**c** $20+30 = 50$, **k** $37+43 = 80$,
**d** $40+50 = 90$, **l** $56+34 = 90$,
**e** $13+10 = 23$, **m** $31+39 = 70$,
**f** $47+20 = 67$, **n** $28+62 = 90$,
**g** $10+4 = 14$, **o** $14+66 = 80$,
**h** $20+7 = 27$, **p** $29+12 = 41$

**2a** $9-3 = 6$, **i** $15-8 = 7$,
**b** $10-2 = 8$, **j** $40-28 = 12$,
**c** $50-20 = 30$, **k** $80-37 = 43$,
**d** $90-40 = 50$, **l** $90-56 = 34$,
**e** $23-13 = 10$, **m** $70-31 = 39$,
**f** $67-47 = 20$, **n** $90-28 = 62$,
**g** $14-10 = 4$, **o** $80-14 = 66$,
**h** $27-20 = 7$, **p** $41-29 = 12$

## Page 71
**1**   65p (old price)
$-$ 44p (new price)
21p cheaper

**2** 11

**3a** 6 eggs, **e** 27 minutes,
**b** 13 conkers, **f** 11 litres,
**c** 13p, **g** 34 centimetres
**d** 21 kilograms,

# Chapter 16: Money 2

## Page 72
**1a** 20p, **b** 30p, **c** 40p, **d** 45p

**2a** 8 (5p) coins $\rightarrow$ 40p,
**b** 5 (5p) coins $\rightarrow$ 25p,
**c** 6 (5p) coins $\rightarrow$ 30p,
**d** 9 (5p) coins $\rightarrow$ 45p

## Page 73
**1a** 10p 2p 2p 2p 1p
10p, 12p, 14p, 16p, 17p.
**b** 10p 5p 1p 1p 1p
10p, 15p, 16p, 17p, 18p.
**c** 5p 5p 5p 2p 1p
5p, 10p, 15p, 17p, 18p.
**d** 20p 5p 2p 2p 2p
20p, 25p, 27p, 29p, 31p.
**2a** 10p 2p 2p 1p
10p, 12p, 14p, 15p.
**b** 10p 5p 2p 1p 1p
10p, 15p, 17p, 18p, 19p.
**c** 10p 5p 2p 1p 1p
10p, 15p, 17p, 18p, 19p.
**d** 20p 10p 10p 5p 5p 2p
20p, 30p, 40p, 45p, 50p, 52p,
2p, 1p
54p, 55p.
**e** 20p 10p 10p 5p 5p 2p
20p, 30p, 40p, 45p, 50p, 52p,
1p 1p
53p, 54p.

## Page 74
**1a** liquorice, **b** 5p, **c** 3p
**d** 11p

**2a** Toffee        9p
Mints      $+$ 4p
13p

**b** Large icecream    12p
Orange drink    $+$ 11p
23p

**c** Ball point pen    17p
Note book      $+$ 8p
25p

**d** Pencil         6p
Crayons       $+$ 10p
16p

**e** Choc-bar        8p
Choc-drops     $+$ 7p
15p

**f** Felt pen        20p
Humbugs      $+$ 6p
26p

**g** Toffee          9p
Liquorice      $+$ 3p
12p

**h** Mints          4p
Choc-drops     $+$ 7p
11p

**i** Felt pen        20p
Fruit         $+$ 5p
25p

**j** Choc-drops       7p
Fruit         $+$ 5p
12p

**k** Choc-drops       7p
Liquorice      $+$ 3p
10p

**l** Fruit          5p
Liquorice      $+$ 3p
8p

**m** Choc-bar        8p
Crayons       $+$ 10p
Ball point pen   $+$ 17p
35p

**n** Pencil         6p
Note book      $+$ 8p
Toffee        $+$ 9p
23p

**o** Liquorice        3p
Mints        $+$ 4p
Choc-drops     $+$ 7p
14p

**3a** 12p,    **d** 32p,    **g** 3,
 **b** 25p,    **e** 32p,    **h** 6
 **c** 24p,    **f** 2,

### Page 75
**1a** 9p,    **d** 27p,  **g** 6p,   **j** 45p
 **b** 15p,   **e** 38p,  **h** 36p,  **k** 33p
 **c** 19p,   **f** 42p,  **i** 21p,  **l** 17p

### Page 76
**1** 18p

**2a** 15p spent,     **d** 13p spent,
 **b** 13p spent,     **e** 13p spent,
 **c** 11p spent,     **f** 11p spent.

# Chapter 17:
# Multiplication 2

### Page 77
**1a** $5 \times 3 = 15 = 3 \times 5$,
 **b** $7 \times 4 = 28 = 4 \times 7$,
 **c** $5 \times 6 = 30 = 6 \times 5$,
 **d** $4 \times 8 = 32 = 8 \times 4$

**2a** $4 \times 3 = 12$,    **k** $9 \times 2 = 18$,
 **b** $3 \times 4 = 12$,    **l** $2 \times 9 = 18$,
 **c** $5 \times 3 = 15$,    **m** $4 \times 8 = 32$,
 **d** $3 \times 5 = 15$,    **n** $8 \times 4 = 32$,
 **e** $5 \times 6 = 30$,    **o** $4 \times 7 = 28$,
 **f** $6 \times 5 = 30$,    **p** $7 \times 4 = 28$,
 **g** $3 \times 7 = 21$,    **q** $9 \times 3 = 27$,
 **h** $7 \times 3 = 21$,    **r** $3 \times 9 = 27$,
 **i** $8 \times 3 = 24$,    **s** $7 \times 5 = 35$,
 **j** $3 \times 8 = 24$,    **t** $5 \times 7 = 35$

### Page 78
**1a** $7 \times 7 = 49, 8 \times 8 = 64$

### Page 80
**1a**
$$\begin{array}{r} 5 \\ \times\ 2 \\ \hline 10 \end{array} \qquad \textbf{g}\ \begin{array}{r} 2 \\ \times\ 6 \\ \hline 12 \end{array} \qquad \textbf{m}\ \begin{array}{r} 6 \\ \times\ 5 \\ \hline 30 \end{array}$$

**b**
$$\begin{array}{r} 6 \\ \times\ 3 \\ \hline 18 \end{array} \qquad \textbf{h}\ \begin{array}{r} 4 \\ \times\ 4 \\ \hline 16 \end{array} \qquad \textbf{n}\ \begin{array}{r} 5 \\ \times\ 5 \\ \hline 25 \end{array}$$

**c**
$$\begin{array}{r} 10 \\ \times\ 3 \\ \hline 30 \end{array} \qquad \textbf{i}\ \begin{array}{r} 10 \\ \times\ 5 \\ \hline 50 \end{array} \qquad \textbf{o}\ \begin{array}{r} 4 \\ \times\ 6 \\ \hline 24 \end{array}$$

**d**
$$\begin{array}{r} 4 \\ \times\ 3 \\ \hline 12 \end{array} \qquad \textbf{j}\ \begin{array}{r} 4 \\ \times\ 5 \\ \hline 20 \end{array} \qquad \textbf{p}\ \begin{array}{r} 4 \\ \times\ 1 \\ \hline 4 \end{array}$$

**e**
$$\begin{array}{r} 5 \\ \times\ 6 \\ \hline 30 \end{array} \qquad \textbf{k}\ \begin{array}{r} 6 \\ \times\ 1 \\ \hline 6 \end{array} \qquad \textbf{q}\ \begin{array}{r} 3 \\ \times\ 4 \\ \hline 12 \end{array}$$

**f**
$$\begin{array}{r} 6 \\ \times\ 2 \\ \hline 12 \end{array} \qquad \textbf{l}\ \begin{array}{r} 3 \\ \times\ 5 \\ \hline 15 \end{array} \qquad \textbf{r}\ \begin{array}{r} 6 \\ \times\ 6 \\ \hline 36 \end{array}$$

**2**
$$\begin{array}{ccc} 21 & 24 & 9 \\ 6 & 18 & 30 \\ 27 & 12 & 15 \end{array}$$

# Chapter 18: Length 2

### Page 81
**1** Line A is 5 cm long.
    B is 7 cm long.
    C is 11 cm long.

### Page 82
**1** Line **A** is 7 cm long,
   Line **B** is 9 cm long,
   Line **C** is 4 cm long,
   Line **D** is 7 cm long,
   Line **E** is 5 cm long,
   Line **F** is 8 cm long,
   Line **G** is 15 cm long.

### Page 83
**1** From ★ to point A is 5 cm.
   From ★ to point B is 9 cm.
   From ★ to point C is 7 cm.
   From ★ to point D is 12 cm.

**2a** 7 cm  **b** 8 cm  **c** 6 cm

### Page 85
**1a** 10 cm,   **d** 14 cm,  **g** 17 cm,
 **b** 10 cm,   **e** 16 cm,  **h** 16 cm,
 **c** 10 cm,   **f** 18 cm,  **i** 18 cm

**2a** 7 cm + 3 cm = 10 cm
 **b** 3 cm + 7 cm = 10 cm
 **c** 6 cm + 9 cm = 15 cm
 **d** 8 cm + 6 cm = 14 cm

**3a** 4 cm,   **d** 4 cm,  **g** 8 cm,
 **b** 6 cm,   **e** 5 cm,  **h** 10 cm
 **c** 10 cm,   **f** 10 cm,

**4a** 3 cm,   **c** 5 cm,  **e** 3 cm,
 **b** 5 cm,   **d** 8 cm,  **f** 14 cm

# Chapter 19:
# Introducing fractions 1

### Page 87
**1a** half,   **c** third,  **e** third,
 **b** half,   **d** half,   **f** third

**2a** third,   **c** half,   **e** tenth
 **b** quarter,  **d** fifth,

### Page 88
**3a** 12 cm ÷ 3 = 4 cm
    or $\frac{1}{3}$ of 12 cm = 4 cm,
 **b** 12 cm ÷ 4 = 3 cm
    or $\frac{1}{4}$ of 12 cm = 3 cm

### Page 89
**1a** 20 cm ÷ 2 = 10 cm
    or $\frac{1}{2}$ of 20 cm = 10 cm,
 **b** 8 cm ÷ 4 = 2 cm
    or $\frac{1}{4}$ of 8 cm = 2 cm,
 **c** 24 cm ÷ 2 = 12 cm
    or $\frac{1}{2}$ of 24 cm = 12 cm,
 **d** 20 cm ÷ 10 = 2 cm
    or $\frac{1}{10}$ of 20 cm = 2 cm
 **e** 16 cm ÷ 2 = 8 cm
    or $\frac{1}{2}$ of 16 cm = 8 cm
 **f** 18 cm ÷ 3 = 6 cm
    or $\frac{1}{3}$ of 18 cm = 6 cm,
 **g** 35 cm ÷ 5 = 7 cm
    or $\frac{1}{5}$ of 35 cm = 7 cm

**2a** 60 ÷ 2 = 30
    There are 30 minutes in $\frac{1}{2}$ hour.
 **b** 60 ÷ 4 = 15
    There are 15 minutes in $\frac{1}{4}$ hour.
 **c** 60 ÷ 3 = 20
    There are 20 minutes in $\frac{1}{3}$ hour.

**3a** $100 \div 2 = 50$
$\frac{1}{2}$ a bar weighs 50 grams.
  **b** $100 \div 5 = 20$
$\frac{1}{5}$ a bar weighs 20 grams.
  **c** $100 \div 10 = 10$
$\frac{1}{10}$ a bar weighs 10 grams.

**4a** $24 \div 2 = 12$
$\frac{1}{2}$ of a day is 12 hours.
  **b** $24 \div 4 = 6$
$\frac{1}{4}$ of a day is 6 hours.
  **c** $24 \div 3 = 8$
$\frac{1}{3}$ of a day is 8 hours.

**Page 90**

**1a** $8 \div 2 = 4$    **g** $\frac{1}{10}$ of $30 = 3$
$\frac{1}{2}$ of $8 = 4$    $30 \div 10 = 3$
  **b** $15 \div 3 = 5$    **h** $\frac{1}{4}$ of $16 = 4$
$\frac{1}{3}$ of $15 = 5$    $16 \div 4 = 4$
  **c** $20 \div 4 = 5$    **i** $\frac{1}{5}$ of $30 = 6$
$\frac{1}{4}$ of $20 = 5$    $30 \div 5 = 6$
  **d** $16 \div 2 = 8$    **j** $12 \div 2 = 6$
$\frac{1}{2}$ of $16 = 8$    $6 = \frac{1}{2}$ of $12$
  **e** $10 \div 5 = 2$    **k** $15 \div 3 = 5$
$\frac{1}{5}$ of $10 = 2$    $5 = \frac{1}{3}$ of $15$
  **f** $24 \div 4 = 6$    **l** $40 \div 10 = 4$
$\frac{1}{4}$ of $24 = 6$    $10 = \frac{1}{4}$ of $40.$

**2a** 6,    **b** 2,    **c** 2,    **d** 3,
     4,      3,      4,      8,
     8,     20,     9,      5,
     7      8      7      9

# Chapter 20 : Time 2.

**Page 91**

**1a** 8 o'clock,    **d** 11 o'clock
  **b** 3 o'clock,    **e** 6 o'clock,
  **c** 10 o'clock,    **f** 12 o'clock

**Page 92**

**1a** 5, **b** 12, **c** 24

**2** 2

**3a** 4 o'clock,    **c** 3 o'clock,
  **b** 11 o'clock,    **d** 1 o'clock

**4a** 2 o'clock,    **c** 8 o'clock,
  **b** 12 o'clock,    **d** 9 o'clock

**Page 93**

**1** quarter to one or 12.45

**2a** half past seven or 7.30,
  **b** quarter to six or 5.4̇5̇,
  **c** 15 minutes to ten or 9.45

**3a** 3.04,    **d** 10.59,
  **b** 12.15,    **e** 7.22,
  **c** 8.35,    **f** 6.33

**Page 94**

**1a** 10 minutes past 12.    12.10,
  **b** 13 minutes past 11.    11.13,
  **c** 20 minutes to 3.    2.40,
  **d** 3 minutes to 6.    5.57,
  **e** 4 minutes past 5.    5.04,
  **f** 27 minutes to 10.    9.33

**Page 95**

**1a** 20 mins.    **c** 30 mins.
  **b** 45 mins.    **d** 65 mins.

**2** 6.12, 7.27, 7.52, 10.07

**4a** 6.30,    **e** 10.35,
  **b** 8 o'clock,    **f** 6.03,
  **c** 8.15,    **g** 5.12,
  **d** 9.55    **h** 8.33

# Chapter 21 : Division 2

**Page 96**

**1a** $4 \times 3 = 12$    **e** $6 \times 3 = 18$
     $12 \div 4 = 3$      $18 \div 6 = 3$
     $4 \times 3 = 12$      $6 \times 3 = 18$
     $12 \div 3 = 4$      $18 \div 3 = 6$
  **b** $5 \times 6 = 30$    **f** $7 \times 4 = 28$
     $30 \div 5 = 6$      $28 \div 7 = 4$
     $5 \times 6 = 30$      $7 \times 4 = 28$
     $30 \div 6 = 5$      $28 \div 4 = 7$
  **c** $5 \times 4 = 20$    **g** $4 \times 4 = 16$
     $20 \div 5 = 4$      $16 \div 4 = 4$
     $5 \times 4 = 20$    **h** $5 \times 5 = 25$
     $20 \div 4 = 5$      $25 \div 5 = 5$
  **d** $9 \times 3 = 27$    **i** $6 \times 6 = 36$
     $27 \div 9 = 3$      $36 \div 6 = 6$
     $9 \times 3 = 27$
     $27 \div 3 = 9$

**Page 97**

**1a** $5 \times 4 = 20$    $20 \div 5 = 4$
  **b** $3 \times 6 = 18$    $18 \div 3 = 6$
  **c** $7 \times 3 = 21$    $21 \div 7 = 3$
  **d** $6 \times 4 = 24$    $24 \div 6 = 4$

**Page 98**

**1a** $6 \div 2 = 3$    **g** $8 \div 4 = 2$
  **b** $4 \div 1 = 4$    **h** $18 \div 3 = 6$
  **c** $10 \div 2 = 5$    **i** $24 \div 4 = 6$
  **d** $12 \div 3 = 4$    **j** $20 \div 5 = 4$
  **e** $20 \div 4 = 5$    **k** $15 \div 3 = 5$
  **f** $5 \div 5 = 1$    **l** $30 \div 6 = 5$

**2a** $2 \times 6 = 12$    **i** $4 \times 7 = 28$
     $12 \div 2 = 6$      $28 \div 7 = 4$
     $12 \div 6 = 2$      $28 \div 4 = 7$
  **b** $8 \times 4 = 32$    **j** $6 \times 4 = 24$
     $32 \div 4 = 8$      $24 \div 4 = 6$
     $32 \div 8 = 4$      $24 \div 6 = 4$
  **c** $5 \times 3 = 15$    **k** $3 \times 4 = 12$
     $15 \div 5 = 3$      $12 \div 3 = 4$
     $15 \div 3 = 5$      $12 \div 4 = 3$
  **d** $5 \times 6 = 30$    **l** $7 \times 3 = 21$
     $30 \div 6 = 5$      $21 \div 3 = 7$
     $30 \div 5 = 6$      $21 \div 7 = 3$
  **e** $3 \times 8 = 24$    **m** $6 \times 3 = 18$
     $24 \div 8 = 3$      $18 \div 3 = 6$
     $24 \div 3 = 8$      $18 \div 6 = 3$
  **f** $5 \times 4 = 20$    **n** $3 \times 10 = 30$
     $20 \div 4 = 5$      $30 \div 10 = 3$
     $20 \div 5 = 4$      $30 \div 3 = 10$
  **g** $7 \times 5 = 35$    **o** $7 \times 2 = 14$
     $35 \div 7 = 5$      $14 \div 2 = 7$
     $35 \div 5 = 7$      $14 \div 7 = 2$
  **h** $8 \times 3 = 24$    **p** $6 \times 6 = 36$
     $24 \div 3 = 8$      $36 \div 6 = 6$
     $24 \div 8 = 3$      $36 \div 6 = 6$

**Page 99**

**1** $14 \div 4 = 3$ remainder 2

**2a** $9 \div 2 = 4$ remainder 1,
  **b** $17 \div 5 = 3$ remainder 2,
  **c** $20 \div 6 = 3$ remainder 2,
  **d** $17 \div 8 = 2$ remainder 1,
  **e** $11 \div 4 = 2$ remainder 3,
  **f** $10 \div 3 = 3$ remainder 1,
  **g** $23 \div 4 = 5$ remainder 3,
  **h** $33 \div 6 = 5$ remainder 3

**Page 100**

**1a** $22 \div 6 = 3$ remainder 4,

**b** $25 \div 4 = 6$ remainder 1,

**c** $13 \div 4 = 3$ remainder 1,

**d** $15 \div 2 = 7$ remainder 1,

**e** $32 \div 6 = 5$ remainder 2,

**f** $18 \div 4 = 4$ remainder 2,

**g** $20 \div 6 = 3$ remainder 2,

**h** $21 \div 5 = 4$ remainder 1,

**i** $28 \div 5 = 5$ remainder 3,

**j** $27 \div 4 = 6$ remainder 3

**2a** ③ 6 8 ⑨ 12 ⑪ ⑮ 18 ⑰

**b** The ringed numbers are odd.

**3** ⑦ 13 ⑫ ⑰ 20 23 ㉒ ㊲

# Chapter 22: Weight 2

**Page 102**

**1a** 100 g

# Chapter 23: Area

**Page 105**

**1a** 6, **b** 7,

**c** D has the greater area.

**Page 106**

**1** Shape **A** has an area of 13 units.
Shape **B** has an area of 9 units.
The area of Shape **A** is greater
than the area of Shape **B**.

Shape **C** has an area of 16 units.
Shape **D** has an area of 18 units.
The area of Shape **D** is greater
than Shape **C**.

Shape **E** has an area of 14 units.
Shape **F** has an area of 12 units.
The area of Shape **E** is greater
than Shape **F**.

Shape **G** has an area of 5 units.
Shape **H** has an area of 6 units.
The area of Shape **H** is greater
than shape **G**.

**Page 107**

**1a** The area is 9 squares.

**b** The area is 10 squares.

**c** The area is 11 squares.

**d** The area is 10 squares.

**e** The area is 10 squares.

**f** The area is 11 squares.

**g** The area is 10 squares.

**h** The area is 9 squares.

**i** The area is 13 squares.

**Page 108**

**2** Shape **A** has an area of 9 squares.
Shape **B** has an area of 8 squares.
Shape **A** has a greater area than
Shape **B**.

Shape **C** has an area of 7 squares.
Shape **D** has an area of 6 squares.
Shape **C** has a greater area than
Shape **D**

Shape **E** has an area of 8 squares.
Shape **F** has an area of 7 squares.
Shape **E** has a greater area than
Shape **F**.

Shape **G** has an area of 10
squares.
Shape **H** has an area of 11
squares.
Shape **H** has a greater area than
Shape **G**.

Shape **I** has an area of 6 squares.
Shape **J** has an area of 7 squares.
Shape **J** has a greater area than
Shape **I**.

Shape **K** has an area of 10
squares.
Shape **L** has an area of 11
squares.
Shape **L** has a greater area than
Shape **K**.

Shape **M** has an area of 9 squares.
Shape **N** has an area of 10
squares.
Shape **N** has a greater area than
Shape **M**.

Shape **O** has an area of 13
squares.
Shape **P** has an area of 12
squares.
Shape **O** has a greater area than
Shape **P**.

# Chapter 24: Capacity 2 and Volume

**Page 110**

**1** 2 times

**2** activity

**3** activity

**Page 112**

**1a** 12,

**b** yes,

**2** activity,

**3** activity

**4a** Box A takes 27 cubes. Box B
takes 40 cubes.

**b** Box B takes more cubes than
Box A.

**c** The volume of the cubes in B is
greater than the volume of the
cubes in A.

**5** Activity

# Index

# Nuffield Maths 5–11

*Nuffield Maths 3 Teachers' Handbook*
## Contents